NO SAFE PLACE

NO SAFE PLACE

by

Warner Troyer

CLARKE, IRWIN & COMPANY LIMITED,
TORONTO/VANCOUVER

Canadian Cataloguing in Publication Data

Troyer, Warner, 1932-
    No safe place

Bibliography: p. 246
Includes index.
ISBN 0-7720-1117-6

1. Mercury – Environmental aspects –
Ontario.
2. Mercury – Environmental aspects.
3. Pollution.
4. Environmental policy. I. Title.

TD196.M38T76   363.6   C77-001153-5

1 2 3 4 5 JD 81 80 79 78 77

Printed in Canada

Contents

For the people of White Dog and
Grassy Narrows — with hope that
they will have many better
testaments, but never need memorials.

It is from the mercury mines that there issues the most cruel bane of all that deals death and destruction to miners. . . .

We all know what terrible maladies are contracted from mercury by goldsmiths, especially those employed in gilding silver and copper objects. This work cannot be done without the use of amalgam, and when they later drive off the mercury by fire they cannot avoid receiving the poisonous fumes into their mouths, even though they turn away their faces. Hence craftsmen of this sort very soon become subject to vertigo, asthma and paralysis. Very few of them reach old age, and even when they do not die young their health is so terribly undermined that they pray for death.

— BERNARDINO RAMAZZINI,
1731 A.D.

Acknowledgments

First, to the many, many anonymous contributors. Our society has grown too complex for us to survive without the help of the real experts – the people in government, business, industry, who know what's going on and are prepared to disclose that data. Our mutual responsibilities to avoid a permanently silent spring have far outstripped the need to avoid embarrassing a deputy minister, an executive vice-president or a shareholder.

To the researchers who provided the mountain of data which is the foundation of all that follows. Their patience, ingenuity and enthusiasm matched the purposeful endurance with which they pursued every lead, every document, every scrap of intriguing information. Especially to Glenys Moss for whom this ''second job'' consumed virtually every free hour for half a year, and to her family, who bore her absences and preoccupation. To Michael Perley whose energy was outstripped only by his dedication. To too many others to dare mention many without being certain of missing many more.

To the scientists who made their data freely available and gave great help in the Herculean chore of assimilating and understanding the jargon and the scholastic minutiae. To the other scientists who would have helped more if they'd not felt bound by their relationships to government.

To Marion and Barney Lamm, Aileen Smith, the Minamata patients and the researchers at Kumamoto University – there and at Grassy Narrows.

It's been a long journey, made, mostly, in sorrow. But no one ever had better companions.

List of illustrations

Photographs not taken by the author all appear by kind permission of the photographers, who are credited below.

Minamata disease victim (Aileen and Eugene Smith)
Mercury-killed fish in Japan (Aileen and Eugene Smith)
Minamata disease victim (Aileen and Eugene Smith)
Three brains (Aileen and Eugene Smith)
Grassy Narrows reserve
The Wabigoon River (Aileen Smith)
Wild rice near Grassy Narrows (Takeshi Shiota and Koichi Enishi)
Outside Grassy Narrows school (Takeshi Shiota and Koichi Enishi)
Children of Grassy Narrows (Takeshi Shiota and Koichi Enishi)
A fishing guide (Takeshi Shiota and Koichi Enishi)
The Kumamoto Study Group visits the reserves — summer 1975 (Takeshi Shiota and Koichi Enishi)
Jimmy Tanguay
Shore lunch (Takeshi Shiota and Koichi Enishi)
Barney Lamm and poster outside Ball Lake Lodge
Dryden and the mill (Aileen Smith)
The main effluent outflow pipe
One of the pits where Reed buries mercury-laden sediment (Michael Perley)
The ''backyard'' of the mill (Takeshi Shiota and Koichi Enishi)
Foam and fibre on the Wabigoon River downstream from the Reed plant (Michael Perley)

Introduction

Any author is tempted to explain the "why" of a book. In this case the overriding reason was simply that an ongoing problem – mercury pollution in Northwest Ontario – still existed as the book was begun, and completed. Moreover, the lessons inherent in a study of that problem seemed still to be unlearned. I believed better perception of those lessons would help us all in other cases and times of need – now and later.

However, there is another much more personal motive behind this book. Journalism, in my twenty-five years experience, fails more than it serves. We in the trade rarely achieve the jump from trade to craft – hardly ever the quantum leap to art. The reasons for our failures are too many, too obvious. Here are just a few:

-laziness
-ineptitude
-lack of time, money, research resources
-lack of expertise in complex fields which, nonetheless, bear directly and radically on everyday living
-lack of imagination, initiative
-preoccupation with day-to-day trivia (the engineer's credo: "When you're up to your ass in alligators, it's hard to remember that what you're here for, is to drain the swamp.")
-lack of space for "thorough" coverage
-chronic failure to follow-up ("We did that piece last year.")
-"Me-too-ism" ("So-and-so has already done a story on that; they're on to something new; we should be, too.")
-lack of continuity (Toronto daily newspapers covering this story –

damned good newspapers – assigned different reporters to it almost every time there was a new development to cover.)

In the spring of 1976 this journalist was given a national award for the script of a film made on the subject of this book; it was telecast on the Canadian Broadcasting Corporation's national network in late September of 1975. I was proud of the award then; I still am. But horrified, after having the time and using the resources available to me in preparing this book, at the superficiality of my documentary film. There was nothing in it I would retract at this date – no egregious error of fact or emphasis; just, instead, an overwhelming sense of having done the topic – and the people involved – less than justice through having less time, fewer resources, than were required to fully develop the story.

Television journalism, the brand at which I've spent a preponderance of my time since 1961, is a magnifying glass, almost a carnival mirror for journalism of all sorts: the beauty spots and warts are all the more visible – the grace of a reporter under fire; the banality of one over-his-head; the crudity of one seeking a reputation as fastest-lip-in-the-east; the temptation to over-simplify, cosmetize, dramatize, bear-bait; the failure to probe deeply, to follow-up, to deal with stories which might be judged dull and therefore fail to generate a 14-point byline – or a 14-point audience rating.

TV journalists, even more than print reporters, tend to be hit-and-run artists – going for the gravy, or the groin – the honey-badgers of their trade, ripping out the dramatic, erotic meat of the story's corpus and leaving the rest to rot, off-camera.

But there are solutions: demand for higher standards from readers, listeners and viewers; insistence that stories continue to be covered after the first blush of scoop and drama have faded; a conviction that "dull" stories and events critical to our community must be explained, made interesting.

We need more specialists in journalism – people who study and stay with specialized areas of events. Outside of medicine, labour, police, business, courts, sports, movie and record reviews, there's precious little of it today. And much of what exists is uncritical, smacking of the sycophantic and groundless anxiety that clear-eyed reporting might "burn the sources" and eliminate future tips and stories. Canada is probably the least adventurous of all the western nations in developing specialist journalists, an appalling situation in a society which grows more complex day by day, where a "good reporter with a lot of common sense" can no longer assume an ability to avoid being the terminal victim of doubletalk by nuclear power planners, defence hardware merchants, petroleum executives, government-bought economic planners, industrial managers, super-sophisticated trade union movers and shakers, academics or even, heaven forfend, second-generation citizen activists and street radicals. They are getting too smart for us, too supple and subtle, too knowledgeable.

Today we need journalists who can tell us whether super-rice and the green revolution are real and helpful, whether nuclear power is truly our best energy alternative, whether our children's lives will be governed, inexorably, by lifeboat ethics. Few journalists, proportionately, are given the time, resources, contracts to write books – so we need more specialization. And more input, too, from everybody outside journalism.

There are, clearly, many facts not in this book – and there are many reasons. There were wide variations in what data was available from institutional sources, and by what means. Sometimes, when research turned up the existence of a government study, a simple request was enough to elicit a copy of the previously "unpublished" report; sometimes not. Sometimes data in the hands of a government department or agency for a year, three years, five years, was described as "incomplete" or "unfinished" or "not checked-out yet." Sometimes a civil servant, frustrated by his/her senior management or by political (cabinet) level inertia would "send along" some data – a report, a study, an internal memo. Some arrived with a signed note, in envelopes bearing a return address – some bore neither, though recapitulation of recent conversations, interviews, trips and phone calls made the origins plain.

Many of those who contributed material to this book wish to remain anonymous. They will; but none of the factual data that follows is from a single source, unless that source be a formal document; the rest has at least one cross-reference in our research files – most have two or three. Some seductive data, not confirmed from independent sources, have been omitted with whatever regrets one acquires from inability to follow up unsubstantiated reports.

What follows is journalism; not science, history, economics, demography, sociology or philosophy. But the data are sufficient for some conclusions. The raw meat of my trade has enough protein here, I think, to provide some of the nourishment we need for those other component parts of our community corpus.

My conviction is that our community's dynamic, its structural integrity, survival, depend on an informed people – and that journalists, with teachers, managers, public men and women, are essential to the educative process.

The assistance given me in the preparation of this book has been beyond description or the compass of written gratitude. Whatever strengths and merits exist on the following pages spring from and belong to those identified in the Acknowledgements. Where there are errors of priority, of emphasis, of interpretation, they are mine. All italics in quoted matter are mine unless otherwise specified.

WARNER TROYER
Toronto
July 1975 – January 1977

NO SAFE PLACE

1 THE WITCHES' BREW

People have been poisoned by methyl mercury in Northwest Ontario. That's fact, just as it's fact that the economies of two Ojibway Indian communities have been destroyed in large measure by the consequences of mercury "spills" from a chemical and pulp mill at Dryden, Ontario, owned by the Reed Paper Company.

What's still at issue in Ontario is the degree of poisoning in any one individual. The 1,200 people at risk aren't consoled by suggestions they are just a little bit pregnant from the mating of the toxic heavy metal with delicate brain tissue. What's at issue, too, is the matter of how the industry and governments involved have responded to the hazard and to the needs of the people living in the target zone.

Mercury is only one element of the witches' brew of industrial pollution in our society. Asbestos, lead and uranium play havoc of a different sort but with similar tragic results. So do DDT, and PCBs, Dioxin and a galaxy of toxic, sometimes carcinogenic, chemicals. One recently published "partial list" of industrial substances-to-be-feared lists 300 separate elements and compounds. Northwest Ontario, too, is just one place on a map dotted with locations of mercury emissions. Forty American states and five Canadian provinces have banned fishing in some lakes and streams because of mercury contamination of fish beyond levels safe for human consumption.

But it's because there is, literally, no safe place any more, no place where people can comfortably believe themselves safe from the hazards of pollution, that we need to study the forces which create the problems – and which can delay, even prevent, solutions. And in Northwest Ontario almost all possible elements and interests are

3

present: federal and provincial governments with their complex of departments, boards, agencies, divisions and branches; the factory of a huge, multinational conglomerate; an isolated society directly affected by the pollution; a social ambience in which the victims have become "an embarrassment" because other area residents fear panic and economic loss in a tourist-based economy; scrutiny and research (some say interference) by the international scientific community; dramatic and emotional (some say sensational and irresponsible) coverage by the world's mass media; a web of interlocking political, cultural, financial and social relationships impinging on every decision and policy.

We are said to differ from other species in our capacity to learn from experience. This is not just the conditioned reflex of the pet which, once burned, will never again touch the front burner. We are the sophisticated animal. We go on to learn why the burner was hot, to elaborate systems through which we can avoid future injury. But nothing in the experience of Northwest Ontario between 1969 and 1977 suggests that we humans learn from observed experience, and act on the data our research yields.

The following are a few of the questions raised in this book. It's frightening that most of them are not different, fundamentally, from those to be asked in every major case of industrial pollution anywhere in the world:

Why were a whole series of federal and provincial studies and reports – medical and environmental – hidden from public view between 1970 and 1977?

Why are anglers still permitted to fish in the area and a handful of fishing camps and tourist lodges still allowed to operate there?

Why have 1,200 people whose livelihoods, culture, pride and bodies have been poisoned by industrially dumped mercury still not been adequately tested seven years after that poisoning was detected, still not been provided with proper alternate diet or alternate employment, still not been compensated or even told that compensation was a possibility?

Why in 1977 has the government of Ontario yet even to threaten to prosecute, fine or sue Reed Paper Company for dumping more than ten tons of mercury into the Wabigoon River between 1962 and 1970? This, though best scientific estimates are that the contaminated river systems will not be safe for upwards of fifty – possibly as many as 100 – years?

Why has no governmental agency sought compensation for costs incurred in responding to the problem? Costs to the tax-paying public are somewhere in at least the seven-figure range – none of it recovered.

Then there is the matter of mercury poisoning, Minamata Disease. Still a matter of passionate controversy seven years after the danger was first officially established, the case is, according to government, "not proved."

What is proved is that local Indians have alarmingly high mercury blood levels and that some area residents have neurological symptoms "consistent with" Minamata Disease.

What's acknowledged by every government agency and research-er is that the situation is sufficiently grave to warrant much more research aimed at getting definitive answers to the key questions: Has anyone got Minamata Disease? How badly? Has anyone died? Is anyone going to?

Data from suppressed government reports and files, the correla-tion of material already published, and the examination of scientific research ignored until now by government all lead to the irresistible conclusion that there are dozens, probably scores of people who now have the clinical signs and symptoms. A further probability is that a number of deaths in the communities have been mis-attributed to other causes when the real killer was mercury-contaminated fish.

There's abundant documentation of the pollution. Once again, however, much lies in unpublished and suppressed government reports and memos – some published for the first time in this book. What's been missing, since the problem surfaced in late 1969, has been any political or bureaucratic will to deal effectively with the dangers, either through strong action or preventive legislation.

From the formal discovery of the problem in 1969, through 1976, the bureaucratic posture was one of "no panic." By late 1976 both Ontario and federal employees and government-hired scientists were down-playing the mercury hazards, suggesting the Byzantine labyrinth of surveys and reports had answered most questions; not that they weren't in favour of more studies.

The extraordinary coincidence apparent to one studying these events was that every scientific researcher and physician outside the governments' services who looked at the problem reacted with alarm and demands for urgent action, while virtually every scientist, researcher and physician on the staffs of government departments and ministries, or contracted to do studies for them, was exuding comfort and complacence. Difficult to avoid recalling George Orwell's response to co-option: "A bought mind is a spoiled mind."

In 1973 a still-unpublished report by a federal task force said: "At present, the federal government's approach to the special problems of White Dog and Grassy Narrows [the Indian reserves affected] is fragmented and lacks cohesion. ... The free flow of information and data on mercury in the environment with the Province of Ontario is impeded for reasons that are not clearly understood."[1]

Northwest Ontario's mercury pollution illuminates how industries can ignore public safety, how governments fail those they are employed to protect, how fear of economic loss can immobilize populations, and how parliament and the press can miss alerting us to danger. If we can't extrapolate from Northwest Ontario, there'll be more diaries of despair, maybe in your neighbourhood, on your bedside table. Later we'll look at other jurisdictions, other industries and other poisons, and see that without constant vigilance and questioning there is no safe place for any of us.

2 THE POISON

Mercury is one of the oldest known and most fascinating metals. Its ore, cinnabar, was probably used to provide the red colouring in pre-historic cave paintings in Europe; cinnabar and the red, crystalline sulphide of mercury are still used to make red sealing wax and the vermilion paint that so delights artists seeking a pure and perfect scarlet.

To ask how poisonous mercury can be is to ask "how high is up?" Mercury, a heavy metal, has much in common with arsenic and lead. One toxicologist put it this way: "If you dumped one tablespoon of mercury into a body of water the size of a football field, and fifteen feet deep, that would be enough to result in unsafe mercury levels in fish in that water; they wouldn't be fit to eat." A lethal dose of mercuric chloride is less than one-quarter of a gram. It would take 113 such doses to make up a single ounce. A gram of mercuric chloride was once the most common United States vehicle for suicide – the death-of-choice before the introduction and availability of barbiturates.

The first written record of mercury comes from Aristotle, who in the fourth century BC described the metal as "liquid silver." In 380 BC Theophrastus of Eresus was writing of what is still the largest and most productive mercury mine in the world, at Almaden, Spain; in the first century AD Pliny described the mine as "the most famous for the revenues of the Roman nation." Pliny also mentioned that the mine was worked exclusively by Roman convicts and slaves, and wrote of the hazards of poisoning.

There were industrial hazards from mercury in ancient city of Rome, too. The metal, then as now, was used to harden gold and silver, and as a refining agent with which dirt and impurities could be removed from gold; but the heat used in these processes gave rise to deadly mercury vapour. Said Pliny of the goldsmiths in Rome: "Persons employed in the manufactories ... protect the face with masks of loose bladder skin to avoid inhaling the dust, which is most pernicious."

Mercury had already become a medical aid as well. In the first century AD the Greek physician Dioscorides was using mercury as it occurred in crushed cinnabar. It was, he said, "good for eye medicines ... heals burnings, and the breaking out of pustules" although he added that it was dangerous if swallowed. Centuries later, when mercury ointment became a commonly used treatment for syphilis, sixteenth- and seventeenth-century physicians took to wearing leather gloves while applying the therapy, since they became ill from absorption of the mercury through the skin of their hands. Eventually some frightened doctors began forcing the patients to treat themselves, aiding their own recovery from the pox at the possible expense of developing the tremors, kidney problems and temperamental instability of characteristic sub-acute mercury poisoning.

The first medically documented case of lethal mercury poisoning involved a miner in the fifteenth century, and, throughout history, hazards to mercury miners have been horrendous. When the Spanish Conquest struck the Americas, the Conquistadores found they didn't have to ship mercury to the New World from their own mine for use in refining the gold they plundered: the Mayans had been using cinnabar for decoration from 500 BC onwards. The Spaniards developed mercury mines in Peru and used forced labour. Peruvians were required to work in the mines for six months every two years, but few managed a second tour of duty, since they worked almost constantly near the deadly fumes (the life expectancy of the miners was precisely their term of indentured service: six months).

Even today the risks are so great that in Almaden, Spanish mercury workers, governed by a health law passed in 1665 (surely the earliest of industrial safety regulations), are permitted to work only a six-hour day, eight days a month, in the shafts and refinery; most have other occupations as clerks, shopkeepers, barbers and so on. Despite that, today in Almaden there are former miners who cannot write, walk or feed themselves – men who have such violent tremors and muscle spasms that they must be strapped to the beds they will never leave alive.

Nor are the super-hot temperatures of a mercury refinery needed to vapourize the killer metal – it readily evaporates at normal room temperature if left exposed, say from a broken thermometer. The mercury simply "disappears" as it forms an invisible and odourless gas.

The phrase "mad as a hatter" grew from the use of mercury in treating woollen hats in Europe – mercuric nitrate was used to improve the felting quality of wool and fur. "Hatters shakes," the classic tremor induced by poisoning from mercury vapour, became known as "Danbury shakes" in the United States in the late nineteenth century, when Danbury, Connecticut, became the centre of the continent's wool and felt hat industry. Mercury is rarely used now in such industries; the Danbury shakes have instead become mostly a risk for lab workers and people employed in the paint and electrical industries.

Enthusiasm for mercury has known few bounds since Pliny. At Almaden production records kept since before the Middle Ages show "spikes" of output which accompanied early industrial development, the invention of the mercury fuse and detonator in 1814, declarations of war, and the growth of the pulp and paper industry. World production/consumption now averages 10,000 tons annually; known commercial reserves exceed 200,000 tons.

The new uses have tripped over one another making more and more occupations vulnerable. Munitions workers joined mirror-makers, thermometer-fillers and laboratory workers as frequent victims of mercury poisoning; next came policemen, as numbers of British Bobbies developed serious symptoms of the poisoning after prolonged work with a mercury-based fingerprinting powder compound (still used in most of the world). Dental assistants, too, are vulnerable. A 50 per cent mix of mercury with an equal amount of tin and silver – or gold – dissolves that alloy which then hardens when applied to a cavity. In mixing the fillings, half the mercury mixture usually evaporates or is lost down the dental laboratory drains – at .75 grams per filling, half that weight mercury, and with 160 million such fillings annually in the United States at present, that's 132,262½ pounds of mercury down the drain in the USA each year.

Mercury is used in paints; electronic controls; as an amalgam and catalyst in metallurgical processes; and as a disinfectant and preservative in hand lotions, vaginal deodorants, etc. But the major single use of mercury is in chlor-alkali plants built to serve the paper industry. Here mercury is used in the electrolytic production of caustic soda and of chlorine, a bleaching agent used in pulp mills. In chlor-alkali plants mercury is lost in great volume relative to its toxicity, both in waste water from the chemical processes and through exhaust gases. While the electrical industry uses almost as much mercury as the paper industry, it loses very little, in comparison, in the production of batteries, switches, fluorescent lights *et al*.

Mercury poisoning in industry often passes undiagnosed or unnoticed, unless symptoms are severe. Moreover, in cases of relatively mild-to-moderate poisoning from inorganic mercury or its fumes, symptoms often disappear if the affected worker is moved away for a time.

But to demonstrate that such cases continue to occur, take the experience, between 1955 and 1975, of the Workmen's Compensation Board of Ontario. In that period, as reported to a researcher for this book by a Board official, compensation was paid to twenty-two workers who had been afflicted by mercury poisoning. Given Ontario's population base of 8 million, an extrapolation to cover North America and Western Europe, would mean 71,785 reported and compensated cases annually between the Volga and the California coastline. Ontario's cases involved hat manufacturing; gold refining; fungicides; a dental lab; battery manufacturing; the electrical industry; firefighting (from inhalation of mercury vapour at a fire); mail handling (when a parcel containing mercuric chloride was dropped and the mercury spilled); and a laboratory. Finally, there were two compensated cases involving chlor-alkali plant workers, exposed while working in the mercury cell division of the Reed paper mill (see p. 111).

Metallic (inorganic) mercury, especially as vapour, can be just as deadly as methyl (organic) mercury. In 1948 Dr. J. A. Campbell reported on a case of "Acute mercuric poisoning by inhalation of metallic vapour in an infant" to the *Canadian Medical Association Journal*. The circumstances were so commonplace that the tragedy they triggered is hard to accept. The father of a four-month-old infant accidentally spilled a half-teaspoon of mercury onto the kitchen stove, where it was immediately vapourized; intrigued by the event, the man called his wife to come and watch him repeat the action, this time deliberately, so she could watch the quicksilver disappear. The baby, present in the kitchen at the time, showed symptoms of mercury poisoning within two hours – it died four days later of acute "pulmonary edema." (Many Minamata Disease victims died of pneumonia, at the terminal stage of their illness.)

In 1958 three small children died after being exposed to the fumes from mercury/aluminum paint. The toddlers, aged 1½, 2½ and four, all contracted fatal pneumonia while sleeping in a room in which a space heater had been painted, then fired-up to "help the paint dry" more quickly.[1]

In 1956 in an outbreak of poisoning in Iraq, where seed grain treated with mercury to prevent mildew was diverted to be milled for flour, at least 100 of those who baked their bread from that flour were hospitalized; more than a dozen died.

In 1960 there was a second outbreak in Iraq, with over 1,000 patients and an undisclosed number of deaths. In 1971 a third "epidemic" triggered in the same way had disastrous results. Estimates indicate that a total of 3,723 victims died from methyl mercury intoxication – and over 10,000 people suffered symptoms, most of them fated to carry the neurological claw-marks to their graves.

There were other, smaller outbreaks: in Guatemala in 1966, in Pakistan in 1969. In that same year, 1969, Ernest Huckleby of Alamogordo, New Mexico, got a truckload of free grain. The mercury-treated grain spilled from its sacks at the Golden West Seed Company in Texico, New Mexico, as rats gnawed the sacks, and poisoned themselves. Ernest Huckleby's family raised hogs, loved pork – and he mixed the treated seed with slops and fattened his pigs with it. Some of the hogs died of "the blind staggers," as Huckleby said, and three of his children developed symptoms of Minamata Disease. This was in January 1970. By the end of the year four Huckleby children had been affected: Amos is still blind, but can walk a little with help; his sister Dorothy Jean can walk about 100 feet, with crutches, in ten minutes. She was twenty when the disease struck, Amos was fourteen. Ernestine Huckleby was only eight when, on 4 December 1969, she fell off the monkey bars at school. She is a permanent resident of the Gerald Champion Memorial Hospital in Alamogordo, blind and mute; the youngest Huckleby child, Michael, was born on 20 March 1970. His mother's doctor pronounced Michael fit and healthy at birth. But

Michael cried a lot after being taken home from hospital, before it was discovered he was the first diagnosed case of congenital Minamata Disease in the United States. At age six he could not sit up, or speak. Michael is blind too.

And in Canada and the United States, a year after the Huckleby tragedy, the use of mercury-treated seed grains was banned.

But the most significant outbreaks of mercury poisoning remain those in Japan, where investigation has been the most thorough and continuous. Before Canadian outbreaks, it was only in Japan that mercury poisoning triggered by industrial contamination of the marine food chain could be observed and studied, and only there that symptoms developed, not from a brief, huge, intake of mercury but from prolonged fish diets and a relatively slow onset of clinical signs.

3 "CAT-DANCING DISEASE"

The outbreak which was to claim over 100 lives and leave perhaps 1,000 people with permanent symptoms of irreversible brain damage, was first seen in Kumamoto Prefecture – a suburb of Minamata City on Japan's southern island – on a sunny April afternoon in 1953. A group of children saw a cat behaving strangely. Leaping into the air, turning in feverish circles, screeching and howling, the cat would run wildly a few steps, fall, run again, stumble again; the children followed the tortured animal for a short while until finally it plunged into the sea water of Minamata Bay, struggled for a moment, and drowned. The children had seen nothing like it before: "*Kibyo*," they said. "Strange illness."

Wild birds were afflicted, too. Crows and sea birds were seen falling into Minamata Bay, or onto the land around Minamata; the birds were unsteady when walking, showed symptoms of spastic paralysis and abnormal movement. Sometimes birds would plummet from the sky, catch themselves just before striking ground or sea, fly unsteadily back into the air, only to fall again and die.

The "kibyo" soon acquired a new name, based on the dervish-like spinning the cats exhibited: "Cat-dancing disease." There's a fascinating historical link here. The oldest-known mine in the world was at the Hittite community of Iconium (now Konia). In the thirteenth century AD, Iconium witnessed the birth of a new and fanatic religious movement which became known as the Order of the Whirling Dervishes. It is hard not to speculate that the founding society of believers may have been inspired by the same symptoms of mercury poisoning.

The first well-documented brain histology of a mercury-killed

13

human patient was reported in Britain in 1954. The precise descriptions by Doctors D. Hunter and D.S. Russell of the selective brain tissue damage and atrophy gave Japanese scientists at Kumamoto University a major "assist" in their attempts to identify the silent killer which struck Minamata between 1953 and 1966.

Although retrospective study of local medical records showed that mercury poisoning had caused at least fifty-two cases of illness and death in Minamata before the mid-fifties, these cases had not been diagnosed.

The first recognition came in late April 1956 when a six-year-old girl was admitted to receive medical examination for some cerebral symptoms at the Pediatrics Clinic, Chisso Factory Hospital. Her three-year-old sister followed eight days later. Dr. Noda, Chairman of the Clinic, reported to Dr. Hosokawa, Director of the Hospital, on the conditions of the two patients in detail, and asked his permission to commence closer investigation. After investigation people were warned to stop eating fish taken from the bay, and research centred on efforts to identify the poison. Three years later it was officially published that mercury was most suspicious as the causative agent. The actual killer, methyl mercury, was formally identified and the results of the studies published (in English) at the Seventh International Congress of Neurology in Rome in September 1961 – and later at a conference funded by the US National Institute of Health on 6 February 1963.

Some of the patterns which developed from the mercury intoxication problem at Minamata were echoed clearly in Canada twenty years later.

Minamata, a community of 40,000, is neither village nor city, but a combination of both. Its only major industry is the Chisso factory: its other economic base split between commercial fishing and tourism. The first and loudest response of the local citizens was that the matter must be hushed up. Workers in the Chisso plant, and their families. feared for the future of their jobs and incomes. Other citizens worried about the loss of fish markets and still more agonized over the potential loss of money from holiday-makers who came for the fishing, the swimming, the magnificent scenery. All of that still being echoed, in Ontario, as late as 13 October 1976, when the Dryden *Observer* declared;

Once again erroneous reporting is threatening the life-style, industry and economy of this part of Northwestern Ontario. Once again the reports on mercury pollution, mercury content in fish and probable dangers of mercury to people eating fish have been clipped, mangled and misquoted in reports in newspapers, radio and TV reports. ...

The Dryden *Observer* has been trying to have residents of this area and other parts of Northwest Ontario register concern and do something positive about this harmful type of publicity. We have pointed out before that there are individuals who are exploiting the mercury situation for their own needs. ...

It is a heartening sign that tourist outfitters, Chambers of Commerce and other organizations are finally awakening to the harm these individuals are doing. ...

Those who are exploiting the situation for their own selfish ends must be exposed and prevented from doing further harm. In the interests of truth and the interest also of an area that has been maligned all over the country by false, malicious and ignorant publicity, it is time that people all over this part of Northwestern Ontario begin a campaign on their behalf.

The *Observer* is owned and published by Dryden citizen Alex M. Wilson, whose firm has substantial business associations with Reed Paper (see p. 59).

In Minamata, as in Northwest Ontario, those afflicted tended to be the least advantaged members of their community. "It's only a few fishermen," was a not uncommon response. "It's only Indians, anyway," is still heard in Ontario's boardrooms and in the private conversations of some bureaucrats and politicians discussing the mercury problem.

At one point in Japan, resolutions were passed by local groups demanding that researchers and others find a new name for the poisoning epidemic: stop blackening the town by calling it Minamata Disease. When, in 1975, Japanese disease patients visiting White Dog and Grassy Narrows carried signs reading "Arrest Dryden/Minamata Disease," the Ontario outcry was as anguished as it was outraged.

In Japan, as in Ontario, the polluting company began by denying responsibility: then took cover in the declaration that it had, at all times, emitted only those poisons permitted by law. (In 1958, unhappy with photographers snapping shots of their effluent outflow pipe, Chisso temporarily transferred their dumping to the other side of the town, to a river flowing into the Shiranui Sea beyond Minamata Bay; within six months people in this area, too, were developing symptoms of Minamata Disease.) Both companies spoke often of the enormous cost of anti-pollution programs; privately both were known to suggest often that no company could survive the economic disasters consequent on evidence of legal liability for damages done by the pollution. In court, Chisso was assessed over $86 million in direct damages to disease victims and their families; they are still in business. Government observers and journalists told the author in Tokyo, in 1975, that Chisso would be the last company ever to be allowed to fail financially in Japan; it was, they said, being openly supported by Japanese banks and by other large industrial concerns – and for good reason: "If Chisso was bankrupted by the damage suits," said one, "there would be a run on the stocks and shares of every industry which pollutes; small shareholders would run like hell and those huge companies would face a disaster in terms of raising capital. So Chisso won't ever fail – the other big industrial companies don't dare let it go down and thus scare off their investors."

And in Japan, as in Ontario, it was difficult to get data from the polluting companies. In Minamata it was only, literally, with a 1969 death-bed confession that the public learned that Chisso's management had been given evidence ten years earlier demonstrating a direct link between Chisso effluent discharges and Minamata Disease – a link the company continued to deny, in public and in court, for a decade.

The confession came from Dr. Hajimé Hosokawa, the Director of the Chisso Factory Hospital, to whom Dr. Noda had turned for direction and help after admitting the first two patients to his children's ward in 1956. Those little girls both had obvious symptoms of brain damage. Both, known to their neighbours as "bright and energetic" children, were delirious, incoherent, unable to walk or co-ordinate. Within days Dr. Noda had found a neighbouring five-year-old with the same symptoms; then that child's mother developed the symptoms; followed, in under a month, by her eleven-year-old and eight-year-old sons. The epidemic was on.

Dr. Hosokawa reported to the Public Health Department that "an unclarified disease of the central nervous system has broken out," and began searching for its nature and cause. Chisso had hired Dr. Hosokawa right at the beginning of his career. But he believed himself a free man and knew himself to be an excellent physician and intelligent researcher. A man whose favourite reading was Ibsen's *An Enemy of the People*, he had a profound sympathy for the individual at odds with the establishment. In late 1956, Dr. Hosokawa began feeding poisons to cats. He tried toxic heavy metal pollutants known to be in Minamata Bay, with cat after cat: thalium, selenium, arsenic, lead, manganese. His procedures were scrupulous, his records meticulous. It all took a long time as he tested ten cats, then 100 – another 100, and another, and another.

In early 1969 attorneys representing disease victims who were suing the Chisso Corporation came to Dr. Hosokawa's home. He was retired, bed-ridden, dying – he did not live to see the end of the trial. But he made a sworn statement that revealed what had come of his experiments – and one of them in particular. "I was a bit hesitant and found it difficult to begin that experiment. I did not talk about it," Hosokawa told the lawyers. But he did it. On cat number 400. The doctor had his assistant draw a container of liquid from the acetaldehyde effluent pipe on the Chisso property – and he introduced that fluid into the cat's diet. "On 7 October, 1959, Cat #400 fell ill. While Hosokawa watched, it convulsed, salivated, and then suddenly whirled at terrific speed, crashing into the laboratory walls – exactly the behaviour he feared he would see."[1] He reported the result to Chisso management. The next time his assistant went out to get acetaldehyde waste water, he was stopped by a guard. In a November meeting, Hosokawa was told that there would be absolutely no more experiments connected with Minamata Disease.

All of this at a time when the Chisso executive and their representatives were attempting to get the disease victims and their families to sign quit-claim documents in return for token compensation payments – and telling those victims, "There is absolutely no scientific evidence that Minamata Disease is caused by Chisso."

Hosokawa testified, "I asked them to please let me continue the experiments. But it was no good. ... " Until mid-1960, when the Chisso management changed its mind, or appeared so to do, and allowed the doctor to resume his work, but only with waste water delivered to him by the new factory manager. In 1969, Hosokawa said, "I don't know whether it was or was not the real – the same waste water as before."

He continued his studies for a while, but when he sent cats to

Tokyo for post-mortem examinations at the university there, they "disappeared." He retired, grew ill, held his peace and tongue until 1969. A year after his death Minamata Disease victims built a shrine to his memory in front of the courthouse; they decorated the shrine, and prayed there.

By 1958 the first post-mortem studies of human victims had been completed. The clinical symptoms of the disease were clearly identified:

> ... progressive numbness of the fingers and often of the lips and tongue, clumsiness in the hands or an ataxic gait. This is followed by dysarthria [slurred speech] ... deafness and constriction of visual fields. ... From the pathological point of view, this mysterious disease was ... characterized by degeneration of cerebellar cortices and destruction of brain cells and tissue.[2]

In addition, about one year after the general outbreak, not a few infants were born with cerebral palsy in those villages where there were many patients suffering from the disease. After some years of investigations all these infants were announced to be victims of fetal Minamata Disease, the cause being intoxication from organic mercury acquired prenatally from the mother, although the mothers did not show manifestations of Minamata Disease. Research into congenital Minamata disease has shown that not only can methyl mercury pass through the placenta to the fetus, but that the fetus, like the heart, liver, kidneys, brain of a postnatal victim of mercury, actually concentrates the lethal toxin.[3]

Equally horrible studies in Iraq, Japan and Sweden indicated that some infants showed an increase in blood mercury levels in their first year of life. One Iraqi infant, the only test subject among fifteen born with a mercury level lower than that of the mother, surpassed her level at twelve months of age, having continued to ingest and concentrate the poison after birth at its mother's breast.

By 1962 there were many cases of congenital idiocy amongst children who had not eaten fish or shellfish from Minamata Bay. Their clinical characteristics, as described by Dr. Masazumi Harada, probably the world's leading diagnostician of Minamata Disease, consisted of

> serious mental retardation, primitive reflexes such as oral reflex and

grasping reflex [many such children could not even suckle] ... disturbance of co-ordination, ataxia ... intention tremor [tremor which begins during attempts to perform any "intentional" physical act], dysarthria, salivation, character disorder – unfriendly, indifferent, shy, nervous, excited, restless, obstinate – psychomotor seizure, loss of consciousness, myclonic jerk [a muscle spasm or twitch of a muscle or group of muscles – a facial tic on a much grander scale], deformity of limbs, strabismus [squinting] and pathological reflex.[4]

For anyone who has seen such children, these clinical signs are horrifying. And although congenital Minamata Disease has many similarities to other forms of cerebral palsy, Dr. Harada found that "in ... idiocy caused by other factors cerebellar symptoms and strabismus were rarely observed. ... In general, among cerebral palsy patients, as compared to these Minamata patients, intelligence disturbance was slight."

Post-mortem studies of the brains of such victims are graphic witness to the ravages of organic mercury. There are, first, underdeveloped and malformed tissues in the central nervous system, evidence of damage during fetal development; but most starkly, and in common with non-fetal victims, there is a marked atrophy, a shrinkage of the brain caused by the disappearance and decrease of cortical nerve cells. That shrinkage is observable in most victims of the disease who have died – with the remaining nerve-cell tissue described as "pulpy" or "spongy." But in the case of congenital victims the reduction is as much as one-third or more of normal brain size and weight.[5]

Although the mothers were first believed free of the disease, closer examination showed that "certain neurological symptoms were present in 73 per cent of the mothers; for example, ataxia ... nystagmus [a rhythmic rolling of the eyeballs or a vertical or horizontal oscillation], dysarthria, sensory disturbance."

One factor which makes mercury poisoning horrible beyond the normal sense of the word is that ten years after they first appeared those "certain neurological symptoms" in the mothers had increased. Attacking brain tissue, mercury observes no timetable: damage done one year may not manifest itself symptomatically until five, ten or more years later. Also mercury goes on with its destructive work long after the potential victim has stopped eating poisoned fish. It is quite possible for more than 25 per cent of the original mercury burden to be still active in the cortical tissue more than a year after all mercury ingestion has stopped.

There is absolutely no data on when and how the disease may strike those who have been exposed to a heavy diet of mercury-poisoned fish. Some people at Niigata with a history of heavy intake and high hair mercury content manifested diagnosable symptoms only three to four years later. And Niigata, where more than 500 people contracted the disease in a second outbreak, also provides incontrovertible evidence that even brief exposure to heavily contaminated fish can create dangerous blood levels of mercury in humans. In one case a boy who ate a lot of contaminated shellfish over a period of only ten days in 1953 was, eight years later, still so incapacitated that he was unable to attend school – he had forgotten even the alphabet, and couldn't learn it again.

4 "MINE THE RIVER"

In Northwest Ontario, as in Minamata, we are concerned with mercury transferred from water or sediment to marine life and then moving up the food chain in ever greater concentration. Marine algae, for example, will concentrate 100 times as much mercury by volume as the surrounding mercury-contaminated water. The mercury is first concentrated by the marine plants, then eaten by small marine animals which in turn are eaten by minnows, small fish, larger fish, and so on. The large fish, those most prized by sportsmen and commercial fishermen, achieve the highest, most dangerous mercury levels.

In Northwest Ontario, as in Minamata, we are concerned with methyl mercury – the more dangerous of the two fundamental kinds of mercury.

Structurally, organic (methyl) mercury differs from inorganic (metallic) simply through the addition of one or more carbon atoms to the mercury atom. Both are toxic, but inorganic mercury does not do as much damage when taken by mouth. Methyl mercury has an ability to move through body tissue, finally penetrating the brain where it destroys cells in the cortex, crippling or killing its host, while much greater amounts of inorganic mercury consumed by humans – or any animal – pass through the body and are excreted by the digestive system. Inorganic mercury, taken by mouth, starts being expelled within hours and has mostly gone within a week. Methyl mercury, concentrating in vital and vulnerable organs and the brain, has a half-life of at least seventy days. In other words after that prolonged period half the poison still exists in the system, with the amount halved again every seventy days.[1] But brain damage can be caused by minute amounts of mercury and it takes years for all mercury to clear the system.

The crucial factor in the development of methyl mercury in the water system is a process described as biomethylation – the methylation of inorganic mercury in the marine bio-system. In lay terms, inorganic mercury is "eaten" by bacteria in the water system sediment; the bacteria then "excrete" organic mercury. Best scientific estimates are that only about one per cent of the sediment's inorganic mercury burden is transformed into methyl mercury each year – so the process of contamination of marine life is generally expected to go on for seventy years or longer after mercury is no longer being added to the water system.

Because of ignorance of biomethylation, for a long time industries and governmental regulatory agencies assumed there was no great harm in spilling a certain amount of inorganic mercury into the environment. And when mercury poisoning became a real and present danger, both Chisso Corporation and, fourteen years later, Reed Paper took pains to point out that it was *inorganic* mercury they were using in their plants, whereas the contaminated fish were carrying a mercury burden that was mostly *organic* (methyl) mercury. And that was true. In Chisso's case, in the 1950s, it was almost a palatable excuse, putting aside the multitude of other toxins the company was pouring into Minamata Bay. But it was less of an excuse in the several years before 1970 when the Wabigoon/English river systems were closed to commercial fishing in Ontario because, as we shall see, it was known by then that inorganic mercury could be changed to methyl mercury through biomethylation.

It was in 1962 that Dryden Chemicals first began using its new mercury cell process, discharging somewhere between ten and twenty pounds of mercury daily into the river – and a like amount into the air.

In that same year, 1962, the cause of Minamata Disease had been pinpointed as mercury-laden waste water; there had already been forty-six deaths; it had been known for six years that the disease was caused by eating contaminated fish; and in 1959 the poison had been identified and the medical account of the disease published. In September 1961 the Japanese data had been fully published in English (see p. 14).

Throughout the 1960s, when, according to a later federal task force estimate, Reed Paper was dumping from ten to twenty pounds of mercury into the Wabigoon River *every day* (remember that table-spoon) there was a series of international conferences on heavy metals and on mercury in particular. Beginning at least as early as 1966, Canadian delegates to those conferences were warned that industrial uses of mercury should be monitored for potential danger. US delegates were given the same warnings. Both came home, informed their health authorities in Ottawa and Washington, and were told not to worry: "That's all being watched. ... We have no problems here. That's something that's happening in Japan and Sweden, not North America." The map on p. 24 shows some of the rivers and lakes in North America later found to be dangerously polluted with mercury.

In 1966 and 1967 the Canadian Federal Health Department was warned by at least three sources that mercury contamination could be a serious health hazard. Scientists from the National Research Council approached federal health authorities and were told there was "no problem." Dr. Robert Jervis of the University of Toronto echoed the warning and sought funds for research. He was refused. That same year direct communication with Ottawa from the World Health Organization in Geneva failed to move the federal bureaucrats to act.

Then, in the winter of 1966-7 a graduate student at the University of Western Ontario, advised and assisted by frustrated officials of the Canadian Wildlife Federation, made an end run around the bureau-cratic blockade. Norvald Fimreite, a Norwegian graduate student, applied for and received a federal grant for research connected with his doctoral studies. He wanted to study the effects on upland birds of eating mercury-treated seed grains and the effects on fish of industrial mercury losses – specifically from chlor-alkali plants. Fimreite's studies, in 1967 and 1968, revealed very high mercury levels in fish in the Saskatchewan River, in seed-eating pheasants and partridges in Alberta, and in fish in Lake St. Clair, between Ontario and Michigan.

The government of Alberta acted early on Fimreite's warning, closing the upland bird hunting season in 1969.

When Ontario and federal health authorities showed no enthu-siasm to move quickly on his findings, Fimreite published his studies and by late 1969 officials of Ontario's Water Resources Commission were moved to undertake studies of their own. The fish collected in 1969 were finally analysed in California for mercury content on 3

March 1970. The Water Resources Commission had no difficulty deciding from which waters to take fish for sampling; they simply worked downstream from Ontario's six chlor-alkali plants. The Ontario government now found itself obliged to act.

In 1970 a reporter for the Toronto *Globe and Mail*, Frances Russell, asked an Ontario Water Resources Commission spokesman why the province hadn't moved to check for mercury danger in Canada after reading the Japanese and Swedish studies. There were two answers. First: "The Japanese eat far more fish than we do, and they don't have any pollution controls." (Nor, in terms that mattered, did Canada or the US in respect of chlor-alkali plants like the one at Dryden). Second: "We have all their papers," said the spokesman for Ontario's chief environmental regulation agency, "but they're written in Japanese and Swedish and we couldn't read them."

Asked why fish hadn't been tested in 1969, after sediment tests revealed very high mercury levels, the reply was: "Why, back then, we didn't know that the mercury could get into the fish."

Even before the 1960s, a little was known about biomethylation.[2] But in 1960, *ten years* before that newspaper interview, a *World Neurology* article in English pointed to organic mercury in fish at Minamata – this in the sub-title – and also said, "if [the mercury] is lost as inorganic compounds, it presumably would have to be converted to more complex (organic) forms by plankton or other marine life after it has reached the bay."[3] The authors of the article examined all the available research data and wrote a comprehensive account of the then-available knowledge. Their concern that we find out "whether or not similar situations may occur in other areas of the world where mercury is used as an industrial catalyst" went largely unheeded. In Washington it was March 1969 before the Federal Food and Drug Administration discovered hazards from a chemical plant and one chlor-alkali plant. In Japan it was five years *after* this article that a second outbreak of Minamata Disease struck – this time at Niigata – killing 25 people. This time the polluting factory, Showa Denko Company, closed down.

In 1965 a Swedish scientist Dr. Alf Johnels and his associate, M. Olsson, published a paper stating that inorganic mercury of the kind used in chlor-alkali plants could be converted to methyl mercury in oxygen-free surroundings such as muddy lake bottoms. (In 1965 chlor-alkali plants were the biggest single users of mercury in the United States and Canada.)

On 1 February 1966, the Swedish government banned the use of mercury-treated seed grain.[4] Swedish farmers used two tons of mercury pesticides in 1965; US farmers pumped 400 tons of mercury products into the ecosystem that same year. On a basis of pesticide-per-acre the Americans were out-spraying the Swedes forty to one. In 1966 the Swedes sponsored an international symposium on mercury pollution. Five United States delegates, including one from the White House Office of Science and Technology, Dr. John L. Buckley, returned home apparently unaffected by the Scandinavian alarm about mercury dangers, since they did not act.

In 1967 two more Swedish researchers, Drs. Arne Jernelov and Soren Jensen confirmed that methylation was transforming inorganic mercury into the killer form. Still no response in Canada or the US, although by now chemists, environmentalists and toxicologists in both nations were asking their government agencies whether they were entirely certain that all was well. The Food and Drug Administration in Washington was "sure." So were Ottawa's Ministry of Health and Welfare and Ontario's Health Ministry.

Later in 1967 just a few months research led to identification of the micro-organism, "methano-bacterium omelanskii," which actually converts inorganic mercury to methyl mercury in bottom sediment and mud. In April 1968 the paper reporting this finding was refused for publication by the US journal *Science*, but six months later it was printed by the British journal *Nature*.[5]

But claims that in 1969 "we didn't know" were still being made in 1976. In that year a team assembled by the Ontario Government to study mercury poisoning in Japan and Iraq published their report. It includes the words: "Studies reported in 1969 in Sweden and Japan also showed that methyl mercury could be produced from inorganic mercury by the action of bacteria in the sediments of rivers and lakes." (Well, that's true. The 1960, 1965, 1967 and 1968 studies were all reported and reprinted in Sweden and Japan in 1969 – as were continuing studies in those countries.)

The Ontario team was composed of the most senior and best informed of the men directly involved in the mercury problem in Northwest Ontario, scientists who had kept "on top of" developments in Canada and abroad.[6] The author of the team's report was generally said to be Dr. G. James Stopps.* Doubtless one of the documents in their files was "The Public Health Significance of Methyl Mercury" printed on 18 February 1972, by the Environmental Health Services Branch of the Public Health Division of the Ontario Ministry of Health. Published, that is, by the five-man shop of which, on 18 February 1972, Dr. Stopps was boss. Said that report, in part: "In 1966 the cause of the disease was traced to methyl mercury poisoning which came from two sources, one being the outfall of the chemical plant and the other the production of methyl mercury from inorganic mercury by the action of micro organisms present in the sediments of Minamata Bay." In 1966. According to the report of Dr. Stopps' office. That the argument over when biomethylation was discovered still rages speaks only for the suggestion that government agencies are in our society either blind or hamstrung by insufficient research resources – or *aides memoire.*

At all events, on 26 March 1970, the Hon. George A. Kerr,† Ontario Minister of Energy and Resource Management, ordered Dryden Chemicals to stop "discharging mercury to the environment under any circumstances" and spelt out in detail how this should be achieved.[7] The order referred solely to mercury lost into the Wabigoon River and not to losses through exhaust gases.

At the same time a similar restraining order under Section 50 of the Ontario Water Resources Act was issued against Dow Chemical, operators of a similar plant on the St. Clair River. Four other Ontario

---

*Dr. Stopps was born in England in 1926 and took his medical training in the UK before doing post-graduate work at Cornell and in Toronto and Montreal. Dr. Stopps was for thirteen years an employee of Dupont at their Haskell Laboratory in Delaware, one of the largest toxicology labs in private industry.

Dr. Stopps moved from Dupont to the Ontario Health Ministry in 1971 and was shortly Chief, Environmental Health Services Branch. In February 1976, he left the government to become an associate professor of preventive medicine in the Occupational and Environmental Health Unit of the University of Toronto's Faculty of Medicine. Dr. Stopps also became Ontario's representative on the International Joint Commission, monitoring pollution of the Great Lakes.

†Hon. George Kerr, Ontario Minister of the Environment since 1974, represents the provincial constituency of Halton which includes the steel city of Hamilton and a large open sewer known as Hamilton Harbour. Mr. Kerr was born in 1924, called to the Ontario bar in 1955 and made a QC in 1967.

plants using mercury as an electrode were ordered to "virtually eliminate mercury losses": CIL in Hamilton; CIL at Cornwall, on the St. Lawrence River; Dow Chemical at Thunder Bay on Lake Superior, and American Can Company at Marathon, on Lake Superior.

By 1970 there was no question about the presence of unsafe levels of mercury in the fish downstream from Reed's mill for 100 and more miles, no question of the potential danger to people eating those fish – no question, from the beginning, of the source of the mercury, whatever fudging of the issue Reed might attempt through inaccurate talk about "high background levels of mercury."[8] In the words of a 1976 Ontario Ministry of the Environment study: "An estimated 20,000 pounds of mercury were introduced into the Wabigoon River at Dryden, Ontario, between 1962 and 1970 by Dryden Chemicals Limited. ... This has resulted in significant biological changes in the Wabigoon and English river systems and to a lesser extent in the Winnipeg River."[9]

In a speech to the Kenora Camp Owner's Association in April 1973 Ontario's Natural Resources Minister, Hon. Leo Bernier,* taking care to seize every opportunity to extol and promote the mineral wealth of Northwest Ontario, said, "If mother nature planted a curse on fishing in some lakes, she did leave an alternative. If you can't eat it, you might be able to stake it."

There are doubts about mother nature's role in mercury contamination of North American waterways, and doubts, too, that anyone will be filing a mineral claim on sediment in the Wabigoon or English rivers. Nonetheless in 1970 Norvald Fimreite was told by an official of the Ontario Water Resources Commission that mercury levels in the sediment of the St. Clair River, near the dumping location of the Dow Chemical plant, were measured at 1,400 parts per million of mercury by the government's labs. Reporting these facts in its issue of May

---

*Hon. Leo Bernier was born at Sioux Lookout in Northwest Ontario. The Natural Resources Ministry he headed until 1977 controls or profoundly influences: the mining industry; the forest industry; commercial and sports fishing; fur management and trapping; wildlife conservation; provincial and historic parks; thirty-seven conservation authorities. The printed description of his occupation on 1975 Ontario general election ballots was "statesman." Bernier later told a *Star* reporter in Toronto, "That was just my over-enthusiastic campaign workers. They thought 'politician' wasn't dignified enough." In February 1977, Mr. Bernier was made Minister of a newly created Ministry of Northern Affairs.

1971, *Esquire* Magazine checked with a chemistry professor with a special interest in mercury, Dr. David H. Klein of Hope College at Holland, Michigan, and gave him the figures. Said Klein, "Mercury in such concentrations in the sediment was approaching the commercially mineable level."

A cynical wag suggested that, as governments seemed unable or unwilling to force the polluting industries to clean up the mercury-wasted waterways, and as known methods of removing or de-fanging the mercury were inadequate anyway, a better solution might be to add some more mercury to the polluted rivers, to bring them up to strength and thereby attract other industrialists who could realize a profit by "mining" the sediment.

In May 1970, commercial fishing was banned on the Wabigoon/ English river systems as well as on Lake St. Clair. Letters were written to tourist camp operators on the affected waterways, recommending that their guides and guests "fish for fun," and not eat their catches. That summer, Fish for Fun posters were printed and stapled to trees along the contaminated streams and lakes. (Some tourist and fishing camp operators were said to be paying a two-dollar "bounty" to Indians who tore the signs down and brought them in. These operators didn't want their $100-a-day guests frightened away. Other signs reportedly were less of a nuisance; some area people say that they had been posted by employees of the Ministry of Natural Resources on trees one hundred yards and more from the shore of polluted water-ways. "Not even the moose could have found the damn things," snorted one area resident.)

Three fishing camps closed voluntarily, including the largest and best equipped, Ball Lake Lodge. Unable to divert some guests already en route, Barney Lamm, the owner, took fifty-four guests and guides to Minaki Lodge, thirty miles away. The Ontario Minister of Natural Resources Rene Brunelle,* assured Lamm personally that the fish in the area of Minaki were safe. All of this on 13 May, the day on which the Ontario Government announced that sports fish from the contam-

---

*Hon. Rene Brunelle was first elected from the riding of Cochrane North in 1958. Mr. Brunelle owns a tourist resort at Remi Lake near Timmins, Ontario. He has been Minister of Lands and Forests, Minister of Mines and Minister of Community and Social Services, and Chairman of the Cabinet. In February 1977 he became Provincial Secretary for Resources Development.

inated waters should not be eaten – just forty-eight hours before the opening of the 1970 game fishing season.

Still not satisfied that all the facts were out, Lamm pressed Mr. Brunelle by telephone for guarantees that fish around Minaki Lodge, 150 miles downstream of Reed's Dryden mill, were fit to be eaten. After repeated assurances the Resources Minister reversed himself and said he'd learned that those fish, too, had mercury levels above the 0.5 parts per million accepted as the maximum safe level for human food. It later transpired that many fish in the water systems downstream of the Reed mill carry mercury burdens ranging from six times to twenty times the recommended safe limit – burdens as high and higher than those found in fish in Minimata Bay. Lamm bought meat in Kenora and trucked it to the Lodge as alternate diet for those of his clients staying there. He then cancelled all reservations for the balance of the summer – and every summer since.

5 THE PLACE AND THE PEOPLE

The area generally described as Northwest Ontario lies just west of Lake Superior, extending north from the US (Minnesota) boundary along the eastern border of Manitoba and reaching 200-300 miles north from the international line. It isn't far northern country, although its winters can feel arctic enough for most.

The overall district is not urbanized, not industrialized, not thickly settled, not farmed. It is what's most easily described as Canadian Shield country: rough, rocky, heavily treed and dotted with countless lakes. Boreal forest, spruce, pine and birch trees everywhere; rivers and lakes abundant in gamefish; deer and wolves adjusting nature's balance between them from year to year; beaver and lynx patrolling the shorelines – occasional bays with their strands of sand or gravel – more often burly shoulders of ice-age rock dropping in sculpted curves into still water.

Stillness is the hallmark outside the towns of Northwest Ontario. The ubiquitous bush planes, the outboard motors and chain saws of summer, the snowmobiles of winter, only punctuate the peace they interrupt. Loons still call on a thousand lakes each dusk; sunsets have palpable texture. In winter the Northern Lights wrap the horizon in girdles of cold, green fire, pulsing towards the black sky zenith, always failing, falling back to the horizon and the arctic pole beyond.

It's beautiful country; for those in love with North America's wilderness, maybe the most beautiful. Cottage sites in Northwest Ontario have drawn summer residents and sportsmen from Winnipeg, Minneapolis, Toronto and Detroit for more than fifty years. Hunting's

31

here: moose and bear, deer and gamebirds. Fly a few hundred miles further north and the bear come with white fur, the deer become elk.

And the fishing? This is the fishing country of legend. There's a story of the old-timer, fishing in an aluminum boat with an excited neophyte on the Winnipeg River: "This guy landed a nice pike, maybe 14-18 pounds, but it scared him flopping around in the bottom of the boat. First thing I knew, he'd pulled a pistol out of his tackle box and put four shots through the pike, and straight through the bottom of the boat. The boat went straight down, motor and all – with our tackle and our beer – and we swam for shore with the guide. Fellow told me later some friends in Chicago had told him the pike was the most dangerous gamefish on the continent, so he'd figured it'd be a good idea to shoot any he caught."

Lake trout as big as coffee tables; muskie heavier than the boats from which they were caught. Talk to anyone who has fished Northwest Ontario – the stories are the stuff of epic poetry, the ones-that-got-away fit companions for the lady of Loch Ness; the ones that got caught impressive enough, toothsome enough, to satisfy the most over-achieving angler. The bourbon and scotch consumed over instant replays of the day's catch at most area fishing camps would themselves fill a not inconsiderable lake. It's difficult not to feel a bit taller, stalking over the rocky shore in high boots; shoulders seem to stretch shirt seams a mite; the air and the country give an heroic cast to the simplest acts – building a fire, carrying water for the tea, filleting fish on the shore.

Before 1730 the Wabigoon River, its fish, game and wildlife were the exclusive property of the Ojibway Indians. They were not renowned warriors. A contented people, living prosperously with nature, they fished, hunted and harvested the succulent wild rice strewn so lavishly near the shores of shallow, marshy lakes. And they trapped for meat and the furs they needed in winter. From the early eighteenth century the trapping served other purposes and needs, the furs sold to the Northwest Company, the trading credits used for tobacco and flour, sugar, tea, lard and whiskey. The river became a major route of fur traders ferrying loads from the Northwest trading post on Ball Lake.

But there was more in Northwest Ontario than fish, fur and claw. There was, to begin, gold and silver, and iron, copper, nickel. And timber – wood for lumber and pulp – for paper, hardboard, all the

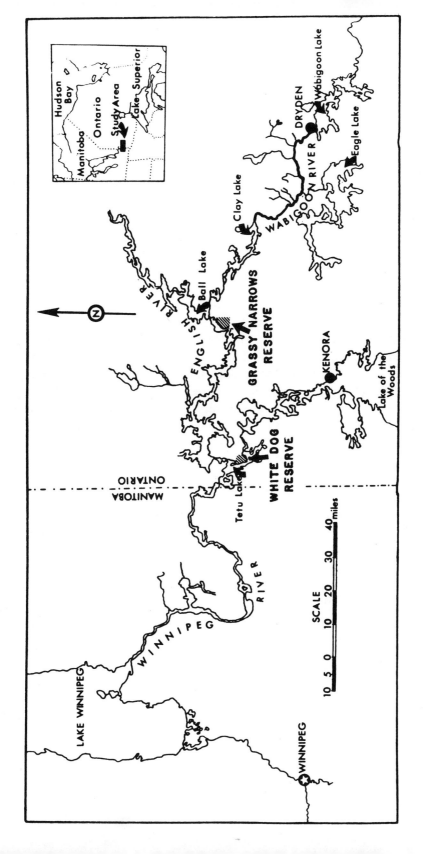

cellulose-based products of modern society. There were also the Great Lakes to the south and east – a water highway first used by the voyageurs, now opened to the lake steamers carrying ore and timber to the smelters, blast furnaces and fabricating plants of the industrial east in Canada and the United States; a route to take the resources out, and bring the developers in.

But still a remote country, an easy-to-forget appendage to Ontario's body politic. More than 1,000 miles west from Toronto over forbidding terrain; more allied geographically to Winnipeg – Manitoba's capital, just 130 miles beyond Kenora to the west; as much in common with Duluth, Minneapolis or Chicago as with Montreal or Toronto.

The towns are small with less than 10,000 people in any of the three main centres: Dryden, 100 miles east of the Ontario-Manitoba border; Fort Frances, nestled hard against the US boundary; and Kenora, barely inside Ontario. All three are wrapped around the security of a local industry – pulpmills, sawmills their base; tourism the sweetener of their economic nourishment. Radiating out from them are networks of secondary roads, the strictly utilitarian truck routes built by mining companies, timber cutters, hydro project engineers. Then there are the tiny communities – most serving only one isolated industry, some growing a little with the fly-in tourists, the fishing enthusiasts. Towns like Red Lake, Ear Falls, Hudson, Minaki. Fly over them in a float-equipped Beaver, bend your head to light a cigarette or check the instruments and you've missed them. Communities, mostly, with one general store-cum-post office; one small, frame hotel; one restaurant, maybe a bakery, a pool hall, a beer parlour in the hotel.

And the characteristics peculiar to small communities in remote areas: a sense of "us-against-those-city-slickers"; an openness and generosity foreign to larger places – unusual, here, to have a car break down without the first vehicle along stopping to help. There is more drinking, probably, especially in the winter. ("What else would you do, here, in February? Can't go skidooing or ice-fishing at night.") A sense of some isolation, of a precarious toehold on security and survival, when the summer's tourists have left.

Strikes here are rare, but bitter. There is a feeling that, when there's just one industry, just one game in town, it should be a "straight" game, and should be supported by everyone. Easy, in small, remote communities to get out-of-step. Less tolerance, maybe, of difference here, of dissent from the community's sense-of-the-meeting.

Sometimes, in such towns, there is a feeling of being left out, left behind. The summer visitors leave; children finish school and go off to college, marriage, careers in centres of wider opportunity. The last generation of Kenora's children are in Winnipeg, Chicago, Denver or Vancouver; not many of them in Kenora. So resentment, too, when outsiders are critical of local circumstances, local ways, local methods of dealing with problems perceived to be local. No family wants its linen aired on the national TV networks, in the international press. Dryden, Kenora and the others are still small enough to be "family." This is especially true of one-company mill towns.

The Reed paper mill at Dryden was built in 1913, and looks it. Sprawled along the west bank of the Wabigoon River immediately downstream (north) of the dam at the outlet of Wabigoon Lake, the complex of industrial buildings combines the least attractive architectural features of a grain terminal, turn-of-the-century warehouse, chemical refinery and missile bunker. As with most aging paper mills, buildings have been added and expanded when they were needed, wherever they fitted. After sixty-five years the overall appearance is one of jumble, even chaos. Linked and wrapped by steam pipes, catwalks, causeways, enclosed conveyor "tunnels" sloping crazily high above the ground, the buildings are mostly clad in time-scarred concrete or weather-abused, corrugated metal sheathing. Many rise, blind and featureless, for thirty or fifty feet from the plant yard. Where there are windows pocking those grey walls they are blind eyes, coated with a generation of scummy dust. Flanking the main driveway to town is the tidy, geometric, three-storey brick executive office.

The mill yard bears the scars of sixty-five years of aerial bombardment from the industry it surrounds. Three generations of wood fibre, bark and chips suffused with chemical fallout have long buried any trace of natural earth or vegetation. There is often mud inside the chain link fence girdling the plant, but no sense of contact with the living earth until, past the administration building and outside the factory gate, sickly grass struggles to keep a tidy carpet under a pair of flagpoles and a slick, logo-topped REED pedestal and sign. For miles downwind, as with every pulp or paper mill, a miasma of attar-of-rotten eggs; the clinging, tongue-coating presence of hydrogen sulfide gas is inescapable.

The Wabigoon is moat for the industrial fortress. Like the real moats of earlier medieval enterprise, it serves double duty as sewer, is shallow, unattractive, slow, dead and rancid as it grumbles north from the main effluent outfall pipe skulking beneath a creaking metal railway bridge just yards downstream.

The rail line is Reed's connection with a world eager for Reed Fine Papers. A road and bridge lead from Dryden to the plant gate, flagpoles, executive block, guardhouse. Dryden sends its workers over the bridge, three times a day. The town of 7,000 has four industries. Reed employs about 1,500 men, the others combined less than 150. One hundred or more of those work for Alex Wilson in his newspaper, printing and related enterprises. Traffic from the mill nourishes the community as surely as Dryden's workers sustain Reed International; payroll and taxes replace the green of foliage lost to mercury, hydrogen and chlorine.

Less than 1,000 yards north of the railway bridge that ties Dryden to its "main source of economic wellbeing" (Reed's phrase), the Trans-Canada Highway arcs out of the northwest corner of town, back into the "environs" where, driving through the restored green and sapphire of forest and clean lakes, the Reed monument to economic wellbeing can be scrubbed from the mind's eye – until the next town, and the next mill.

Scattered between the towns and villages are the Indian reserves; places the Ojibway agreed to settle and, in return for certain treaty rights negotiated with the federal government 80 or 100 years ago, cleave to. The areas are identified by the number of the treaty – for the area around Dryden and Kenora, the dozen-and-a-half reserves of Treaty Three; for the area from Red Lake and north, Treaty Nine. White Dog and Grassy Narrows reserves are in the Treaty Three district, ninety minutes' drive north from Kenora (in good weather).

The reserves are even more isolated than the towns. But until recently they were nourished by the surroundings; good game in many places, blueberries in the summer, wild rice, fish in abundance. Work, sometimes, cutting timber for the sawmills and pulp companies; work as guides in the fishing camps, as cooks, mechanics, carpenters, electricians, serving staff, housekeepers and maintenance staff; work catching fish for sale. A good and happy life, in good and happy times.

The educational opportunities are not up to those in the towns in every way, but there are now schools on the reserves; young children needn't leave home for the high-starch diets and high-starch regimes of Indian Residential Schools. In some ways, a more open society than in the towns; less sense of ownership, less anxiety about property, material possessions, and appearances. More ribaldry here, more joking, singing, strutting. Greater closeness to nature, more intimacy with birth and death since they are so much more often witnessed at home. More sense, too, that nature's whim can tip the scales from abundance to impoverishment or back. High water means no wild rice; storms mean miserable nights sleeping cold under the canoes during the harvest. Maybe more acceptance of hardships imposed by nature. Social disciplines, state disciplines may seem less important – harder to understand. ("Children should be loved, not spanked. They spanked my kids in that school.")

There's also more time for communication on the reserves. The rhythms of speech are nature's rhythms; pauses between thoughts, unhurried reflections on undemanding questions. Hard, here, to imagine the urgency of answering a government letter on the day of its arrival.

All of Ojibway history, legend, religion, is oral – passed from generation to generation. Even today there is no written Ojibway language and, given that about one-quarter of the nearly six hundred souls on each of the two reserves speak only Ojibway, small chance of any response to many of the letters from government. As Ignatius E. La Rusic noted in that unpublished 1973 federal report: "There is clearly a problem in initiating an information programme in both communities ... a programme to correct rumours and misinformation is not simple – especially as one cannot use written Ojibway materials since no one reads the language. This means all communications to about a quarter of the population will have to be in oral Ojibway."[1] (A lesson still unlearned, by both federal and provincial officials, four years later.) M. La Rusic, in his study, noted other communication pitfalls which have since trapped or frustrated many bureaucrats, at the ultimate expense of the local people:

It is easy to fall into the trap of publishing something like the Canada Food Rules, which reflect the White, middle class preferences of those who prepare them. For example, in the Northwest Quebec situation two years ago, the Department of Health and Welfare erred in suggesting that the fish in their diet be replaced by fruit and vegetables. Even if these were available in the region (which they were not in sufficient quantity) the suggestion was laughed at by the meat-eating Cree who wanted nothing to do with "rabbit food.". ... Equally important is that any information programme not be confused with some sort of face saving manoeuver on the part of the government. The people have been told many stories of the seriousness of mercury. They will have seen the Minamata films. ... Therefore, to report, that levels over 100 ppb are not really serious, is to strain the credibility of the people when they know that the levels in a "normal" population are around 10-20 ppb. ... There is the great danger that any attempt to assuage the concern of people who feel they are in danger will be seen by others as an attempt to set the stage to renege on the acceptance of responsibility for any possible compensation that such people might be in a position to claim.[2]

Not easy for organization folk from Ottawa and Toronto to communicate with the Ojibway. In addition Indians find it hard to be rude. The Ojibway don't like to contradict, to offend. Rather than give a negative reply to a request they will smile, say "yes," and do nothing. Rather than press for explanation of a system, process or document foreign to them, they will nod understanding to avoid embarrassing the official who has failed to communicate effectively.

Dr. R. B. Sutherland, then Chief of the Ontario Health Studies Service in the Ministry of Health, was served an object lesson in Ojibway desire to please when he visited the reserves in 1972 to research the fish-eating habits of the populations at risk from mercury. He recalled the experience in a research interview in 1976:

After I had talked with the first three or four people I began to realize that the rest were all giving me precisely the same answers, word for word. It was impossible to believe each individual and family was eating exactly the same amount of fish, day-by-day.

Finally, I realized what had happened. After the first three or four interviewees left the office, they told the others waiting outside what they had told me – and said I had seemed to be pleased with the answers. So those still waiting made sure they would please me, too, by giving the same answers.

The Indian bands are largely self-sufficient communities, the white population of Northwest Ontario largely mistrustful and uninterested in their Ojibway neighbours. Close and enduring relationships were formed with some employers, fishing camp and tourist lodge operators. But the towns are strange turf; places where one has to shop. The journey is long, the roads bad, so the visits infrequent. The townspeople see the Indians as very different, easy to identify in their appearance. Prejudice is easy. No one in Kenora has ever been heard to say, "There goes another drunken WASP." Nor does anyone in Kenora ever hear, "He's a good, steady, reliable white man."

So with the bureaucrats and politicians in the area. Their friends, campaign managers, fund raisers and colleagues are from the towns; their perceptions mutually reinforcing. Only natural to ignore – even to faintly dislike – those "other folks." Usually the white prejudice, like the Ojibway eloquence, is muted. But not always. When Ontario Treasurer, Hon. W. Darcy McKeough, visited Kenora in September 1976, the town council requested that he arrange to move the government liquor store to a spot remote from the main business intersection where it now stands, so that tourists visiting Kenora wouldn't be obliged to see drunken Indians while strolling on the main street.

Then there are these comments extracted from a tape-recorded research interview with a scientist who undertook to study some of the people affected by mercury consumption for one of the governments involved. At the start he is referring to the faking of symptoms, which he says he sees all the time in Workmen's Compensation cases.

> It's kind of easy to talk yourself into these things if you know this is the kind of thing you should have wrong. ... I see a lot of people, a lot of children 12, 13, 14, 15 years old, particularly girls, who have all sorts of subjective phenomena, which are hysterical. ... When you saw_____
> [a man with particularly high mercury blood levels interviewed by the author], he couldn't balance on one foot, eh? Probably had a few whiskeys, eh? Is this damn machine [the tape recorder] on?
> When a friend of mine asked a Regional Director of Health and Welfare what would solve the problem, he said, "Two generations." They [the Indians] have a value system that is unsatisfactory in our society; they are a lot different from us and I think this difference makes it hard for them to live. For instance, I was at White Dog and some guide

had just shot a moose there and everyone helped themselves to a steak; the moose was collective property. They have their houses – but they don't own property. It is OUR reserve, not MY reserve. Territorial imperative is very important to me, it's not to them, you know. And this is a value system ... born of their past. They were nomads not too long ago. They're not acquisitive and as they're not acquisitive work is unimportant. They'll do a job for a couple of weeks until they have enough money and then they'll bugger off. So it all comes back to the question of property.

Time is a lot different to them. ... Ever tried to make an appointment with these birds? They live in a huge North American culture where time is important. These fellows are in an enclave with different property values, time values, education – and how you tie this in to our society, I'll be goddamned if I know.

If I were God I'd wave my scimitar or whatever and say "Get the hell out of Grassy and White Dog." It's an anathema, it's got ghosts all over it. I'd push them someplace else.

The WASP catalogue of Indian vices is the familiar refrain of the "better" element in every society: "They're lazy, shiftless, unreliable; they drink too much, have no ambition, don't care for their families; they're slow, hard to educate, uninterested in self-improvement; they lack initiative, prefer to live in filth and garbage; don't have 'our' values, 'our' sensibilities."

There can be something of the self-fulfilling prophecy in such pejoratives. In the early 1970s when Ontario and federal bureaucrats were often heard to bemoan the Indians' lack of "get-up-and-go," a common comment at White Dog and Grassy Narrows was, "We just can't make it. No matter what we do, we can't make it." That attitude has changed somewhat since 1975 when the interest and moral support of Japanese scientists and Minamata disease patients revived hope at Grassy and White Dog. But there was a good deal of apathy between 1970 and 1975; there still is some. To suggest that government agencies have been less than effectual in communicating with the residents of Grassy Narrows and White Dog is an egregious under-statement. The causes, whether roots in culture shock, arrogance, or simple, bureaucratic indifference, are less important than the results: Indian bitterness, reflexes conditioned to anticipate rebuff and resent-ment from any governmental representative, cynicism and apathy. To understand the degree to which these people have been programmed for failure is to marvel at their continuing tenacity. To close this chapter here are four anecdotes which supply the blue-prints for negative conditioning.

"THEY HAVE NO INITIATIVE"

Robert Keesick was janitor at the school on Grassy Narrows reserve. Most of the reserve, in the 1960s, had no hydro, so Mr. Keesick bought a diesel motor and generator, set them up in a log cabin, and began generating electricity for his home. He was shortly supplying about ten other homes nearby with hydro.

Four years later, Mr. Keesick decided to expand his enterprise. With no electricity in most of the community, with his generator proven efficient, with the nearest town fifty-five miles away, he thought it would be a good idea to open a laundromat. He prepared a building for that purpose and approached the federal Department of Indian Affairs for a $5,000 loan to buy two commercial washers and dryers.

Indian Affairs sent a representative to Grassy Narrows to look at Mr. Keesick's set-up and advise on the loan. This in 1970, when the river at Grassy Narrows had been closed to commercial fishing because of mercury contamination, and two years after the general marketing, in Canada, of non-phosphate detergents. The representative of the federal government talked with Mr. Keesick, looked at his plans, and vetoed the loan. There was too much risk, he reported, that the laundromat would "pollute" the waterway.

"THEY PREFER TO LIVE ... IN GARBAGE":

The residents of Grassy Narrows for some years tried to find a system for disposing of garbage – the bane of small rural communities around the world, where there are no municipal services, no government organizations or budgets for such needs. In 1975 the federal Indian Affairs office at Kenora informed the community there was a $600 annual allocation available to pick up, transport and dump garbage from the community – $1.64 per day.

This was less than ample, but the people of Grassy decided to make an attempt, perhaps adding some welfare funds or other cash, to make the garbage collection a combination work project and town site service. But six months later, in the spring of 1976, an Indian Affairs representative, visiting the reserve, found garbage conditions as bad as they'd been a year earlier. It took him a while to find out why.

The Indians had collected and bagged all the garbage on the reserve in a clean-up drive; they had intended trucking it to a dump site, some 200 yards off the road, which had been in use as such (by the local Hudson's Bay store) for ten or more years. Then the provincial Ministry of Natural Resources sent a man to forbid the dumping. The site, said the Ministry, was too close to the main road. The Indians regrouped and cut a new road through the bush, a full mile further into their own reserve property; at the end of that road they cleared a site for use as a dump. But the available money had all been used up by now, the workers needed income, and the collected garbage, left over the winter, was scattered by dogs and wild life.

In the spring of 1976 the Indians tried again, but as their new "road" went through a gully which flooded in the spring, they went to work with their chain-saws to clear yet another site as a dump. Again the road proved to be so muddy after any rain as to be impassable. Indian Affairs came to look again, made a survey again, and declared that the Indians should truck their garbage the fifty-five miles to Kenora since it would cost $16,000 to fix the road. The Indians were also told that they would be taken to court if they used the accessible garbage dump site, although it was located on their own reserve property. After a protracted series of conversations, assisted by Dr. Peter Newberry, an American Quaker physician who lived at Grassy Narrows for eighteen months in 1974-5, the Ontario Ministry of Natural Resources and the Federal Department of Indian Affairs relented and "permitted" the folk of Grassy to use the original dump site.

"WE DON'T TAKE THE INDIANS INTO ACCOUNT ... "

The traditional and bitter description, by Indians, of governments speaking, "with a forked tongue" never seemed more justified than in the years from 1963 to 1977, in the area around White Dog reserve in particular. While spokesmen for both the federal and provincial governments were proudly describing make-work projects, plans for vocational training and studies designed to develop industry on the reserves, an agency of the Ontario government was, in 11 of those 14 years, engaged in destroying an industry with a potential annual "payroll" of up to $150,000 annually at White Dog alone.

The industry was wild rice harvesting; the mechanism of destruction the release of water from hydro dams each spring with, in eleven years, consequent destruction of the downstream wild rice crop on which the Indians depended both for diet and cash income. Said one spokesman for Ontario Hydro when asked about the flooding, "We don't take the Indians into account," when deciding how much water to release from the hydro dams.

The major control dam, at the south end of Goshawk Lake on the Winnipeg River system, 1½ miles upstream from White Dog, was built on reserve land in the spring of 1958. When it was completed Hydro closed the dam and flooded the area behind it without notice of the day to the 100 local residents; many of them had to flee their homes over piled-up blocks of ice on the shore, escaping with only their canoes and the clothes on their backs. Moved, perforce, to the main community at White Dog, the evacuees were offered Ontario Hydro frame and tar-paper construction shacks as homes although some wintered in tents before the shacks were provided.

The White Dog people built an earthen control dam to keep Hydro's spring releases of water from backing into White Dog Lake, a major wild rice growing area and a tributary of the river system. The dam protected their crops in 1972 and 1973, when harvests were ten times those of the earlier years. But in 1974 a Hydro release even greater than those of previous years washed out the dam; there was no crop in 1974 and 1975. The Indians asked Leo Bernier for the assistance of a government engineer in planning a new dam. After interminable delays, the people of White Dog were still waiting, in the early spring of 1977, for some of the control mechanisms without which the new dam was useless to protect their crop. And, in 1977, Ontario Hydro still had not agreed to compensation terms for the use of Indian land and resources used in the construction of roads, rights-of-way, dams and boat landings almost twenty years earlier. For details, including a description of the destruction of the community at One Man Lake, and its cemetery, see Appendix One.

"APPARENTLY DELIBERATE SABOTAGE ... "

In the spring of 1976 Indians at Grassy Narrows reported that a freezer supplied by the Ontario government to hold mercury-free fish supplies for them wasn't working. Leo Bernier acted quickly and decisively. He told the Ontario legislature he suspected an act of "apparently deliberate sabotage," and announced he'd asked the Attorney General to order an immediate probe by the Ontario Provincial Police.

The freezer in question held 7,500 pounds of whitefish, all of it rotten. Mr. Bernier hinted darkly at politically motivated sabotage and said friends in Kenora had told him "that outside leadership was involved." He was especially suspicious because the incident had come to light during a visit to the reserve by Stephen Lewis, opposition leader in the Ontario legislature.

The OPP inspector dispatched to Grassy Narrows reported the freezer had been damaged during "a boyish prank," when a thirteen-year-old threw pebbles into the freezer fan to see them expelled by the fan blades. He reported there was "nothing more to it" – and added evidence that anyhow the fish had already been spoiled *before* the child broke into the freezer building.

Mr. Bernier refused to withdraw his allegations in the legislature and claimed the Indians had failed to report the breakdown to make immediate servicing possible. Research for this book revealed that an Indian telephone report about the failure of the freezer, made at least two weeks before they told Ontario officials at a meeting the fish were now rotten, had somehow, in the minutes of the meeting (kept by an Ontario official) been made to appear to have been first received at the meeting. For further details of the legislative debates and provincial police probe, see Appendix Two.

Mr. Bernier's relationship to the people of Grassy Narrows and White Dog, and to the people of Kenora, is both intimate and complex. As Minister of Natural Resources he was responsible both for preserving the resources of the area, and for plans through which those resources are industrially exploited. It was his Ministry which stimulated and regulated the mining and pulp companies that comprise the major industry of Northwest Ontario; he is a frequent public advocate of resource-based industries, both in general terms and in specific cases. Bernier's original jurisdiction of Mines and Northern Affairs, became the Ministry of Lands and Forests in February 1972. On 28 September 1972, new stationery had to be ordered yet again, this time for the new Ministry of Natural Resources. Mr. Bernier's personal power and control of the Ministry was said to have grown throughout the years between 1971 and 1977, but what was never resolved was the paradox implicit in the definition of the Ministry: the need to be both promoter of resource exploitation and protector of the resources and those they nourish.

More than the Minister whose pen-stroke could save or destroy the economic bases of towns like Kenora and Dryden, Indian reserves such as Grassy Narrows and White Dog, industries including Dryden Chemicals, Leo Bernier is also the member of the Ontario legislature for the area. He personally represents those people and places; and his financial campaign resources and electoral survival are both rooted in the area.

Mr. Bernier first won the right to serve the area at a by-election on 22 September 1966 and was re-elected in the general election contests of 1967, 1971 and 1975, with ever-mounting majorities at the polls; many describe the riding as his personal and closely held fiefdom. But there were chinks in the impregnable pluralities after public disclosure of the mercury problem. At Grassy Narrows and White Dog, Mr. Bernier's share of the total vote dropped from 58.69% in 1967 and 62.58% in 1971, to 27.72% in 1975.

One reason for Leo Bernier's unpopularity on the reserves is that he has failed to answer Indian requests that he amend the game laws to allow them to hunt year round to increase the protein in their diets.

People seeking "trophy fish" have sometimes had somewhat more understanding treatment. This from a Canadian Press story of 26 March 1976:

> Leo Bernier said today he has used his influence as a cabinet minister to help persons convicted of offences under the Game and Fish Act ... [and] has had guns, confiscated for hunting offenses, returned to their owners.
>
> He said he has also taken his daughter's father-in-law fishing on a sanctuary lake, forbidden to those without ministerial approval. ...
>
> Mr. Bernier said some persons will be critical of him for using his ministerial influence, but nothing he had done was illegal.
>
> In the case of his fishing trip on Muskie Lake sanctuary, Mr.

Bernier said: "But Gordie Howe [the hockey player] and his two sons Marty and Mark have been on that lake, too." He said members of his staff took the Howe family to Muskie Lake a number of years ago.

It is considered hospitable of the province to take celebrities into special fishing spots to promote Ontario's tourist attractions, the minister said, and a number of United States generals had also fished there.

He said game wardens seized two fish which Ralph Cast, his daughter's father-in-law, had left to be stuffed and mounted. But Mr. Bernier said he interceded and had the fish returned to Mr. Cast.

In an interview with Toronto *Star* reporter Daniel Stoffman, published on 28 April 1976, Leo Bernier responded to criticism of the Muskie Lake family outing, as reported by Stoffman: " 'You can't satisfy everyone,' he said, with a big smile, as he relaxed the other day in the huge Queen's Park Office decorated with pictures and mementos of Northern Ontario."

On 3 February 1977, Premier William Davis made fact out of the jocular description of Leo Bernier used by friends and critics in previous years: "Czar of the North." The Premier created a new provincial portfolio of Northern Affairs and installed Mr. Bernier as its first minister; the gap at Natural Resources was filled by another man who had said that the mercury poisoning problem was "greatly exaggerated," the Health Minister, Frank Miller.

6 DESIGN FOR DISASTER

One research scientist in Ottawa told the author: "It couldn't have been arranged more efficiently if the company had set out to destroy the Indians at White Dog and Grassy."

We've already seen some examples of the Indians' defencelessness in the previous chapter; but the vulnerability of the two communities far exceeds that fostered by callous government bureaucrats. The area is peculiarly fragile for three other reasons: its isolation; the narrow economic base on which it has developed; and the destruction, before mercury was ever used at Dryden, of the life of the Wabigoon River. As a result, the effects of the 1970 Ontario government order to stop dumping mercury were immediate and catastrophic.

Let's begin with the nature of the Wabigoon River below Reed's mill. The river, assaulted for over fifty years by continuous dumping of chemicals and wood fibre from the mill, and effectively "dead" when mercury losses began, was ideally suited to the process of biomethylation. According to a report prepared by the Ontario government's Ministry of the Environment in the early 1970s,[1] the Wabigoon River simply cannot support a pulp mill. The volume and flow of water in the river isn't adequate to handle pulp mill wastes. A short walk along the bank of the Wabigoon below the mill, past its chain of islands of wood fibre and other mill excretions is graphic confirmation of the conclusions in the report (prepared in 1973-4, but first published, in summary form only, in the winter of 1976-7). The Reed mill at Dryden is described as the worst polluter in the industry, in Ontario, and the plant most vulnerable to government legal action. There have been government grants to Reed since the report – but as yet no fines,

47

though some charges for general pollution were finally laid in December 1976.

Complaints about the deterioration of the river were first aired in 1937. There is life, such as crayfish, just two hundred yards upstream from the mill's effluent discharge, above a dam. But for forty miles below the dam the Wabigoon is a dead river. At that point crayfish are found, and they have extremely high burdens of methyl mercury.

To make matters worse, there is the combination of wood fibre and inorganic or ethyl mercury. Wood fibre destroys oxygen in a water system, and fish life requires the presence of at least five ppm of dissolved oxygen in the water. In a survey made in 1968 by the Water Quality Surveys Branch of the Ontario Water Resources Commission, sampling of the Wabigoon showed readings consistently under that minimum need, to the point thirty-nine miles downstream from Reed Paper, where a waterfall naturally aerated the stream. A full twenty-seven miles downstream from the mill the river contained only 2 ppm of oxygen. At a dam site downstream from the mill, the fibrous sediment lies forty feet deep on the river bottom.[2]

But the fibre and sludge do more than kill the oxygen and the marine life of the river. Research into biomethylation demonstrates that the process occurs most efficiently where there is least oxygen. What better "soup," then, for rapid conversion into the organic mercury killer than the Wabigoon River, where walking on the waters seems an all too plausible exercise, where torpid rafts of fibre and assorted particles and chemicals suck up the stream's oxygen as they join the countless thousands of tons of sludge already resting on the river bed? The river is too small, too slow-moving to scour its own bottom, flush its own poisons rapidly downstream where they might be more dilute, less deadly in their concentration.

There's one more chemical irony in the chain of circumstances: any salts added to a mercury-bearing sediment will release mercury more quickly. Take that fibrous sediment in the Wabigoon, add that ten tons plus of mercury and let cook via the biomethylation process. Then add one further element: build a section of the Trans-Canada Highway and of Ontario Highway 105 along the northern escarpment above the river, on the western outskirts of Dryden. Finally, as on all major highways in Ontario, slather the road liberally with salt after every snowstorm – and Dryden gets a lot of snow. Spring run-off will do the rest – carry a heavy load of winter-accumulated salt into the river and provide a fresh burst, a fresh release of mercury just before the opening of another fishing season.

Next there are the human factors in the target area. The men of Grassy Narrows and White Dog worked, happily and faithfully, as guides at the tourist lodges and fishing camps. They cooked and shared those ambrosial shore lunches with their guests, fishermen from Toronto and New York, from Chicago, Detroit, Dallas, Los Angeles and St. Louis. Some of them still do, as we'll see. Most don't. The largest lodge, Barney Lamm's Ball Lake Lodge, put a $300,000 annual payroll into Grassy Narrows reserve, and alone employed virtually every employable Grassy Narrows adult. It closed down immediately and voluntarily when informed that its guests couldn't safely eat the fish they caught. Its closure means, over the minimal forty years estimated for the rivers to flush themselves free of mercury, lost wages totalling $12 million. This in a community of fewer than 600 people.

Then there was the commercial fishing. On both reserves. Men who worked as guides during the day would set their nets and harvest them at night. Their wives and children, too, would tend the commercial fish nets. The closure of the Wabigoon/English river systems to commercial fishing in May 1970 reduced the Ontario catch of commercial fishermen by not less than 200,000 pounds annually.[3] Ten million pounds of fish were impounded and destroyed in 1972. Revenue to fishermen in that area was expected to average from $30,000 to $50,000 annually. Multiply those figures by that minimal forty years and the commercial fishing losses in those areas alone – where the fishing is largely a part-time activity by local Indians – approach $2 million in lost income. For the province as a whole, if other affected water bodies take as long to be safe, nearly $35 million.[4] And there are four other affected provinces, and forty of the American states.

In addition, the main staple of the communities was and is fish – both as their main source of protein and as a source of bulk in their diets. The soil is poor, rocky, unkind to gardens or those who would raise animals for meat – a foreign activity, anyway, to these hunters, fishermen, trappers.

The economic deterioration since 1970 has been dramatic. For example, despite their own fairly effective efforts coupled with provincial and federal employment and training programs, the number of

Indians receiving welfare at White Dog doubled between 1969 and 1974. In that same period actual welfare payments tripled, reflecting inflation-forced increases in payments as well as the doubled number of recipients. Unemployment in Grassy Narrows and White Dog jumped from 20 per cent to over 80 per cent following pollution-caused job losses. All of this, after seven years, without a nickel of compensation or a dime's worth of hope that conditions will improve substantially during the lifetime of any resident in those shattered communities.

This deterioration has been accompanied by cultural and human depression and by social apathy. One measure of the disintegration is in the suicide rates. Between 1970 and 1973 there were 36 confirmed and suspected deaths by suicide in the area. The annual Canadian suicide rate varies by sex and age, but averages less than five deaths by suicide for every 100,000 of population. Even ignoring the absence from the area of many White Dog and Grassy residents seeking work and income off the reserves since losing their economic base, the suicide rate in these communities averages 999.6 deaths per 100,000 of population– 200 times the national rate for the same period. Three years is not a long sample, nor is 1,200 people a large one; but with such differences, some inferences are hard to avoid.

On 31 October 1975, the community representatives had asked the province to declare their reserves a disaster area. Mr. Bernier explained that would be of little help, since existing legislation required local municipalities to match "disaster" relief on a dollar-for-dollar basis, and there was no municipality to help. Instead, Mr. Bernier proposed establishing a new government position, someone posted in the area who would have "special powers" to co-ordinate all government ministries and agencies in Ontario, crossing petty jurisdictional lines and over-riding anxieties about areas-of-responsibility. Good idea, said the Indians. Two and a half months later, the local representative of Ontario's Indian Community Secretariat, Jeff Perkins, was named the first (and last, as it turned out) "Co-ordinator." (Prior to 15 January, he'd been called a "Community Resources Officer.")

Perkins, widely respected both by the Indians and his bureaucratic masters, set out to meet his new and wider responsibilities with what he thought were his new and wider powers. It didn't work. When Perkins asked for action on various specific programs, the requests were fed through precisely the same interminable bureaucratic channels. When Perkins asked Natural Resources staff in Kenora to move on his needs he was told they'd had no word from government in Toronto that he had "any special" authority. When Perkins enquired about the fate of the detailed sixteen-page briefs presented to the Cabinet representatives in October by the Band Councils, he was told by Natural Resources personnel in Kenora: "Mr. Bernier has them in his files in Toronto, we don't know anything about those requests." Seeking action on many specific requests to Natural Resources (Bernier had told the 31 October meeting: "I want to emphasize to you that I recognize from looking through these briefs that there are a lot of areas where my Ministry can become involved"), Perkins was told, by Natural Resources, to channel his suggestions in the usual way, through his own Secretariat.

In early March 1976, Jeff Perkins resigned in disgust. His successor, Hume Martin, was given a different title by the Indian Community Secretariat. He was called a "Community Resources Officer" – again. Martin was also, literally, given wider responsibilities. He was to look after a total of nine Indian reserves, instead of just the two suffering from the consequences of mercury pollution.

The Kenora office of the Secretariat, once home to four or five staffers was back to a single employee and business-as-usual; the wheel had come full circle.

In 1975-6, when Ontario's government was refusing to establish a disaster area, downgrading even the minimal staff responsibilities suggested and set up by its own cabinet ministers, there was already a wealth of evidence of many people in the communities with dangerous blood mercury levels and, more frightening, with probable symptoms of Minamata Disease. Some of the data we'll discuss in detail later was in supressed federal government files – possibly unknown by the province; some was dearly held by provincial authorities, as reluctant to share their studies with the "feds" as with the public or the Indians themselves. But in 1975 the Indians knew, intuitively and from observation, what has now been revealed by a search of some of those government files: that many of their neighbours and relatives had classic symptoms of mercury poisoning – constricted vision, loss of feeling in the hands and feet, reduction in co-ordination, tingling sensations in the face and hands. Moreover, although they lacked knowledge of the scientific studies we will examine later, the Indians knew there was more violence in their reserves; there seemed to be more deaths related to alcohol, to exposure, to pneumonia, more deaths by suicide, and they suspected links with the mercury in fish – links which data assembled for this book appear to prove. They knew, and they were growing bitter amid their continuing inability to move governments to act effectually.

Perhaps the most eloquent statement of that frustration came from Josephine Mandamin. Pass Josephine Mandamin – in a car, on the street in Kenora, in a boat near her home at White Dog; if you're white and unfamiliar with Indians at close range, the word that first crosses your mind probably will be "squaw." She is somewhere near forty; somewhere near 160 pounds; somewhere near five-feet-four; the gross value of everything she wears might be six or eight dollars. Not chic. Not cosmopolitan. Not striking. Not white. But very near the surface of Josephine's persona, there is a philosopher – a woman of extraordinary commitment, and hope.

She is married to Isaac Mandamin, Chief of the White Dog Band Council; they have eight children. She is a community health worker, owner and driver of her own one-ton pick-up truck, tireless labourer at the task of trying, somehow, to cancel the corrosion of hope brought about by mercury poisoning. She is saving her salary so that she can travel to Minamata, Japan.

The words that follow are hers, as was the muted fire and quiet humour with which she expresses her will to endure:

> I don't know why they keep pussy-footing around the mercury problem ... I don't know. Maybe it's because of the money; they don't want to lose the tourist business.
>
> If it was white people being poisoned it would be different; if there was mercury poisoning in Toronto you'd get action. Just like that. But we're just natives here; second-class Canadians. ...
>
> I resent the fact very much when people come here and try to change it all for "progress." Progress to me just means pollution. And killing. Killing our fish, our way of life. Maybe killing our children.
>
> It seems that the whole majority of the people near here ... – when we try to fight for our rights ... we seem to antagonize them. I don't understand that at all. It isn't our intention to antagonize anybody. We just want to be treated fair. But even, in Kenora, when people there see

an Indian dressed in nice, clean clothes; when they see us driving a good car; when they see us sober, they seem to resent that. It seems like they prefer us to be drunk, to be dirty. Then they can keep us where they want us. We don't like drunks any more than them; we don't like dirt. We just want people, the government, to recognize that our livelihood is being destroyed. ...

The way government treats us – I think the government would prefer to see all the Indians dead; it would be so much easier for them. No more Indian problems. Look at all the movies that John Wayne makes: he beats the shit out of the Indians, every time. Kills them. I won't feel so bitter the day I see an Indian beat the hell out of John Wayne. Then I'll be satisfied.

My kids still go fishing; they still eat the fish from the river, here. With inflation, now, I can't afford to eat meat all the time; and my husband is too busy to go and get fish from the clean lakes. ... Kids can't realize that this beautiful river is contaminated. ... They say, "It can't be. Something that beautiful can't be poisoned." And it tastes so good. So when my kids bring back a mess of fresh walleye, pike, we eat them. ... The government has been giving us some whitefish lately, in the freezers they built here; but they have no flavour; we just don't like whitefish much, they're so dry. ...

I don't believe in militant tactics, you know. But you know; we know, because we live close to nature: any creature, any creature, if you push him too far into a hole, into a corner, he will have to try to fight, to get out. ...

I tell my kids the only hope for Indians is through education. ... I say, someday they may get to sit in the Indian Affairs chair, in the job as superintendent, where they can help their people. ...

But still, I blame the government. For the pollution. For refusing to recognize that the paper company is responsible for polluting our lakes, our river. I can't understand why they won't get after the paper company. Maybe they're getting some money from the companies. If I was the Prime Minister I'd make the polluters responsible for the damage they've done. That's how it's supposed to work. I'd make them compensate the people in some way ... I know money isn't the answer to everything ... You can't ever replace a human being. ... But money could be used to build new jobs; to get back some pride, some dignity.

I'm scared for the future – for the mothers who've been eating the contaminated fish; nobody knows what might happen to their babies, when they're born. I'm worried about my daughters, when they have children. No one knows what might happen.

We don't need money for individuals; compensation. We need long-term employment; money to create long-range jobs. We're sick of welfare.... We want to stand on our own two feet. But when they take our commercial fishing licences away, ... when they flood out our wild rice crops, then, for the time being that's all we've got left. Welfare. ...

Sure that makes us bitter. ... Our children [are] bitter, too. ... All the kids here. ... They can't strike back at government ... so they strike out in small ways: vandalism, fires, destroying things, breaking things sometimes. You know, school property, government property. ... Then the law system makes it worse. They send those kids to "training schools." That's what they call them. And those kids are trained to be hard-rock criminals. They come back harder, more bitter. They are educated to be mean when they come back. That doesn't help.

I try to tell my kids not to be bitter. It does no good to hate. ... There are times when I can't stop being bitter, though. ...

People hear about us on TV. But they don't care. They watch. But they care more about their colour TVs and their cars and their payments. They have other things to worry about. Most of the time they don't even have to see us.

We're here alone.

7 REASSURING THE TOURISTS

Imputation of motives is heady stuff – dangerous stuff. It can be said, with certainty, that bureaucrats involved in the problems of Northwest Ontario are concerned, respectably concerned, with the economy of the area, with possible loss of employment and tourist revenue. Bank spokesmen at a Kenora Chamber of Commerce meeting in 1972 estimated that Kenora lost $6 million or more in US tourist revenue between 1970 and 1972 alone. Given the common multiplier of three-to-five times used by economists in measuring the overall benefit of "foreign" currency in a community, the economic loss to Ontario's economy, and to Kenora area businesses and wage-earners from that source was between $18 and $30 million (another loss in respect of which there's been no talk of compensation). Small wonder that local businessmen, employees and bureaucrats find it easy to blame the "messengers" of trouble.

THE SMEAR

As Josephine Mandamin noted, people unable to strike out against the object of their frustrations will often seek the handiest target and despoil it, instead.

The white businessmen and tourist operators of Kenora and Dryden have been frustrated by seven years of painful publicity, during which they have somehow felt guilty about a problem not of their making – a problem they often feel, sincerely, may not be all that serious after all; after all, the government hasn't thought it serious enough to close the rivers to sports fishing. But still the acid of ongoing publicity and continuing charges corrodes the public's confidence in the area; corrodes, too, self-respect and pride in communities and businesses built through generations of labour.

Businessmen, though, don't break schoolhouse windows when frustrated, nor do they light fires in garbage dumps or privies. Adult "vandalism" more often involves the smear – the individual or concerted attempt to discredit the bearers of ill tidings and thereby bolster confidence that the bad news may not have been true, after all.

Just about every journalist who has reported on events in Northwest Ontario has been attacked as seeking sensation or ignoring "the facts." But nomadic journalists are somewhat unsatisfactory punching bags. When the pain persists a more handy scapegoat is infinitely more satisfying. Marion and Barney Lamm have filled that need since 1970.

In 1969 the Kenora Chamber of Commerce named Barney Lamm their "Man of the Year," recognizing the fact that Lamm had made a greater contribution to the economic growth of the area, through his air services and lodge, than any other single individual. Barely two years later Marion Lamm had been forced to the verge of a nervous collapse and the Lamms had been persuaded to sell their beloved Kenora home and move their three daughters to a new home at Gimli, Manitoba, almost 200 miles to the northwest.

In spring 1970 Barney Lamm was something of a folk hero among his fellow camp operators. He had come to the area from his native United States immediately after World War Two and started at Ball Lake on a shoe-string, some wartime gratuities and the confidence of a pretty, blonde bride. Over the years the couple built both camp and airline into multi-million dollar businesses. They took out Canadian citizenship and raised their daughters to love the area, as they did. Many of the Indian families employed at the camp lived on a nearby island during the summer. Marion soon became the best-known midwife in the area, delivering many of the wives when there wasn't time for Barney to fly them to Kenora.

From the first warnings in 1970 Barney Lamm took a lead role in seeking redress and resolution of the problem. Thanks to his successful businesses, he had the resources to commit to the investigation, and the battle; he used them unstintingly. In the first few months the Lamms spent more on fish tests in the area than the provincial government –

something in excess of $50,000. Barney provided pilots and aircraft for any scientists and journalists wishing to visit the area, as he provided transportation "out" for Indian spokesmen who wanted to meet with government officials or attend meetings. It was through the Lamms that Eugene and Aileen Smith heard of the problem in Northwest Ontario and, later, as a direct result of their interest that the Japanese study group from Kumamoto University tested Indians at White Dog and Grassy. Marion Lamm kept voluminous tape recordings, speech texts and newspaper clipping files from the beginning and soon "Marion's scrapbooks" were an indispensible research source for any journalist seeking background on the story. With the airline and ancillary services their only operating business and their base moved to Gimli, the Lamms' economic interests in White Dog and Grassy ended; but not their personal interest. Barney Lamm's planes still commute regularly into the reserves. Government and scientific researchers on the reserves depend on Barney for fast transport to town, deliveries of urgently needed equipment and supplies. The number of injured and ill reserve adults and children flown to Kenora for emergency treatment are beyond computation.

When it became clear the area fish were going to be contaminated for more than the "few weeks" first suggested by the Ontario government, Lamm filed a "statement of claim" against Dryden Chemicals and Dryden Paper in the Supreme Court of Ontario for his losses in closing Ball Lake Lodge. The companies filed a "statement of defence" some time later. In the intervening years, although the suit has not been pressed, it's been used as a major lever in attempts to discredit the Lamms. ("Barney's just trying to make a few million bucks out of Reed.")

The smear began in Kenora, with whispers and rumours. The Lamms had been in trouble anyway, said the gossips, and needed an excuse to close down. They were in financial difficulty; they weren't getting enough guests; a new road driven through relatively near their lodge had taken away the romance of its isolation. None of the stories true, but all hurtful.

Even in 1975, in July, a New York editor of *People* Magazine, Sally Moore, was told by Frank Newstead, Manager of the Kenora Tourist Bureau, that Barney Lamm's lodge had been closed down because the sewer system was below standard. Mr. Newstead added that the lodge was in financial trouble anyhow. Confronted by the Lamms, Newstead (whose tourism publication is supported by advertising from area fishing camps and businesses) said he'd "heard it"; but he apologized and promised not to repeat the wholly inaccurate statements. One year later, on 20 August 1976, perhaps not knowing the man who engaged him in conversation, he repeated the charges to Dr. Frank D'Itri of Michigan University.

A few months later in Kenora, some "Cleopatras" more anxious to discredit the messenger than deal with the ill-tidings, attempted to muzzle the messenger as well. During the September 1975 Ontario general election campaign a supporter of the local government candidate Leo Bernier, took to his typewriter. Using the letterhead of his employer, Bell Canada, Mr. Frank Lillicoe of Kenora wrote to the local radio station, CJRL (a station which leases its broadcast lines from Bell Canada) to suggest that Barney Lamm, who had been on a radio "hotline" phone-in program ought not to be allowed to go on the air during an election period.

Then there were the telephone calls. To Marion Lamm at her Kenora home, usually late at night. Repartee like, "Do you know where your husband is?" "If you know what's good for you, you'll get the hell out of Kenora." "If you're smart, you'll keep your doors and windows locked." And, from a woman: "Where's Barney? He was supposed to meet me in room so-and-so."

And finally, for Marion Lamm, the last straw, when her twelve-year-old daughter was attending an early evening movie: "Do you know where your daughter is?"

The letters-to-the-editor, callers to local radio hotline shows weren't a great deal more imaginative or sophisticated. Such folk wondered "How [Barney Lamm] sleeps nights" while destroying an area for his own selfish purposes.

Then there was the financial smear. Barney Lamm, the "millionaire," was financing all the unpleasant publicity. Lamm had bribed the Cousteaus to film the area for a documentary on industrial pollution for world wide TV distribution. Barney Lamm had financed this book and "bought" the author. Lamm paid for a massively detailed 28-page study into mercury pollution published by the Ontario Public Interest Research Group at the University of Waterloo and titled "Quicksilver and slow death." All untrue.

The Dryden *Observer*, quoting allegations that the study had been financed by Barney Lamm, ran an extensive front-page story headlined "Quick-gold and fast death" (17 November 1976). On 29 November Terrence Moore, co-ordinator of the Waterloo Research Group, wrote to the editor of the Dryden *Observer* to deny the allegation. The *Observer* did not publish the letter. (It continued to find space for such protestations as we saw on p. 15)

The *Observer* hasn't entirely stopped publishing letters to the editor, however. On 8 December 1976, over the name of Robert L. Rolls, there were these comments from a correspondent with more success in meeting publication standards than Mr. Moore: "Having read your reports about Barney Lamm I wonder if he is a Canadian? ... Is Barney Lamm a Canadian or a displaced person who wishes to make his money in Canada? ... He may sleep with his money but he can't take it with him."

Alex Wilson, publisher of the Dryden *Observer*, owns and operates Coldstream Paper Products, which wholesales Reed papers to other businesses (including Alex Wilson's office supply and stationery store in Dryden) and prints and distributes a number of specialty paper products ranging from post cards to paper place-mats for restaurants.

BAD PUBLICITY

Government was no less sensitive to criticism than the area's businessmen and camp operators. In 1970, the Ontario Department of Tourism and Information issued the following press release:

AULD MOVES TO OFFSET BAD FISHING PUBLICITY
An all-out campaign is being waged by Ontario Tourism and Information Minister James Auld to offset damaging publicity resulting from mercury contamination findings in certain provincial waters.

On the heels of an emergency cabinet meeting and the announcement last week by Lands and Forests Minister Rene Brunelle that the ban had been lifted on all sports fishing where the contaminant exists, Mr. Auld moved to initiate:

*A $70,000 newspaper, radio and television advertising program aimed at audiences in the US and neighbouring provinces which includes the beefing up by 50 per cent of the department's TV commercials on fishing and lakeland country.

    *A 900-word press release to more than 1,000 outdoor writers and outdoor newspaper editors in both the US and Canada.
    *Up-to-the-minute bulletins. ...

At the same time, summer 1970, a senior official of the Health Ministry was making the first of a series of recommendations that the river systems be entirely closed to all fishing. Said he, in a research interview for this book in the late autumn of 1976:

> I recommended that all waters which contained fish with 2 ppm or more of mercury be closed to fishing. ... The Department of Health recommended that the tourist camps be closed down; and then there was a hassle in Kenora because the Chamber of Commerce and the Minister of Lands and Forests were advertising the fishing at the same time we were recommending that there should be no fishing and it all be closed down.

And the Kenora Chamber of Commerce had powerful allies. On 13 August 1970, Leo Bernier "interviewed" George Kerr over the Kenora radio station. Said Kerr, as excerpted from the transcript of a tape recording of that broadcast:

> Well, I think it was unfortunate that any camp operator felt it was necessary to close right down at the beginning of the season. A lot of people are happy to come here and fish for fun. ... I feel that by closing a camp down and then making a great to-do about it, publicizing information that possibly isn't exactly accurate and maybe a little bit too emotional, this is how it has hurt the whole industry in this area. ... The fact is that the situation in these areas that have been closed to fishing is improving. ... The mills that have been using mercury, we are monitoring those mills, we're satisfied that *there isn't any mercury loss now.*

That wasn't true, as we shall see, but it gave the Kenora Chamber of Commerce heart. Indeed on 13 August 1970, Mr. Kerr was a virtual well of misinformation. Some examples:

> We have monitored and checked these industries continually from last April or May and we're satisfied that there is no mercury now going into these rivers.

It is impossible to find mercury in water just by analysing water as you can with other pollutants.

Now there is still a great deal of uncertainty about mercury contamination in fish, how long it will take fish to lose it, to lower their mercury count. The statement that we have had from our scientists is about 12 weeks. This was the original statement, assuming that that fish is not subject to any more contamination. We're hoping, therefore, by next spring that the problem will be over.

Mercury "losses" from the Reed plant at Dryden continued for fifty months after the radio interview; mercury *can* be analysed in water; and the half-life of mercury "in some fish is 700 days," according to "Mercury Levels in Fish from Northwestern Ontario," published by the Environment Ministry, Hon. George Kerr, Minister. That report cites research done in Sweden by three scientists who published their findings in 1970. One fish with a mercury half-life of almost two years is pike – a preferred gamefish in Northwest Ontario.

A little earlier, on 10 June 1970, the Federal Fisheries Minister, Hon. Jack Davis, had replied to a question in the House of Commons: "... The level of mercury of fish in Canada is a very small fraction of the level which was found, for example, in Japan where there was an effect on human beings. In other words, the levels in Canada are very safe levels indeed."

In that year, 1970, one government report after another noted that mercury levels in Ontario fish were entirely comparable with the situation at Minamata. Walleye at Clay Lake were found with mercury levels of 24 ppm, 45 times higher than acceptable safe levels for human consumption – almost 125 times higher than levels safe for people whose blood mercury burden is already above normal. And Mr. Davis' statement came six weeks after commercial fishing in the area had been banned, by his order.

In 1971 the dichotomy between Ontario Health Ministry anxiety and Natural Resources assurances continued. Interviewed on Kenora radio on 17 March 1971, Leo Bernier was asked about the new season's tourists arriving and eating fish from the contaminated waterways. Said Bernier: "Want my own personal opinion? I think he, the tourist, could come up here for three weeks, eat the fish two or three times a week, and be fine."

Most tourists had shore lunch daily, of course. Writing to one camp operator, Colin Myles on 28 February 1971, seventeen days before the Bernier broadcast, Dr. G. J. Stopps, Ontario's Senior Medical Consultant in Environmental Health, postulated the case of a tourist who, staying at an area fishing camp, ate one meal daily of just seven ounces of fish containing 5 ppm of mercury. Said Stopps: "If the daily intake while at the camp remains the same, the blood level will reach a peak of 1,510 in two weeks, and 2,000 in three weeks. These are blood levels in the same range as reported in persons who were poisoned in Japan and clearly above the safety level." They are, in fact, levels at which deaths occurred in Japan.

But Leo Bernier is a hard man to discourage. As his colleague Rene Brunelle reported to the Ontario legislature on 2 April 1971: "[Mr. Bernier] attended the Sportsmen's Show, and some of the Sportsmen's Shows in Chicago and other areas – the interest was very great and they are looking forward to a good tourist year."

A month later Bernier told the Kenora District Camp Owners Association, as quoted in their favorite publication, *The Tourist Outfitter*, Volume 13, Number 5:

> ... that he believes mercury pollution has been seriously overrated by a great many people. The "fish for fun" signs that many of you found objectionable will not be posted this spring," he said. "The Minister of Lands and Forests has assured me that the Cabinet agrees on a policy no signs will be posted until the Cabinet agrees on a policy and that there are no immediate prospects that these signs will be replaced [*sic*]."

Nor was the Hon. Mr. Bernier inconstant. Legislature criticisms after his government "passed on" some recommendations of the government's own task force on mercury, on 4 May 1973, triggered this exchange, as reported in the Ontario *Hansard* (p. 1644):

> *Mr. Reid*: ... How does the Minister explain that he has completely ignored the major recommendations of his own task force on mercury pollution. ... How does he explain that he is going to continue to allow Indians and tourists coming to that area of his riding to eat mercury-polluted fish. ...
>
> *Hon. Mr. Bernier*: Mr. Speaker, let me first say that I do not agree with the member for Rainy River that we completely ignored the report of the task force because this is not correct and he damn well knows it. ...

Mr. Speaker, I must point out that there are a number of task force recommendations and that this is a civil servant's report. There's nothing to say that we have to accept even one of their recommendations. We've accepted a major number of them. The bulk of them have been accepted.

There was continuing government support for the Bernier position. On 26 April 1971, Rene Brunelle was asked whether he agreed with Leo Bernier "that the problem of mercury pollution has been overstated and too much emphasis put on it." Said Brunelle: "My own personal opinion, Mr. Speaker, is yes, I do believe it has been overstated and exaggerated; because most of our lakes in the Precambrian Shield we find have a natural background of mercury."

Mr. Brunelle was no slouch at the art of obfuscation either. This *Hansard* extract from 11 May 1971:

We have not done away with those "fish for fun" signs. We have not posted any this spring. ... In those areas where we feel there could be a health hazard we intend to put posters up and that position will be made not just by our department, it will be made by the four departments involved, mainly the Departments of Health, Tourism and Information, Energy and Resources Management and our own. And it will be in those areas where there is a high concentration of mercury.

No such areas were evidently agreed upon between the departments – no posters were put up in 1971 or any subsequent year. And on 13 June 1972, Mr. Bernier was able to tell the legislature proudly: "Mr. Speaker, there are no lakes in Northern Ontario that are closed to sports fishing. Every lake in Ontario is open to sports fishing."

Meanwhile, back at Separation Lake Camp, second in size and accommodation in the area only to Ball Lake Lodge, Colin Myles had been following an almost equally difficult course – remaining open in 1970 but candidly telling his guests of the hazards and urging them not to eat the fish they caught, then closing in 1971. Mr. Myles was still seeking guidance and, after two seasons of heavy losses was considering closing his camp permanently. He wrote to the Department of Tourism and Information and got a letter back from R.J. Stone, Regional Manager, dated 11 January 1972. (Evidently pleased with his response, Mr. Stone made a carbon for his boss, the Deputy Minister, guaranteeing that a copy of his reasoning would stay in the Department's files):

> Dear Colin:
>
> Thank you for your enquiry regarding the disposition and future of the Separation Lake Camp.
>
> While we realize your operation is in the centre of the area in which the contamination is prevalent, we point out to you the successful efforts of others in similar situations over the past year. ...
>
> Surely we can learn from their experience that despite the adverse publicity regarding the contamination problem with perseverance and good operation, your resort could continue to operate. ... Research regarding mercury in fish and wildlife is constantly revealing that this situation has existed for many years. ...
>
> My advice to you is to advertise and try to retain your previous clientele as well as attracting new guests and get your resort back on an operational basis.
>
> We will be pleased to assist you in any way within our scope to return the operation to its former successful operation.
>
> Yours truly

Colin Myles declined the advice, and closed – the only major camp operator other than Barney Lamm to do so.

The chief irony running through the misadventures of all tourist operators in the area is that a total ban on sports fishing in affected waterways, made in 1970 when the Health Ministry first urged that action, might well have prevented much of the "bad publicity" and subsequent economic loss. Tourists would then have known that any waterway open to them was a "safe" waterway.

In 1970, the Premier of Ontario, John Robarts, met with fishing camp operators in Kenora and asked them to assemble estimates of their total costs in relocating off the poisoned waterways with a broad inference that the government would pick up or heavily subsidize the costs. On 4 February 1971, not yet a cabinet minister, Leo Bernier issued a press release which says, in part:

> Leo Bernier, M.P.P., Kenora, today disclosed the Ontario Government's intention to assist tourist camps in the [Fish for Fun] areas of the province affected by mercury contamination. ... Each operator requesting assistance will be interviewed. ... It is expected that such a policy would include straight purchase of some tourist camps. ... short-term

operating capital loans: or a combination of long-term forgiveable and term loans for relocation or conversion to multi-activity tourist camps rather than exclusively fishing camps as is the case in many parts of northwestern Ontario.

According to Leo Bernier the cabinet decision was the result of extensive study and consideration for the contamination problem with respect to "fish for fun" areas in Ontario.

He stressed that if the problem is not resolved as proposed, as many as 400 people could be out of work in northwestern Ontario this summer with a probable loss of at least one-third of the tourist trade for this year which would translate into several million dollars of lost tourist revenue.

But that wasn't how things were to be. ...

8 "LET THEM EAT FISH"

Prior to 1971 tourist operators, businessmen and residents had supposed the problem was a passing irritation which would be solved in less than a year. But as 1971 approached and the true dimensions of mercury contamination were revealed it was assumed by everyone, including most of those in government, that the river system would be closed to sports fishing, that camp owners would be compensated or moved, that intense medical study and economic rehabilitation would proceed for the Indian communities. All of these perceptions changed coincident with the change in the leadership of the Ontario government.

On 12 February 1971, John Robarts retired as Ontario leader of the Progressive Conservative party and was succeeded, at a leadership convention, by William Davis. On 1 March 1971, Davis became Premier and Leo Bernier was appointed to his first cabinet.

Now the cost estimates requested by John Robarts and supported by Leo Bernier became a dead letter. The emphasis seemed to shift from corrective response to self-serving alopogia, unremitting determination to downplay the urgency of the situation and elaborately-mounted attacks on anyone suggesting the problem was serious. Useful communication between the Health Ministry staff working closely with the problem and everyone else in Ontario's government seemed to end. The Fish For Fun program ended; mercury information booklets prepared for fishermen by Leo Bernier's cabinet predecessor seemed, by summer, to have disappeared. (They are now collector's items.) The aim appeared to be to keep the camps open, the tourist dollars flowing. The probability of the Ontario government closing the river systems all but disappeared. Indeed, in another three years, as we shall see shortly, that government was itself in the fishing camp business on the poisoned waterway.

But the PR war continued. As mentioned above, early in 1971 the Ministry of Lands and Forests, had published a slim, green-covered, twelve-page booklet titled "fishermen ... ABOUT MERCURY IN FISH". The booklet, written in question and answer format, was designed to acquaint anglers with basic data on mercury contamination. No figures on the number of booklets printed is available – the number actually distributed is a whole separate question. Some weeks after the booklets were printed and distributed Marion Lamm went looking for one. At the public office of the Lands and Forests Ministry in Kenora, jump-off point for the affected area, Mrs. Lamm was told by the official in charge of the office that there was no such booklet, that he'd never seen or heard mention of any such booklet. Marion Lamm persisted, suggested he speak to his colleagues, make enquiries. After an argument lasting at least twenty minutes, the Lands and Forests man reached under the counter separating them, pulled a booklet from a large stack stored there, and gave it to Mrs. Lamm.

But even if widely distributed and read, the booklet was, at best, written to reassure. Some extracts follow:

> How are mercury concentrations in fish measured, and how are the results reported?

> ... the results of mercury analysis are reported in parts per million ... one ppm indicates one part of mercury in one million parts of fresh fish flesh, and is equivalent to one ounce of mercury in approximately 60,000 pounds of fish.

Reassuring. Until one recalls that a lethal dose of mercury is just one-quarter gram.

> What is the maximum acceptable concentration of mercury in fish for human consumption, and how was this standard chosen?

> The legally accepted level in Canada for mercury in edible parts of fish is set at ½ ppm by the Federal Food and Drug Directorate. This standard ... contains a safety factor to protect heavy fish eaters or those who may be unduly susceptible to mercury poisoning.

Some safety factors. The 0.5 ppm "safe" level is computed as "safe" for people eating one meal a day of only 3½ ounces of fish. An average shore lunch on the Wabigoon/English system would comprise anything from a half pound to two pounds of fish per person. Moreover, in season, some residents of the area commonly eat two fish meals daily; their daily intake of fish may therefore total from perhaps 14 to as much as 60 ounces daily – from 4 times to 17 times the "safe" intake.

> How much mercury is found in fish from Ontario waters?

> ... where there are no known local sources of mercury from human activities in the drainage system, most fish contain less than ½ part per million of mercury. In waters where there is such a known local mercury source, pike, pickerel and bass often contain 2 or 3 and up to 15 ppm. About 40 waters lacking known local sources of mercury from human activities have been found to contain some species of fish averaging approximately ½ - 1 ppm mercury.
> *The reason for these apparently elevated mercury concentrations is unknown at this time.*

Not entirely "unknown." There are solidly based estimates concerning mercury contamination found in areas remote from "local sources of mercury from human activities," as documented in Chapter 17.

> What is the Ontario Government doing to solve the mercury problem?

> ... sports fishermen have been warned not to eat their catches. ... The Ontario Department of Health is measuring the mercury content in hair and blood samples from persons living in the vicinity of lakes with highly contaminated fish. ... Although sport fisheries in mercury affected waters have remained open to allow continued recreational use, fishermen have been warned not to eat their catches from these waters.

The "warnings" to sports fishermen consisted of the "Fish for Fun" signs which disappeared in 1971-72 and letters to fishing camp operators which were mostly not passed on to guests. Anyhow the warnings of health hazards were coming from Ontario's Ministry of Health, but it was the Ministry of Lands and Forests which regulated and had contact with the fishing lodges, which policed and advised them. Setting aside the three fishing camps which closed voluntarily, the lodge and resort owners' usual custom was to avoid mentioning mercury at all; if the subject came up they reassured their guests that the danger was exaggerated, even non-existent. For example, in the first week of June 1973, Toronto *Star* reporter Robert Reguly chartered a plane and dropped in on a series of fishing parties staying at area camps and spending the day on the water. Reguly asked about mercury and found that "none of the tourists had been warned of the danger of eating fish taken from those waters." Later he found some US tourists who had "heard" of the problem. "The lodge owner told us the Indians eat three times as much fish as the guests every day and no harm has come to them," said lodge guest Adolph Okenfuss. Added the fisherman: "I figure you'd have to eat about fifty pounds of these fish a day for a month for it to do you any harm."

These reassurances to guests came four months after Dr. Stopps, had written a widely published letter to a lodge owner noting that " ... *the World Health Organization recommendation for maximum weekly intake could be exceeded very easily by a very small meal of* [local] *fish.* For instance, it would amount to about *one ounce* of a fish containing 10 parts per million mercury ... "

Throughout the period the lodge owners, undiscouraged, wrote cheerfully to guests who asked for facts about mercury contamination. On 17 March 1972, George Hohnstein, owner of "Grassy Lodge," wrote to a prospective client in Chicago:

> Dear Mr. Henson:
>   Thank you for your letter of March 6, which has been forwarded to us in Milwaukee where we are presently exhibiting in their sports show. ... The "mercury" problem is sort of "fizzling out" as it is now realized that the problem is no where near as serious as first thought. ... It is our feeling that these fish are safe to eat, just as they have been for many many years that people have been eating them. At one time there were signs posted around the lake, cautioning people about same, but they are no longer posted. We kept eating the fish ourselves, as did most of our guides from the Indian reservation. ... As far as I know they are no longer even testing the fish in our waters, for mercury. The last test I have heard of was taken about a year ago.

Seven months after Mr. Hohnstein's letter, the then Ontario Minister of Health, Hon. Richard Potter, was writing to lodge operators in the following words (this particular extract is from a letter dated 16 November 1972, to Mr. Colin Myles now of Ash Rapids

Camp Limited): ". ... The average levels of mercury in the pike and pickerel in the lower English and Wabigoon River *are thirty times the maximum allowable limit set for mercury in fish,* therefore fish from these waters should not be eaten. ... "

Mr. Hohnstein was not intimidated by letters he had received from the Health Ministry. In a letter dated 23 March 1973, he wrote to another prospective guest, Mr. George Hooper of Chicago:

> Dear Mr. Hooper:
>   Thank you for your inquiry. ... Grassy Lodge is a clean and comfortable fishing camp. ... We feel the remors [sic] regarding the so-called mercury pollution have been highly overrated, and reports have been blown way out of proportion, to be highly misleading. We have continued to eat fish from our waters, on a regular basis, without ill-effect.

Other lodge owners, if less blatant, were equally confident. Wrote Tom and Anne Ellis, operators of Rough Rock Lodge, to a Mr. C. Rosenbaum of Southfield, Michigan, on 30 April 1975:

> Dear Sir:
>   Thank you very much for your request for information. ... We fish the very same waters that Minaki Lodge did *and there is no problem with having shore lunches.* [My emphasis.]

In the last week of August 1975, the author interviewed Dr. Tom Clarkson of Rochester University at Grassy Narrows, during preparation of a CBC film documentary on Minamata Disease. Clarkson, perhaps the world's leading toxicologist in the field of mercury poisoning, was asked about the potential risks to a sports fisherman on holiday for three weeks and eating between a pound and a pound and a half of fish every day.

Using a calculator, and working on a daily intake of 500 grams of fish (just over a pound) with allowance made for excretion over the three weeks, he replied: "*Such a person could develop a blood level of approximately 450, about 450 parts per billion.*" (The WHO says 20 ppb is a maximum safe level. The US and Canada say 100 ppb. At 500 ppb acute symptoms of Minamata Disease are to be expected, and 1,300 ppb are known to be lethal.)

Dr. Clarkson was employed by the Canadian Department of Health and Welfare in 1975 to study blood and hair samples in

Northwest Ontario. In his Interim Report, published early in 1976, he revealed the results of blood tests on two women before and after they consumed a small meal of mercury-contaminated fish. Their blood levels had increased, fourfold in one case, almost fivefold in the other, after four hours and after a very small single serving of fish with relatively low mercury contamination.

In his recommendations Dr. Clarkson says,

> Surveys should be made of guests and other residents for exposure to methyl mercury with special emphasis on regular guests and long-term residents in fishing camps and lodges in areas having high mercury in fish.

No such surveys had been undertaken, eighteen months after his recommendations reached the federal government. Of course, fishing camps and lodges are a provincial responsibility – specifically, that of the Ontario Ministry of Natural Resources, to which federal officials would have to appeal for help in implementing the recommendation. In that connection, this quotation, taken from the never-publicly-released 1973 "Final Report" of the federal task force:

> ... The Ontario Ministry of Health is working in close co-operation with the Department of National Health and Welfare. ... *Co-operation with other provincial departments working in the field has not, however, been at the same high level*, with the result that valuable information concerning the environmental effects of mercury pollution has been difficult to obtain.

And again, in the "Conclusions" (p. 18):

> The free flow of information and data on mercury in the environment with the Province of Ontario is impeded for reasons that are not clearly understood. This difficulty has not been experienced with other groups either within Canada or abroad.

Private researchers, too, such as Norvald Fimreite and Dr. Frank D'Itri of Michigan University, were frustrated, thwarted and harassed. (See Appendix Three.)

It can't be ascertained whether federal Health officials ever asked Leo Bernier to arrange meetings with fishing camp owners. What is clear is that no efficacious meetings have been held, no monitoring of lodge guests contemplated or initiated.

When he returned to Rochester in the autumn of 1975, Dr. Clarkson appealed through a Chicago television interview for American sportsmen who had fished the Wabigoon/English river systems to contact him. He explained that blood mercury levels as far back as six months to a year could be determined through hair sample tests.

A number of the fishermen wrote to Dr. Clarkson without exception saying they had heard nothing of the mercury hazard while in the area. This despite the "best efforts" of the Ministry of Lands and Forests which, in that 1971 "green book," had claimed: "Fishermen had been warned ... " and, later, "Every effort is being made to see that sport fishermen are supplied with up-to-date information concerning the safety of a favourite activity – eating their angling catch."

Said Dr. G. J. Stopps during a research interview in the autumn of 1976:

> I can remember on coffee breaks Health Ministry people would complain about Labour Ministry people, Natural Resources Ministry people, not following up on recommendations made by the Health department; but Health people have always had a lot of moral clout with the public ... I could never understand why they didn't simply announce ... to the public ... that their recommendations hadn't been followed ... that would have solved the problem.

Dr. Stopps was among those not heeding his own advice. So his recommendations weren't followed, either.

Asked, "Was there deliberate obstruction of more effective action?", he said

> No. It was just that nothing would happen. No one was trying to prevent action... but somehow all roads did seem to lead to Leo Bernier. ... [who was appointed Minister of Lands and Forests just after publication of the "green booklet."] Bernier would occasionally say things you couldn't quarrel with. It's just that afterwards nothing would be done, nothing would get done. ... Nothing would happen. ... And of course one Ministry can print informative material, but it can't force another Ministry to be enthusiastic about handing it around.

Given that more than 90 per cent of guests at the fishing camps on the polluted waterways were from the United States, and that all non-Ontario residents were and are required to buy a fishing licence, it seemed the booklets could have been given every angler at the time his licence was purchased. That might have helped persuade that, "Every effort is being made ... "

Pollyanna pronouncements from governments and from Reed apologists continued, one set of claims centring on declining mercury levels in fish. A news release of 13 March 1975 from the Ministry of the Environment said:

> William G. Newman, Ontario Minister of the Environment, today announced a significant reduction in mercury levels in fish taken from Ontario waters. ... [He] said, "in both the St. Clair River system and in the English River system we have observed a steady reduction of mercury in the fish specimens we have analyzed from 1970 to 1974 ... as much as 40 per cent reduction in the 1974 sample compared to the levels of 1970. " ... Leo Bernier ... advises me that his Ministry will continue to monitor test results of mercury levels in fish during the next few months to determine which species and which lakes can be re-opened for commercial fishing by the native people." ...

Some fish mercury burdens did drop 40 per cent in those four years – but even that wasn't enough for everyone. Said Reed president Robert Billingsley, speaking to Japanese researchers in August 1975, and making a prepared statement: "We have data on fish biology throughout the area. ... Since 1970 fish levels have dropped 50 per cent." Then, ignoring the fact that only about one per cent of mercury in the river sediment biomethylates annually, feeding a continuous stream of poison to fish in the system, he told his visitors that, "If the source of contamination is from other causes [i.e. other than Dryden Chemicals] the levels of mercury in fish will stay high." A clever argument that; a suggestion that, if things improve dramatically, the dangers have been overstated – while, if there's no continuing improvement, the fault must lie elsewhere. And things were staying bad. A 1975 internal federal memo says "there is no question" that the present environmental conditions in both Northwest Quebec and Northwest Ontario do "not differ significantly from the situation that caused the tragedy [at] Minamata."[1] The following is from a massively detailed report by the Ontario Environment Ministry:[2]

> Mercury levels in fish of similar size from the Wabigoon/English system have not declined from 1974 to 1975. There has been a decline in fish mercury levels for some species in some lakes since large-scale testing began in 1970. ... Most species of fish from lakes on the Wabigoon-English system have mercury levels far in excess of the 0.5 ppm guideline set by the Food and Drug Directorate. *There was practically no species from any lake on the system that could be considered fit for human consumption.* These lakes include Ball, Clay, Grassy Narrows, Separation, Tetu.

Tetu Lake is adjacent to Holst Point Lodge, our next focus of interest.

HOLST POINT LODGE

The "Final Report" of the 1973 federal task force said: " ... it may take up to 70 years for the river system to cleanse itself through natural processes. High methyl mercury fish levels will, therefore, persist for the forseeable future" (p. 6).

The Ontario government wasn't prepared to wait seventy years, or even until after the "forseeable future." On Friday, 8 February 1974, the Kenora *Miner and News* had a new banner headline atop page one: "Government to take over Minaki Lodge." Ontario had already put over $5 million into the privately owned lodge in loans, as well as assisting in the funding of an airstrip, skiing facility and housing project. In the next three years it was to sink a never-disputed, estimated $6 million or more into the lodge in massive renovations, although the lodge was still far from ready for guests with the summer of 1977 in sight. And by spring, 1977, government estimates projected a further investment of $30 million.

When Industry and Tourism Minister Claude Bennett was introduced to a Kenora audience by Leo Bernier on 7 February 1974 he announced that the lodge was not "achieving its tourism potential" in private hands and promised to make the government-operated resort "contribute to the development of northern Ontario." The lodge, said the previous owner, Rod Carey, who was to continue as a "consultant" for the government, closed in the summer of 1971 because business had fallen off after the mercury scare. "Mercury pollution was the lodge's downfall," said Carey. "We re-opened on a year-round basis in January 1972, but it was tough going." It didn't work and the lodge closed again – permanently. Of course in 1972 fish in the waters adjacent to the lodge were still contaminated by mercury, as they have been in every year since.

There was an additional property acquired by the Ontario Government along with Minaki Lodge; part of the same complex, it is called Holst Point Lodge, and is a fishing camp comprising a central log building with dining-room, bar, some rooms and separate tourist cabins, as well as facilities for trailers, campers and travel-homes. Holst Point, accommodating perhaps forty people, is much smaller than the huge and beautiful central log building of Minaki Lodge; but, needing no extensive renovation, and having a much smaller annual overhead, it was able to stay in operation, contaminated fish or not.

Here's a description of Holst Point Lodge, from a brochure printed and distributed after the government took over ownership in early 1974. The brochure was mailed to prospective guests in the winter of 1974-5:

> Today, Holst Point consists of four fine suites in the main lodge, nine modern housekeeping cabins and a limited number of trailer pads for self-contained units with sewer, water and electrical hook-ups provided. In addition, we are presently in the process of expanding the number of suites available for the summer of 1975. ... Whether you fly, come by rail, or drive, plan to spend your next vacation with us at Holst Point Lodge, Minaki, Ontario, Canada.

But a lodge operated by the Ontario government, on waters which its own Health Ministry says contain fish "which should not be eaten" (Health Minister Richard Potter, speaking in 1972)? Not for fishermen, surely; just for a good family holiday?

Turn to page two of the Holst Point brochure:

> At present we have twenty 1974 20hp Mercury motors on 18-foot, high-transom Lund boats. A 5-gallon tank of mixed gas will be included with the daily rental of a boat and motor. We will also have gas and bait available for sale at competitive 1975 prices. ...

There's more, all designed to please the ardent angler; rates for boat and motor rental, for guide fees while fishing ($24 daily for one boat, $30 for two boats, $36 for three boatloads of sports fishermen). And rates, too, for shore lunches – a special charge of $4 per person to have the guide fillet and fry those fresh-caught, mercury-contaminated fish over an open fire. Rods and reels were $4.50 daily.

Way back in 1970, when the Ontario government carefully identified all lakes and waterways affected by mercury and posted its Fish for Fun signs, the waters at Holst Point were among those posted. Fish in those waters had mercury levels well above the maximum safe level of 0.5 ppm and were expected to continue high "into the forseeable future." But Holst Point, now owned by and operated for the people of Ontario by their government, stayed in business. And its business was fishing – including shore lunches, even filletting, packing and flash-freezing the catch for anglers to ship home. Ontario tax-payers, the "shareholders" of Holst Point, weren't asked if they wanted to keep the business in operation, hazard the health of guests.

In late August, 1975, Hon. Frank Miller, Ontario Minister of Health,* was interviewed by the author for a CBC film on mercury poisoning. Here's an excerpt from the transcript:

Question: There's no question in your mind about the danger of eating the fish from those waters?

Miller: None at all ... I agree with you ... I just can't understand why we don't have symptoms showing. ...

Question: I suppose compensation could be a very serious problem in dollar terms, in respect even of the lodges?

Miller: Oh, it would be tremendous. It would be tremendously costly. You know, if I owned a lodge in that area, I'd be screaming along with everyone else. Wouldn't you?

Question: Well you do own a tourist resort. If you owned a lodge in that area, would you have fishermen flying in from the States and staying with you this summer?

*Ontario Health Minister Frank Miller is a chemical engineer and businessman. He owns two Muskoka tourist lodges – both, so far, on waters not believed polluted; one is Patterson-Kaye Lodge, the other, Tamwood Lodge. After three years' experience as a municipal councillor in Bracebridge, Frank Miller was first elected to the Ontario Legislature in 1971. He was appointed Health Minister on 26 February 1974. On 3 February 1977 he succeeded Leo Bernier as Minister of Natural Resources.

Miller: Okay. Let's be human. Yes. I would. Yes, I would. You know, we're going to have to legislate people out of business.

Question: Would you tell them not to eat the fish?

Miller: I hope I would, Warner. That's a hypothetical question. ... I hope I would. Yes. Traditionally, businessmen have been put out of business by the state rather than voluntarily, have they not? I think the responsibility will end up being ours as to whether they stay in business or not.

Question: Given that there are respectable and small 'c' conservative estimates that the river is going to stay fouled-up for fifty or sixty or a hundred years. ...

Miller: Who knows? Yes.

Question: Do you think you may be forced to that?

Miller: We may be. We may be.

Meanwhile, back at Holst Point, it was business-as-usual – fishing in summer, skiing, skidooing and ice-fishing in winter. But surely someone in the Ontario government would spot the ostentatious contradiction between the pronouncements of the Health Ministry and the operation of the Lodge?

In mid-September 1976, a prospective guest telephoned Holst Point to enquire about their facilities and rates. He spoke with the Assistant Manager, a Mr. Frank Robb. Here's a partial transcript of their conversation:

Caller: How's the fishing there?

Robb: It's great. Just great. We've got Great Northern and walleye.

Caller: I haven't stayed there before. Can I have shore lunch if I catch anything?

Robb: Sure. You can have shore lunch.

Caller: Who operates the lodge now?

Robb: The government of Ontario. We're owned and operated by the government of Ontario.

On 18 September 1976, having made a reservation, Mr. Eric Linden of Minneapolis checked into Holst Point Lodge. Mr. Linden attempted to meet the manager, a Mr. Peter Barber (formerly the "chief guide at Minaki Lodge," according to Mr. Robb) but couldn't find him during his stay of two days. Mr. Linden also failed in attempts to engage Mr. Robb in more than a couple of words of conversation. But on 19 September, Mr. Linden did manage to chat with the young lady on the desk at the lodge. Here's part of their transcripted conversation:

Linden: Do you have any mercury problem with the fish around here?

Desk clerk: Oh, no.

Linden: I'd heard you had a problem with mercury pollution contaminating the fish.

Desk clerk: No. There's no problem around here.

Linden: Not anywhere around here?

Desk Clerk: Well, Barney Lamm shut down his lodge; that was about twelve miles from here. But they say he's just trying to get some money out of the government.

Linden: So he shut his lodge down just to try and force the government to pay him a lot of money?

Desk clerk: Well, I don't know. I really don't know anything about it.

Linden: Well, who does know about the mercury? Where could I find out about it?

Desk clerk: I just don't know. I don't know who might know about it. But we're all right here, though.

Linden: Do you know whether fish here have been tested for mercury?

Desk clerk: Oh, sure. Our fish here have been tested for mercury. They're OK. There's no mercury here.

The desk clerk was right. The fish around Minaki Lodge and Holst Point had been tested.

Minaki, and Holst Point are situated on the Winnipeg River, just west of Tetu Lake. In 1970 Barney Lamm learned from Lands and Forests Minister Rene Brunelle that fish there were contaminated. Government readings taken at Minaki in the spring showed mercury levels of 2.7 ppm – more than five times higher than the "safe" level. In 1974 the average readings in walleye 20 inches in length taken from the Minaki area were just under 2 ppm (the bigger the fish, the higher the mercury concentration). In 1975 the readings were higher – just over 2 ppm. Northern pike were tested, too. In 1974 pike averaging 25 inches in length were found to contain a shade over 2 ppm of mercury; by 1975 the readings were in the 3 ppm range.[2]

On 19 September 1976, fishing with a guide supplied by Holst Point Lodge, Mr. Linden caught five walleye. He couldn't have shore lunch, as advertized, because an exceptionally high forest fire hazard in the area had resulted in a ban on all cooking fires outdoors. But the Lodge offered to cook his catch and serve it to him in the diningroom instead; and they did. They also arranged to have Linden's guide fillet, pack and flash-freeze the remainder of his catch, so he could take it home when he left. The author arranged for those two walleye to be tested for mercury levels. One fish contained 1.0 ppm of mercury, the other 0.73 ppm – both well over the "safe" limit of 0.5 ppm.

Before leaving, Mr. Linden encountered a party of five fishermen from Chicago on 19 September.

Linden: Hi. Where you from?

Angler: Chicago.

Linden: Have you been here before? Come often?

Angler: We come here every year.

Linden: Is there any mercury in the fish around here?

Angler: I guess so.

Linden: You got a big catch today. Are you going to eat all that fish?

Angler: Sure. It's OK if you only eat it about once a week.

Linden: You're a lot braver than I am.

Angler: Oh, there's mercury everywhere now. Even in the oceans; they've found it in fish that've never been within a thousand miles of land.

Said the Hon. Frank Miller, then Ontario's Health Minister, in August 1975:

Strangely enough, all the publicity that's now being generated, I welcome. You might not think I would, sitting in my position, but I've learned in the past it takes a lot of publicity even to make some of the potentially ill people worry. ... I don't want to minimize the problem. That's one of the issues I've been trying to make clear. I don't feel there is anything I need to hide; and there have been impressions or almost accusations that things were hidden.

Not Holst Point. Not hidden. Wide open, one might say. Except that brochure mailings generally go to the United States, from which virtually all fish camp clients come. A little easier, now, to understand that letter from the Ellises, at Rough Rock Lodge (see p. 70), comforting a Michigan client with the comment that, "We fish the very same waters that Minaki Lodge did and there is no problem with having shore lunches."

"CLOSE THE RIVER"

On 11 May 1976 at a House of Commons Fisheries Committee meeting, Robert Kaplan, Parliamentary Secretary to federal Health Minister Marc Lalonde was faced with a demand that the Wabigoon/ English river system be closed. It came from Arnold John Malone, PC Member of Parliament from Battle River.

Mr. Kaplan: We cannot close the river.

Mr. Malone: Why not?

Mr. Kaplan: We have closed the river for commercial fishing which is within our jurisdiction to do.

An Honourable Member: Well, close it ...

Mr. Kaplan: We did. We closed it for commercial fishing. We cannot close it for sport fishing. There is suggestion number one, now what is suggestion number two?

Mr. Malone: We can get thalidomide off the market, why can we not get mercury?

Mr. Kaplan: Mercury poison is not on the market.

Mr. Malone: Mercury poison is in the fish.

Mr. Kaplan: Mercury poison is absorbed in the environment. They do not go out and buy it. If they went and bought it we could ban it, and we would.

Mr. Malone: You could quarantine an area, you could restrict an area, you could do lots of things. ... We are failing drastically, terribly, in focusing on these people who have been affected. I think just in a most insensitive way we have not done nearly enough in that regard.

Marc Lalonde himself was questioned several times in Parliament about closure of the Wabigoon/English rivers to sports fishing.

Hansard, 21 June 1976:
Mr. Cyril Symes: ... A special report in the hands of the Ontario minister of health ... recommends that the English and the Wabigoon River system be closed to all fishing. ... Is the federal government prepared to take such action under the Canada Water Act?

Hon. Marc Lalonde: Mr. Speaker, I am not aware of such a report. However, I know that consultations are now underway with Indians, and between Indians and Ontario government ministers on that matter, and I am sure we will have the opportunity to discuss it soon with the Ontario government.

28 June 1976:
Mr. Arnold Malone: Mr. Speaker ... would the minister tell us what efforts he is making to stop the eating of all fish from the Wabigoon and English river systems. ...
Hon. Marc Lalonde: ... My colleagues are to meet the Ontario ministers responsible for those matters in early July. I hope that the government of Ontario will agree to close completely this river to sport fishing.

6 July 1976:
Mr. Cyril Symes: ... Will the minister assure the House that should he fail to get Ontario to agree to his proposal he will exert federal authority to bring about this result by declaring the area a water management control zone under the Canada Water Act.
Hon. Marc Lalonde: Mr. Speaker, this question is not within my departmental jurisdiction.

12 July 1976:
Mr. Arnold Malone: Mr. Speaker, my question is addressed to the Minister of Indian Affairs and Northern Development. Can the honourable gentleman tell us when sports fishing will be banned on the English and Wabigoon rivers. Has he, in his negotiations with provincial cabinet

ministers from Ontario fixed a date when sports fishing on this river system will be stopped?

Hon. Judd Buchanan: At this juncture the federal and Ontario ministers present at the meeting must now take a proposal back to their respective governments. Both levels of government are very much aware of the urgency of this matter but we have to get approval from our respective governments before further action can be taken.

So seven years after dangerous mercury levels were found in Wabigoon/English fish; and three years after the first urgent recommendation from Ontario's mercury task force that the rivers be posted and closed, Judd Buchanan, evidently unaware his cabinet colleagues considered a sports fishing ban an entirely provincial matter, told Parliament that both Ontario and Ottawa would have to "get approval from our respective governments." It might seem too that Buchanan was unaware either of the principle of cabinet solidarity, or of his colleague the Health Minister's statements in the House that he hoped the government of Ontario "will agree to close completely this river." Whatever the jurisdictional and political ramifications, the rivers remained open throughout the summer fishing season of 1976 and there was, at the time of writing, no sign of a likely sport fishing ban for 1977.

Ottawa's failure to move under provisions of the Canada Water Act, like Ontario's refusal to ban fishing through Leo Bernier's Ministry of Natural Resources, may have involved more than reluctance to cross jurisdictional lines or even doubt as to the efficacy of a ban.

Running through the deliberations of both governments and their civil services there has been a constant thread of anxiety about "responsibility" for any damages resulting from the situation in Northwest Ontario. The formal banning of sports fishing on the river systems, reasoned some civil servants speaking during research interviews for this book, might leave the government which acted open to civil law suits brought by fishing camp operators closed down by such a ban. Neither government had moved, by the end of 1976, to require legal or fiscal accountability from Reed for the damage done – but neither was specially interested in making government the target of people seeking compensation, either. So long as fishing is permitted, even sport fishing, the lodge owners might have difficulty proving damages in court, as might Indians not able to work as fishing guides.

Not that the Ontario government, or even Health Minister Frank Miller, were reluctant to move firmly, even dramatically, in some health situations. In the summer of 1976, for example, Mr. Miller shut down an entire metropolitan general hospital to all patients but one, for a period of several weeks – and quarantined essential staff within the building. All of that after a woman with symptoms of severe influenza was taken to the Etobicoke General Hospital after possible contact, on an international flight, with others who might have been in contact with a case of highly contagious Lassa fever. It turned out that the woman did not have the tropical disease, but Mr. Miller was widely quoted at the time as having said it would have been "criminally irresponsible" to keep the hospital open until there was a firm diagnosis.

Not so easy, apparently, to decide on closing the English and Wabigoon river systems to sports fishing; or difficult, perhaps, to persuade cabinet colleagues of the need. Also such a ban would have undoubtedly lost the government its substantial business and revenue from Holst Point Lodge. And as Minister of Tourism and Industry Claude Bennett reported proudly to the Ontario legislature in early 1976: "Mr. Speaker ... Holst Point has been booked to its capacity, which is available for 60 tenants."

Certainly though, that sports fishing ban was "under consideration." Hon. Rene Brunelle told the Ontario House on 5 June 1976:

Again, I would like to reiterate what I said before, Mr. Speaker, that this is a very difficult, complex question. The matter has been discussed and there will be a government decision. The matter will be discussed again tomorrow, so by this weekend we should be in a better position than we are now to make a decision. But it is a very difficult decision, as I think the honourable member appreciates.

9 THE POLLUTER

The links between government regulatory agencies and polluting industries are both intimate and enduring. To understand them one must first try to develop some understanding of the particular industry in question. But in this instance, trying to get a firm fix on Reed Paper Limited, a huge Canadian conglomerate which is, in turn, a subsidiary of an even larger British conglomerate, is a bit like trying to sketch an elephant to scale from a viewing distance of six inches. The temptation is to describe the warts and wrinkles visible at short range. However, here's an attempt at an overall survey.

Reed Limited is the "operating" arm of Reed Paper Limited – a wholly owned subsidiary, as are the pulp and paper mills at Dryden and in Quebec City and most other Reed operations, barring two paper mills in Prince George, British Columbia, of which Reed has a 50 per cent and a 35 per cent ownership respectively.

Reed Limited comprises Reed's Pulp and Paper, Forestry and Wood Products, Packaging, Decorative Products, and Technical Groups – as well as the Pigments Division and Reed's interests in the Prince George mills.

Reed Limited products in Canada include paints (which contain mercury; see Appendix Four), varnishes, wallpaper, draperies, furniture, corrugated and folding boxes, polyethylene bags, lumber, windows, sashes, doors, trusses, wall panels, barns and industrial storage buildings, chemicals and paper products. Data from the Reed annual reports and the Toronto Stock Exchange indicate that Reed net earnings (profits) in recent years have been

1969:	$ 2,603,000
1970:	735,000
1971:	3,478,000
1972:	5,127,000
1973:	19,532,000
1974:	36,447,000
1975:	11,108,000

Total sales in 1975 were $369 million.

Reed Paper Limited, the holding company in Canada for this operation, described by its President, Robert Billingsley,* as "among the 60 largest industrial companies in Canada on the basis of sales, and the fifth-largest publicly held forests products company," has about 9,000 employees in Canada. It is, in turn, a subsidiary of a British company, Reed International Limited of London. Reed International, which owns more than 99 per cent of the Canadian holding company's common shares, has, according to Mr. Billingsley, "approximately 85 per cent of the voting shares of Reed Paper."

Reed International is a real conglomerate. According to the Toronto Stock Exchange it "is one of the largest producers of paper and paper packaging in Europe and has its subsidiary and associated companies in many parts of the world engaged in the manufacture and distribution of paper, paper products, decorative products and building products. In addition, it has a publishing and printing business which

---

*Robert William Billingsley, 40 in 1977, has enjoyed a meteoric corporate career. Born in 1937 of an Oakville, Ontario family, he took a BSc in economics at the University of Pennsylvania, graduating in 1960. Twelve years later, at 35, he was president of Reed. On the way there Billingsley worked for Shell Canada in sales; the Electric Reduction Company of Canada Limited as a divisional manager (from 1967); and the Hooker Chemical Company as product and sales manager (from 1970). In April 1972 Billingsley became Executive Vice-President of Anglo-Canadian. In August he was made President and in 1973 he became President of Reed Paper where he succeeded J. R. Craig. It was as president of Reed that he contracted with his ex-employers, Hooker, in 1975, to design and install a new chlorine production system at Reed's Dryden mill which would not use mercury. By 1976 the young corporation president was commuting to England for one week a month, assuming his new and important duties as a director of the parent conglomerate.

includes the London *Daily Mirror* which is one of the most widely circulated national daily newspapers in Europe." At last count, it operated in 44 countries around the world, some on every continent, and had a corporate family of 80,000 employees. One recent listing showed 583 individual companies, including 37 in Canada. Reed International owns plastics companies, radio stations, a myriad of publishing enterprises; the company is into photo engraving, general insurance, shipping, machinery sales, the music recording industry, textiles, investments, consulting.

Reed International's net profits have shown a steady increase from £10,200,000 in 1970 to over £41,100,000 in 1975. The conglomerate certainly has the resources to back up Mr. Billingsley's somewhat equivocal promise contained in a prepared statement published by the Kenora *Miner and News* on 5 August 1975:

> We have a long term commitment to the Dryden area and we would not consciously do anything to jeopardize the health of our own employees, the residents of Dryden or the people of the surrounding area. We have not and will not take a narrow, legalistic view. We will recognize and fulfill our social and moral responsibilities and will take whatever additional actions are appropriate to the situation.

GOVERNMENT LIAISON

To researchers studying the mass of documentation from and about Reed Paper, the internal and external contradictions seem most to resemble the Augean stable as first encountered by Hercules; the task of compiling the contradictory data seems hopeless, the bland assurances of company spokesmen suffocatingly resistant to the fresh air of fact.

Information for this chapter has not been easy to come by, and government data on Reed Paper Limited is no exception. To illustrate the difficulties, here is a passage from a 7 November 1974 CBC *As It Happens* broadcast where Barbara Frum is asking William Newman, the Ontario Environment Minister, about government grants to Dow Chemical and Dryden Chemicals – the latter owned by Reed Paper – the two plants named by the Ontario government in the spring of 1970 as responsible for mercury contamination of Lake St. Clair and the

Wabigoon/English river systems respectively. Asked about grants, Newman replied, in part:

> *Newman:*... I do have the lists and I'm prepared to give them to you. There's nothing to hide. ... I have a complete list right here – I would have to look it over. It's quite an extensive list – I don't see it on this list, but it's quite a lengthy list. Certainly I'm prepared to give you a copy of this.... I don't see either one of the companies you mention. ... But this is a complete list as far as I'm – this is – I'm, what – I'm given to understand this is a complete list.

> *Question:* For what year?

> *Newman:* Well, I think since the inception of the Act.

> *Question:* The list is clearly inaccurate, because both Dow and Dryden have been given grants under the Pollution Abatement Incentives Act, or whatever it is.

> *Newman:* Well, you – This is the list that's been given to me by our people, and this is the list that will be – that's public information. Would you like to tell me why you think it's inaccurate? Well, in order that we have this clear, I think – while we're on this, and we're recording, in order that we have this clear – you say one thing – This is the report that I have; let's check it out.

It was checked out: Dow Chemical, it emerged, had been given the following pollution abatement grants by Mr. Newman's Ministry:

1971:	$ 46,680.20
1972:	15,767.78
1973:	33,521.87
1974:	2,408.67

a total of $98,450.52, and all of this during a period in which the Ontario government was suing Dow for $35,000,000 in damages arising from the mercury pollution. The suit, filed in 1971 by George Kerr, had not been proceeded with or reached court by the end of 1976. However, government spokesmen explained their failure to act against Dryden Chemicals on grounds that the government's suit against Dow – the "test case" – had first to be resolved.

The same checks, in November 1974, showed Dryden Chemicals,

too, had received grants from Mr. Newman's Ministry as follows:

1971:	$ 3,421.68
1972:	10,210.11
1973:	5,008.42
1974:	317.12

a total of $18,957.33.

Reed fared more handsomely in Ottawa, where by December 1975 the federal Department of Regional Economic Expansion had come up with approval for the following grants:

a) $195,000 for conversion of its chlorine production facility from mercury cells to a non-mercury diaphragm system, which was done, as we shall see, "solely at the Company's initiative."

b) $237,747 towards the capital costs of a wood-chipper and expansion of the lumber industry operated by Reed.

c) $805,273 for expansion of the lumber mill operated by Reed.

d) $1,432,606 for expansion of the lumber industry at Ear Falls, Ontario – an expansion which, a year after approval of the grant, both Reed and the Ontario government were saying was still only "under study." The expansion would give Reed timber rights on 19,000 square miles of northern Ontario boreal forest and was being hotly contested by environmental groups, professional foresters and native groups.

The figures were not especially easy to turn up, despite Mr. Newman's assurances. Not everyone had difficulty getting government data. T.S. ("Tommy") Jones was interviewed on the same 7 November 1974 broadcast as Mr. Newman. Mr. Jones is a Vice-President of Reed and a former Director of Dryden Chemicals[1] as well as Vice-President of the Anglo-Canadian Pulp and Paper Company* – the holding company that operated the Reed mills at Dryden before being absorbed (in name as well as fact) in 1975. The CBC broadcast was in two parts – on 6 November and on 7 November. Mr. Jones responded to some allegations he'd heard on the first half of the program:

T.S. Jones: ... First of all I'd like to say that, you know, I'm a citizen and

---

*In addition, Mr. Jones has served as: President of the Ontario Pulp and Paper Makers' Safety Association; a Director of the Ontario Chamber of Commerce, and as Vice-President and Director of the Ontario Forestry Association – the latter a low key and engaging but unmistakeable "front" lobby for the forest industry of Ontario.

I'm concerned with the health of people and so's our company, and I think we've got to remember that we've got 1,500 employees in that area.

We're not aware of any deterioration in health as specified by your program, and certainly the statements made on the program should be proven, you know, by those who made them because they're of a very serious nature, and I think that if the allegations are true, then hopefully the government will follow through and prove them up.

You see, I was a little surprised at the statement you had trouble getting information from governments, because we never have.

Certainly Mr. Jones seemed to have little trouble getting government information. His job at Reed, as Vice-President, was described in late 1976 by a company colleague as "government liaison ... [It is] Jones' only job. ... He has no other responsibilities."

There follow some examples of Tommy Jones' access to government information.

On 12 November 1970, M.S. ("Mort") Kircher received a memo from Jones. Kircher, now retired from the corporate battlefield, was the chemical engineer who oversaw installation of the mercury cell plant at Dryden in 1962; he was variously Manager, President and a Director of Dryden Chemicals until he left the company on 1 February, 1971. The memo bears quoting at length because of the illumination it provides in respect of Reed/government relations as managed by Tommy Jones. In 1970 the Ontario government had filed no suit against Dryden Chemicals, so the heading of this internal communication makes interesting reading in itself.

MEMO November 10, 1970

TO: Mr. M.S. Kircher
FROM: Mr. T.S. Jones
SUBJECT: GENERAL INFORMATION-MERCURY SUIT
  Attached are:-
1. Fort Frances *Times*, November 4th, re John Reid's proposal for compensating businesses and individuals hurt by pollution. [Reid was the area's MP.]
2. An article from *Chemical Week*, re Kimberly-Clark suing a California rancher for false statements.

I had lunch with Leo Bernier yesterday and I had a general chat about the situation. He reported that Barney Lamb [sic] had been in Toronto last week and had seen him and other political figures. Stephen Lewis, new head of the NDP [who in September 1975 became official Leader of the Opposition in Ontario's legislature] spent last weekend in the Kenora area and visited the Indian Bands at Grassy Narrows and also, I think, White Dog Falls.

Leo Bernier is convinced that the Ontario government has to give some assistance to those affected by the mercury situation in fish and he is finalizing a recommendation to the Cabinet in which there will be aid to fishermen, aid to tourist operators and aid to the White Dog and Grassy Narrows Bands.

He stated that he has reports from tourist operators that they are down about 50% this year, against last year. He admits he can't say how much the economic situation in the country has affected the tourist operators but he reports that the department of Tourism and Publicity has reported general tourist operations in the province up 8% over last year.

He has also talked to Cabinet Members about setting up a joint Federal-Provincial Committee for releases on mercury. With the Federal Fisheries, the Federal Government and Provincial Governments all issuing information it's a chaotic situation and Leo feels that something should be done to restore some sanity to the situation. He doesn't think he has much hope of accomplishing this but he is going to try.

I pointed out to him that George Kerr and others in the Ontario Cabinet and Mr. Green in the Federal Cabinet are still using the phrase, "Sue the Pollutor." He says this is embarrassing and he has spoken to George Kerr about it, but when Kerr gets in front of a microphone he seems to be carried away.

Leo referred to the CBC weekend television program on Sunday, November 1st, which included the report on the chemical situation at Dryden and district. Mr. Kerr hadn't seen the film so he has asked the CBC to run it for him here in Toronto and Leo understands that they are going to do this. For the first time in his career when Mr. Kerr was interviewed at the Indian Reserve the CBC asked him to sign a release and for some reason he signed the release and accordingly, now he has no come-back on them using him in an edited TV broadcast. I don't know whether Mr. Howard [presumably a Reed legal expert] heard the program or not but certainly Mort's voice and my voice were on and I just wonder if there was any come-back re using our voices without permission on a CBC edited report.

So ends my rambling report of my luncheon with Leo.

Now a point to which I need an answer. Dryden Paper Company

has an appointment with the OWRC (Ontario Water Resources Commission) to discuss Dryden's future plans on Thursday, December 3, 1970. Tom Beak is prepared to come to Toronto in the afternoon of December 2, if we wish, so that he can have a further conversation with Mr. Howard and ourselves re the mercury situation.

If Mr. Howard is available and feels this is timely then we could arrange same. I know that Mort and I will be talking in the meantime so we will discuss this further by telephone.

Best regards

When Jones wrote this memo, Leo Bernier, the Kenora Member of the legislature of Ontario, wasn't yet in the provincial cabinet. He was sworn in as Minister of Mines and Northern Affairs four months later.

Access to an occasional confidential document such as this one can help to identify the players and their roles in the mercury drama. The Tom Beak referred to, for example, turns out to be a paid consultant for the Reed group and another avenue through which Tommy Jones was able to pursue his work in government liaison. Witness this memo, from a federal government file, to J. R. ("Jack") Tully– Acting-Director, at this point, of the Special Assignments and Review section of the Department of Indian Affairs in Ottawa:

CONFIDENTIAL
Ottawa, Ontario K1A 0H4
January 10, 1975

J. R. Tully
Interdepartmental Committee
On Mercury Contamination
On January 7, 1975, I established a meeting with BEAK consultants and members of the Mercury Committee. Present at the meeting were:

Mrs. N. Mitchell – IAB (Indian Affairs Branch)

Mr. D. Gimmer – IAB

Mr. J. Dennehy – IAB

Mr. S. Hodd – BEAK

Mr. L. Anthony – BEAK, Ottawa representative

BEAK consultants have been involved with a great deal of mercury studies in the U.S.A. and Canada, including Dryden paper company along the English and Wabigoon river system.

The BEAK representatives stated they would not comment directly on the English and Wabigoon mercury contamination due to the fact of a conflict of interest.

They did, however, give basic general knowledge of the hazards and problems involving mercury and enlightened the group's thoughts on mercury contamination and its effects.

One of the main ideas that developed from the meeting was the possibility of uniting the Federal government, the provincial government and the Dryden paper company in rehabilitating the English Wabigoon river system. If this can be accomplished without relating blame to anyone, it will be a giant step forward towards redevelopment of the area concerned.

The consultants spent two hours with the Mercury Committee at no cost to the department.

Hopefully, good results will develop from this discussion.

> John Dennehy,
> Special Assignments & Review

So, three years after it became clear to other government officials – both federal and provincial – that the mercury in the Wabigoon/ English rivers could not be dredged, covered or flushed away, a federal government committee was going to study "rehabilitating" the system. Two years after the federal task force on mercury issued its final report, the new federal committee turned to private consultants for data on "mercury contamination and its effects," though information was available in several other government offices in Ottawa. Five years after Tommy Jones' memo to Mort Kircher, the Ottawa governmental committee was agreeing, at a meeting with Reed consultants, that "If this can be accomplished without relating blame to anyone, it will be a giant step forward."

On 22 September 1976 George Kerr attended a dinner given by the Medical/Legal Society at Toronto's Osgoode Hall. That evening he took part in a panel discussion of environmental protection and the law. After dinner, a relaxed and expansive George Kerr chatted amiably with a researcher for this book who had also attended the dinner. During the conversation Mr. Kerr touched on the Dow lawsuit (still not at the stage of going before the courts, five years after Kerr had promised the Ontario legislature speedy action and resolution within eighteen months), and on the genesis of the now-defunct notion that a national park expropriating all the land in the area of Grassy Narrows and White Dog might solve everyone's political problems. He spoke first of the Dow contamination by mercury of the St. Clair River and Lake St. Clair, as recorded in the researcher's notes:

> They [Dow] were co-operating. I'd talk to them and tell them how they had to cut down on mercury and they'd agree. ... Then, one day, I called them and they said, "Our insurance company has told us we can't talk to you anymore," and, almost in a fit of pique, I said, "Slap them with a writ." ... We wanted to get that case dealt with before we considered any others. ...
>
> Sure, Dryden Chemical was a better case for us. [On the Wabigoon River, unlike the Lake St. Clair area, there are no possible industrial polluters other than Dryden Chemicals.]
>
> Off the record: Tommy Jones sat across my desk one day and said, "George, you should have sued us. We'd have paid up, any day in the last three years." Tommy Jones is a very persuasive guy. We'd tell them they had to stop dumping mercury – tell them what they had to do; they wouldn't always do it, but Tommy was very persuasive.
>
> Tommy would sit in my office, with Leo Bernier. He'd say, "George, we made $80,000 profit last year – I can't tell my directors we have to spend $15 million to clean up pollution." And Leo would say, "That's right, George. He can't do that. You can see that." ...
>
> I'm glad the press wasn't here tonight. They misunderstand these things. ...
>
> We were up in Ottawa for a federal/provincial meeting. The Indian bands were invited but we had a preliminary meeting – and we were at loggerheads with the feds. But then the Indians arrived and we didn't want them to see that we were in such disagreement; and somebody mentioned the idea of a national park. We grabbed at it – as a way to get out of all those problems.

Government liaison is a two-way street, as practiced by Tommy Jones and Reed.

On 30 March 1973 Leo Bernier announced the appointment of a chairman for a new committee he was forming to advise him on "such things as the use of Crown land, timber limits, hunting seasons and the management of wildlife, forests and mineral resources."[2] The appointee: Tommy Jones who by 1973 had been a Director of Dryden Chemicals for seven years. Mr. Bernier assured critics of the appointment that the advisory committee, which first met in May 1973, would not be considering matters dealing with mercury pollution.

Interestingly, Jones' appointment as chairman of the committee to advise Bernier on, among other things, timber limits came just one year before Reed announced its feasibility study of that 19,000-square mile timber development. Premier William Davis, announcing plans for the study to the Ontario legislature in a formal statement on 7 March 1974, said that "Close co-operation between Anglo-Canadian and the Ontario Government will be maintained. ... "

While Leo Bernier had found no difficulty locating a chairman for his advisory committee, all the committee appointments did not come so easily. Announcing Tommy Jones' selection the Minister told the Ontario legislature that other members of the committee would "represent all segments of society" and include "Indians, sawmill workers and trappers."

A couple of months later, on 12 May, Bernier said he was "still looking for an Indian to sit on the committee," but had two or three qualified people in mind. He had already appointed ten members who represented "interests ranging from the mining, lumber and pulp and paper industries to unionised labor to naturalists, and sportsmen."[3]

But if Reed Paper had lost some of the time of its Vice-President to the needs of Bernier's advisory committee, the government had suffered its personnel losses, too. Since 1971 a young man called Bruce Fountain had worked as an "advance man" for William Davis; by June 1973 he had been made responsible for the Premier's "Appointments and Engagements." But by the spring of 1974 Mr. Fountain's name had been dropped from the catalogue of staff serving the Premier. That was because he had found new employment. A call to the Reed main switchboard elicited the information that Bruce Fountain's proper title now was: "Manager of Corporate Affairs for Reed Paper Limited."

Reed is sensitive to outside criticism. In the summer and autumn of 1976 there was a strike at the Dryden plant, lasting more than three months. According to an employee interviewed for this book "The company heard some Indians were planning to come to Dryden and join us on the picket lines; next thing we knew Reed had hired thirty extra security guards – and they stayed on the job for three weeks."

In the autumn of 1976 it had become a matter of common gossip in Toronto that Reed was taking a leaf from General Motors' book in respect of security. (GM had hired private detectives to shadow Ralph Nader and try to catch him in compromising situations.) Reed, it was alleged, had employed an ex-policeman named Percy Parkes, of Great

Lakes Investigations, to "keep an eye on" Reed's "enemies," particularly anyone critical of Reed policies and Reed's record.

By the spring of 1977 Reed's expansion plans in the Red Lake/Ear Falls area of northwest Ontario were causing the company as many PR headaches as the by-then waning public interest in mercury pollution. The forestry expansion scheme, denounced by conservationists and area Indians, involved an area equal to a twenty-eight-lane super-highway stretching from Rome to the moon, a land mass 25 per cent larger than all of Switzerland. As described in Appendix Five, the plans have led to charges of a "sweetheart" arrangement between a company and government allegedly trying to slide a massive and dangerous forest exploitation scheme past public scrutiny.

10 THE GOOD CORPORATE CITIZEN

I know personally the hardships some of you have felt through contamination of the Wabigoon and English river systems, especially those of you in the tourist industry. Pollution now is abated. The major industrial cause, was the Dryden Paper Company. This company, since 1970, however, has done its best to undo the harm. ... I congratulate the company on its good corporate citizenship.

> – Hon. Leo Bernier,
> Tuesday, 18 May 1971.[1]

I think companies in our capitalistic system must be good corporate citizens. We must be prepared to shoulder our responsibility when it's clear what that is and my statement was simply that we will not take a – if there is a proven case of mercury poisoning or the so-called Minamata Disease – we will not take a legalistic approach. ...

We believe, and I believe personally, as long as I'm president of this company, that we must go beyond that and look at our moral and social responsibilities as people who live in Ontario and Canada and must work there; and I think our employees and shareholders accept that....

Clearly pollution is something that is here and it's topical and it's something that we can't allow to go on. And in 1970, from a technical point of view, we met the government standards. They put in tougher standards. We met them.

> – R.W. Billingsley, filmed interview
> with the author, September 1975.

96

MERCURY LOSSES

In answers to specific charges, as in public relations, Reed prefers to deal in woolly generalities. This is especially true when one tries to extract kernels of responsive and factual statement from the company's defence of its dumping of mercury.

Between 1969 and 1977 Reed officials produced a litany of self-serving nonsense in public statements and replies to questioners. The specifics varied, but the theme was consistent. In terms of mercury pollution: We didn't know the gun was loaded (until 1970); the wounds were probably a result of natural causes, anyhow; our .45 calibre pistol is different from Chisso's .45 calibre pistol because it was made in North America and so inflicts a less fatal wound; we've always acted within the law; we had a license to carry the gun.

In September 1975 Reed Paper Company President Robert Billingsley told the author, in an interview filmed for television, that the mercury biomethylation in the Wabigoon River "isn't the same as in Japan. As I understand it, over there, the mercury was changed into organic mercury inside the factory. Here it's happening in the river, not in the plant."[2]

Billingsley also claimed that methyl mercury "created" in a water system through bacterial conversion wasn't "the same" as "regular" methyl mercury, hinted it wasn't as toxic, and cited as his authority Dr. Leonard Goldwater. (Dr. Goldwater, author of the book *Mercury, A History of Quicksilver*, has been a frequent participant in mercury seminars internationally as well as a consultant regularly employed by private industries, including the Reed Paper Company.)

In a "prepared statement" quoted extensively in the Kenora *Miner and News* of 5 August 1975, Billingsley not only claimed that "it was only in 1970 that it was recognized that inorganic mercury which is used in the chemical plant at Dryden was potentially harmful to the environment." He also stated that "there is good reason to believe that mercury biomethylated in the natural environment, as happened in the Wabigoon, is much less harmful than the chemical substance that was directly discharged in Japan."

And at a Toronto meeting on 21 August 1975, Reed Paper's Environmental Affairs Manager Howard Brown, seated near Dr. Goldwater, repeated the claim: "This situation at Dryden is not comparable to Japan because no biomethylation occurred in Japan. This is a misconception."

The misconception, encouraged by Dr. Goldwater, was entirely Mr. Billingsley's and Mr. Brown's. First, best estimates were that 90 to 99 per cent of the mercury discharged by Chisso into Minamata Bay was inorganic mercury which later biomethylated. Second, there is no difference in the toxicity of commercially-produced and biomethylated methyl mercury. When Dr. Goldwater's public statement (at a meeting, in Ottawa, of a parliamentary committee) about "methyl mercury" being different from "biomethylated mercury" was relayed to Dr. Tom Clarkson of Rochester, a sometime colleague, he smiled and said, "Leonard's being naughty again. Methyl mercury is methyl mercury.... "

There were also efforts to paint over the crimson history of mercury with a liberal coating of whitewash, and to avert any suggestion of responsibility or culpability. The following is an internal document from the files of Dryden Chemicals designed for public relations use. The proposed three-page press release is marked with a rubber stamp reading:

> INFORMATION FOR LAWYER
> re: Possible Legal Suits
> DRYDEN CHEMICALS LIMITED
> OAKVILLE, ONTARIO

The release is headed, in upper case:

> DRYDEN CHEMICALS
> IS PLEASED TO ANNOUNCE
> THAT WHAT IS GOING DOWN *OUR* DRAIN
> IS NOW PROBABLY LESS HARMFUL
> THAN WHAT IS GOING DOWN *YOUR* DRAIN

That rather euphoric defence is explained in the body of the text, on page 2:

> To dispell [sic] the notion that we have wantonly dumped mercury into the river, we should point out that the effluent from our plant even before the installation of the treatment system had a mercury concentration in the order of 1/30 the concentration of mercury in normal human urine.

The logic is not much better than the spelling – few of us manage to excrete 33 million gallons of urine daily.

The 21 August 1975 meeting just referred to was one where representatives of Reed met with members of the Kumamoto University Study Group visiting Canada; others present included representatives of the National Indian Brotherhood, Indians representing the White Dog/Grassy Narrows area. Robert Billingsley was present at the beginning of the meeting, but stayed only for the few moments it took him to make a brief opening statement and field two questions.

At that meeting Howard Brown was asked about losses of mercury from the plant by a member of the Japanese team. Here is part of that transcribed conversation:

Question: How much mercury was lost [before 1970]?

Brown: We do not know because no records were required.

Question: How much mercury did you buy?

Brown: We do not know because no records were required ...

Raoul C. Buser [Technical Group Vice-President, Reed]: We have no records....

Question: In Japan in 1973 the government asked for past data.

Brown: Here the total past amount was not asked for.

The emphasis on Brown's last response relates to a letter written by him and dated 3 October 1975 to Dr. E. Somers, Director General, Environmental Health Directorate, of the federal Health Ministry. Says Brown's opening sentence: "This letter will reconfirm that your August 15, 1975 information request has been referred to me for response."

The request made by Dr. Somers in that letter – six days before the Toronto meeting was told, by the same Howard Brown, that "the total past amount was not asked for" – had been for data on annual purchase figures of mercury.

Mr. Brown's reply raises a doubt about his repeated statements that "we do not know" how much mercury was bought, year by year, from 1962 until 1970: "We anticipate that Environment Canada will request data dating back to the startup of each chlor-alkali operation in Canada. ... When the Environment Canada request is presented *we will consider furnishing annual purchase information."*

Robert Billingsley echoed Howard Brown's statement in his interview with the author: " ... there was no reason to keep records back in 1962 for tax reasons and otherwise. You keep your records about seven years and then you throw them out. We don't have any records."

The records, it would seem, if kept, weren't even kept for the seven years, since Brown, in August 1975, denied having any records before 1970, just five years earlier.

Brown's reply to Dr. Somers lists a total of "measured or calculated losses" of mercury since 1970. They include 37 pounds of mercury admitted "lost" into the Wabigoon River in effluent, 941 pounds of mercury "measured or calculated" as lost into the air over the plant, 322 pounds "lost" in products made by the mill – and 8,355 pounds "cast into concrete and ... not available for reintroduction into the environment." What is especially interesting about the figures given by Mr. Brown, even accepting that they represent an accurate "measurement and calculation" – which governmental spot checks of effluent discharges cast into serious doubt – is the clear and unequivocal statement of mercury discharge into the environment after 1970: 978 pounds into the air and river systems in four years.

Compare this statement from Jack Davis, Minister of Fisheries and Forestry, made in the House of Commons on 22 June 1970:

> Mr. Speaker ... steps have been taken ... to identify areas of the river bottom which have been contaminated with mercury and arrange for them to be dredged out. The answer to the difficulties in the chlor-alkali industry has been *total recirculation of the mercury effluent within the plants' systems. This has been arranged in all cases.*

As for the dredging, six years later it was still not "arranged," on the rational grounds that researchers feared it might stir up the sediment and release even more mercury. It had never been "arranged."

On 15 October 1970, Jack Davis told the House of Commons:

> As Minister of Fisheries, last spring I called a meeting with the top executives in the chlor-alkali industry. I asked them to change their

ways. I asked them to recycle all of their mercury bearing effluents within the factory fence. This the industry did, and promptly.

And, lest there be any sense of equivocation, Mr. Davis made it all perfectly clear to Parliament on 16 May 1973, midway through the five-year period when Dryden Chemicals had apparent mercury losses on every day on which they were monitored:

> Mr. Speaker, the pollution released by the plants in the area ceased over two years ago as a result of initiatives taken by the federal government essentially under the federal Fisheries Act. The plants there have been meeting the federal standards with no release of mercury whatsoever from them. The continuing problem arises from mercury in sediment downstream from the plants which was deposited over a long period, but such release ceased two and a half years ago.

Slightly misleading? The order to stop dumping mercury went to Dryden Chemicals on 26 March 1970 – two years, one and a half months before the Davis comments. It was sent by the Ontario Water Resources Commission, pursuant to Ontario provincial legislation, not exactly "as a result of initiatives taken by the federal government" under Mr. Davis' Department of Fisheries. As for "no release of mercury whatsoever," we have just seen that by the company's own testimony at least 37 pounds of mercury were "lost" into the Wabigoon River after 1970 and 941 pounds into the air.

Compare, too, that statement of losses by Reed's manager of Environmental Affairs with this extract from the transcript of that CBC *As It Happens* program, where Barbara Frum was questioning the then Ontario Environment Minister William Newman.

> *Frum:* Is there an environmental problem now with mercury, in your opinion?
>
> *Newman:* Well, as far as the plants are concerned that were putting mercury into our water system, there's no problem at this point in time.
>
> *Frum:* How can the public of Ontario be assured of that?
>
> *Newman:* Well we put – there were control orders put on in, I believe, 1970, on the big – of course mainly on the pulp and paper industry and they have all switched away from mercury except two. *The other two have what we call a closed circuit mercury treatment. We are monitoring these plants on a very regular basis to make sure there isn't any*

effluent. ... I can assure you that since I came to the Ministry, there has
been [sic]no mercury emissions, and we have made it very carefully.

That year, 1974, by Reed's own figures, surely not exaggerated, 204 pounds of mercury were "lost" into the air and water and 2,051 pounds of mercury in sludge were mixed with wet concrete and poured into plastic-sheet-lined pits on a farm purchased by Reed a few thousand metres from the mill. Mr. Brown, in his letter to Dr. Somers, also notes that Reed recognizes "unaccounted for" loss which is normal in chlor-alkali plants. Dryden accountability averages about 79 per cent, he concludes – leaving 21 per cent of the average annual purchases of "2,661 pounds per year" entirely "unaccounted for." That comes to *a further loss, between 1971 and 1974, of a ton of mercury.*

The 1970 Ontario Water Resources Commission Report notes of Dryden Chemicals Limited that "No major incidents of high mercury (loss) were reported, *although estimated values for certain days are somewhat suspect.*" (Five years later confidential government documents revealed that Dryden Chemicals' assessment of their mercury losses *never* coincided with sampling done by the province. Dryden's figures were sometimes higher than the province's, often lower.)

Apart from the continuing losses of mercury into the air over the chemical plant there were continuing amounts of inorganic mercury seeping into the plant's effluent: from the storm water drains in the chemical plant, from process water and water flushed into the sewers during cleaning processes. Reed probably couldn't have entirely stopped the losses without shutting down the chemical plant, at least temporarily, for a general and thorough clean-up. (Workers reported, in research interviews for this book, seeing "veins of mercury laying in cracks in the rocks out behind the plant," and "puddles of mercury in the yard outside.")

In any event, Reed chose not to shut down, and mercury losses continued. On many days between 1970 and 1975 when Dryden Chemicals says no trace of mercury was dumped, Ontario government examinations of the plant's effluent registered readings ranging from 60 to 6,500 times normal mercury levels[3] – the latter figure on 31 July 1970. On just one day, 13 January 1975, an incident described by Dryden Chemicals as an "operator error" dumped 7.2 pounds of mercury into the Wabigoon River. Three months later, in April 1975, a spot check of effluent, analysed at McMaster University, indicated a loss that day of more than 7 pounds of mercury. Back in 1971 the then Federal Minister of the Environment wrote to an inquiring MP that " ... the total mercury discharged daily by the Dryden Chemical Co., Ltd. of Dryden, Ontario, is 0.05 lbs., or less." At that Toronto meeting in August 1975, Robert Billingsley said, "Since 1970 the Dryden plant has reduced losses of mercury. In 1974 the losses in liquid effluent averaged less than one-quarter ounce per day. ... "

There are some interesting discrepancies in available figures: for example, in the period from August to December 1972, Dryden Chemicals reported very low "averages" of mercury in parts per billion in the plant's effluent. But the averages were arrived at by taking sample readings made on six to eight occasions each month, and dividing the totals by the total number of days in the month, rather than by the much smaller number of days on which samples were tested.

According to Ontario's Ministry of the Environment, in a February 1976 report "Mercury in the Effluents from Chlor-Alkali Plants. Second Survey at Dryden, October 1975" (p.5), " ... the mercury losses reported by Dryden Chemical due to discharges of treated effluent *accounted for only a portion of the total amount of mercury released to the river system.*" And it was based on these "reported" mercury losses that federal and provincial officials said repeatedly from 1970 to 1975 that Reed was living within the law regarding mercury emissions. The report also suggested some drawbacks in the "grab sample" method used by Reed to test effluent at Dryden: "... the mercury concentration in the effluent fluctuated considerably, making single grab samples inadequate for determining mercury loadings." (Some other plants used a continuous sampling method – not Reed.)

But Reed used a second method of sampling effluent, taking a "grab sample" from a bucket below the tap on a draining line – with a small volume of effluent continuously draining through the bucket during discharge of waste liquids. Unfortunately, on pp. 27 and 30 the report says, "the effluent is allowed to sit, unpreserved, until analysis. ... When taking samples for mercury analysis, Dryden Chemical does not add preservatives. Several samples were taken with and without preservatives and a comparison of the two sets of results shows that *the* unpreserved samples yielded lower results. Preservation of samples would appear to be necessary for the accurate analysis of mercury in aqueous solution [water]."

But surely Dryden Chemicals was ordered to "eliminate the possibility of the release of mercury into the environment" way back on 26 March 1970? (One plant employee, in a recorded and transcribed research interview, described how "They sent a carpenter over the day that order arrived; he took a huge wooden plug, wrapped in burlap, and just hammered it into the end of the chemical plant outflow pipe with a sledge. ... They stored the mercury effluent in railway tank cars, big vats, anything handy.")

Of course it didn't quite work out that way – and there was a clause in the "order" permitting the company to appeal the date for ending its dumping. More than five years later, the Reed company knew that its new diaphragm cell system could be installed and ready for use in October of 1975. And on 15 May 1975, Environment Minister William Newman, told reporters in Thunder Bay, Ontario, as reported in the Toronto *Globe and Mail*, that "Dryden Pulp and Paper Co. will be ordered to stop using mercury by November ... Newman told a public session of the Ontario Cabinet that the control order would be delivered to company officials within the next few days." Mr. Newman also disclosed the method by which the five-years-later order was arrived at: "Newman said in an interview the new order, *worked out in consultation with the company*, also will cut down odor from the plant."

The definitive word on why Reed finally stopped using the mercury cell process may have been delivered by Miss M.E. McCormick, a Reed public relations staffer, at that August 1975 meeting with the Japanese researchers. Said McCormick: "This was a change for public relations, not an economic change."

Reed Paper's 1975 Annual Report contains the following extract (p. 13):

> On October 22, 1975, Reed permanently shut down its mercury-cell chlor-alkali plant at Dryden. The plant then was converted to a new process to produce chlorine and caustic soda without the use of mercury. ... On November 19, 1975, the new chlor-alkali plant resumed production. ... The conversion to this new technology, *which was done solely at the company's initiative*, was undertaken to provide the most

environmentally sound system available. ... *Reed believes its initiative here is firm evidence of its policy of responsible behaviour in the matter of environmental affairs.*

The difficulty is that the mercury already in the river systems is still there. As reported in a letter dated 27 September 1976, and addressed to a researcher for this book from L. F. Pitura, Regional Director for the Northwest Region of the Ontario Ministry of the Environment, " ... there is no evidence of significant reduction in mercury concentrations in sediments of the Wabigoon/English River since ... 1970."[4] "The company did comply, however, with much of the regulatory restriction placed on it; no one had suggested it deliberately broke laws or regulations with regard to mercury dumping. However, the federal regulation of mercury emission sets no upper limit on how much mercury can be dumped into a river system; it merely governs the amount which may be discharged in proportion to each ton of chlorine produced. What the regulation missed was the following:

1. It is the absolute discharge of mercury that matters – the amount put, *in toto*, into a water system. Moreover there is ground to believe mercury "losses" were "averaged" against chlorine production, making heavy, occasional "spills" and "losses" legal.

2. The carrying capacity of a waterway which is host to a chlor-alkali plant does not change with changes in that plant's production. In the Wabigoon River, for example, the volume of waste water and effluent released into the system during production at the Dryden mill is equal to one-quarter of the total volume of water in the stream.

So it may be true, as claimed by the company, that the letter of the law was always observed. But it wasn't a very good law. The law, further, controlled only losses of mercury into the water system. But at Dryden, as at most chlor-alkali plants, losses into the atmosphere were as substantial as those going directly into the water system. They were not policed, and continued after 1970 near the high levels registered in years before the company was ordered to stop "discharging mercury to the environment under any circumstances." In 1971, for example, when the company says it "calculated losses" in its liquid effluent of 21 pounds of mercury, the letter to the federal Environmental Health Centre in Ottawa reported that it discharged 257 pounds into the air. In 1972, 7 pounds were reported lost into the river, 245 pounds into the air; in 1973, 5 pounds into the Wabigoon directly, 241 pounds into the air; in 1974 the respective figures are 4 pounds and 198 pounds.

A general rule of thumb is that airborne losses are usually about equal to losses into the water, so the smokestack losses of mercury at the plant, never measured, may have equalled up to ten tons before 1970 and another five tons between then and 1975. All washed from air and foliage into soil, water table and river; dispersed more widely, of course, than mercury dumped directly into a river system – but destined for some river, nonetheless.

During that same period Dryden Chemicals was taking strenuous steps to reduce mercury pollution. Effluent was being held in tanks and ponds on the mill property while the mercury in that water, a "heavy" metal, presumably settled into the sediment at the ponds' bottoms. That sediment was then mixed with concrete and buried in plastic-lined pits on a farm bought by the company, a mile or so from the golf course just west of the mill. That "landfill" mercury loss, a total of 8,355 pounds of mercury from 1971 by the company's reckoning, presumably will not leach into the water table – though, unfortunately, there's even some doubt about that. These comments in an October 1976 tape-recorded and transcribed interview for this book with a worker in the Reed chemical plant:

> We're still treating the contaminated effluent. ... We catch all our contaminated water and hold it in settling tanks and then it's treated so that the mercury is released and settles into the bottom of the tanks. ... This has been going on since 1970 or '71, whenever the government order was. ... The sediment is pumped out of the tanks into big cement trucks, mixed with sand and hauled to the lagoons. ... The lagoons are out on the Hutchison property – they're big pits lined with plastic.
>
> It's a foolish thing. They just do it to make it look good. When you dump cement on the plastic it breaks through; and it rains on top of that cement and you've got run-off from the top of it. ... The old [mercury] cells are buried in the same place.

The Ontario government says it is monitoring the water table around the pits, that the wet cement dumped onto plastic film doesn't lose its concentrated mercury burden into the ground water and thence into the Wabigoon River, just a few thousand metres north.

The last word goes to that unpublished Ontario government study on pollution in the Ontario pulp and paper industry, left unreleased by William Newman. On p. 349 we read:

> The practice of working closely with each mill without public observation, let alone participation in the process, has left the ministry open to accusations of "being in bed with the companies." *Whether or not this is the case*, the method of administering the Ministry's current policy makes it impossible for the Ministry to refute this charge. [The charge had been publicly made in a paper titled "Environment On Trial," edited by David Estrin and John Swaigen for the Canadian Environmental Law Association in 1974.]

ON THE SHOPFLOOR

As noted earlier, Howard Brown acknowledged a loss of 322 pounds "in product" in the years from 1971 to 1974. In February 1976 the Ontario Environment Ministry gave the results of testing the "products" at the chemical and paper plants. They listed the mercury content of the following: 1) filtered caustic; "hypo"; chlorate; and hydrochloric acid – all from Dryden Chemicals, as it was still called; 2) mimeo paper; bond paper; offset paper; envelopes; full bleached pulp; semi-bleached pulp; and "Nu-dry" unbleached pulp – a wide range of Reed fine paper products.

Mercury content of all the paper products was low – and samples gave a constant reading, in each, of 10 ppb. The chemical products were different: the filtered caustic soda checked out at 105.5 ppb; hypo was 140 ppb; chlorate measured 640 ppb; hydrochloric acid registered the record high – 2,600 ppb, or 2.6 ppm.[5]

The Dryden products are, of course, just that – the *raison d'être* of the business and the factories; they are sold. In the case of the paper products the mercury contamination is so slight as not likely to be important, barring losses from fine paper mills in *their* effluent. Said a Dryden worker in a research interview for this book: "I imagine you'd find mercury in every paper plant's effluent because of the 'sizing'[6] they use; but none of the companies would bother to treat that because the government has never thought of it."

Reed's chemical products are more interesting, though, because of their much higher mercury content. It seemed unlikely Reed would provide the author with a list of those customers who bought and used

Reed's caustic soda, hypo, chlorate and hydrochloric acid; but there is this, from an employee in the chemical mill, in a tape-recorded research interview: "All the caustic soda they sold for years to Carnation Foods, it was all contaminated with mercury." (The Carnation Corporation has a plant at Carberry, Manitoba, about 300 miles west of Dryden, which produces processed french fries.) Caustic soda is a by-product, produced in the mercury cells at the same time as the chlorine to bleach the paper in the mill:

> Caustic soda came out of the mercury cells and it was all highly contaminated. When we cleaned the mercury out of the caustic storage there were 30 bottles [flasks] of mercury in there. That's more than a ton of liquid mercury in that place alone [about 2,280 pounds of mercury].

From another employee:

> The caustic soda tankers were never tested for mercury before the caustic was shipped to customers. Then there are the caustic holding tanks in the paper mill – there was mercury in them too. It was washed into the river.

Presumably the tank trucks, railway cars or whatever used to transport the caustic soda from Dryden were also contaminated by the caustic. And housewives weren't the only ultimate consumers of products made with caustic soda shipped by Reed. Other customers include two Winnipeg brewers.

But what about the environmental sampling conducted by the Ontario government – that not simply required of the company on the usual Ontario "self-policing" basis? Here are the comments of a series of Reed plant workers, interviewed on tape for this book:

> The government would check the plant out about once every six months. For mercury contamination. The workers were always ordered to clean the place up and a couple of days later the government inspectors would arrive...

From another:

> The stuff that they put into that river is incredible. They watch the environment people ... and when they know they are going to test again we open the dam [just above the mill]. The environment guys are testing for oxygen in the water so if you have more clean water coming down

from the dam, and more water going through altogether, you have more oxygen.

The company takes their own tests in the plant and they have special guys responsible for what goes into the sewer. Sometimes there's stuff going into the sewer and there's not a thing said; other times they're screaming bloody murder and that means only one thing – that the environment people are expected ...

And another:

Dr. Tidey's people would ship in all their sampling devices, all their meters and boxes, about three days to a week before they came to make their tests. [Dr. V.L. Tidey is Chief of Occupational Protection Services for the Occupational Health Protection Branch of the Ontario Health Ministry.] The boxes and meters and everything would arrive and management would say: "The Department of Health is coming. We'd better clean up." So everybody was working overtime, cleaning up – washing floors – making sure there were no spills. Even at that, when the testers came in, the company got hell for poor readings.

From another:

The raw human sewage goes straight into the river – from 1500 men – they've never been bothered about that as far as I know.

There so much crud in the water that, on a windy day, there aren't even any waves on the river near the plant. ... They'd know when the water resources people were going to come and they'd spill extra water out to dilute the effluent in the river. ...

Another Reed worker said:

Management used to tell us to "walk around" any puddles of mercury on the floor, not to walk through it and stir it up, and to get somebody to wash it away into the drains. And they'd tell us not to spend too much time on top of the [mercury] cells because of the mercury fumes up there. ... We had two kinds of gas masks in the chemical plant: one kind for chlorine gas and one kind for mercury vapour. ...

There was always mercury lying on the roof from where it had come out of the stack with the hydrogen and cooled off and dropped straight onto the roof. ...

There's a lot of chlorine produced in that plant. [Reed's new diaphragm cell process actually produces more chlorine than the old, mercury cell system – stimulating Reed plans to expand their forest operations and add another paper mill to use the chlorine.]

Reed have four storage tanks that each hold 100,000 gallons to store the chlorine when it's produced. But when they run out of storage space they just use railway tanker cars on the siding to store the chlorine. ... I've wondered about that; I mean if the chlorine gas escaped from the tank cars there could be a helluva danger to the town. I don't know if there are any regulations about that, or if anybody ever checks those things. ...

The Dryden phone book used to have instructions in it saying what to do if there was a chlorine gas alarm; but now they've taken that out of the phone book.

From another employee:

When we were being tested for mercury poisoning by Cameron [a Dryden physician employed by the Reed companies to test its employees] we'd go in there and Cameron would give us their spiel about, "How's your taste, your smell, your hearing?" And he'd have us hold a piece of paper in each hand and if you shook so bad the papers fell on the floor he'd never say anything. He'd say, "Touch your fingers, touch your nose," and guys went in there and deliberately did everything ass-backwards and he just said, "Check; check; check."

This, finally, from a transcribed interview the author had with Dr. G.J. Stopps on 16 September 1976. Dr. Stopps said that whenever Health Ministry people went to make any industrial spot-checks, sampling or monitoring procedures in any industry, "They were always accompanied by a representative of the Labour Ministry. I didn't like that much."

Question: It's commonly said that a routine practice in this government – as in many – is that often, before safety or health inspections are made, people in the plant or at the construction location, whatever, are warned so they have time to "get ready" and "clean-up."

Stopps: Yes. It's a shame that happens.

Question: But if the public knew about that, wouldn't it be stopped? It would have to be.

Stopps: I know. But that just hasn't happened. ... Maybe if some health people would complain publicly. ...

In September 1976, it was revealed at Queen's Park that there were plans afoot within the Ontario government to have the Labour

Ministry assume full responsibility for all monitoring of occupational health, removing that job from the Health Ministry.

One final point: the "good corporate citizen" was the only mercury user among six chlor-alkali plants in Ontario, in the years between 1955 and 1975 where workers were paid Workmen's Compensation because of mercury poisoning contracted while working in the chemical plant. There were two such workers, John Kitt and Walter Zuk, at Dryden Chemicals. Dryden Chemicals did not contest the claims of either man and the Workmen's Compensation Board doctors and examiners agreed both should be supported because of disability caused by mercury exposure in their work.

I think there is a responsibility to society as a whole and we must take care of those that are not able to take care of themselves. ... I think there are many instances in our society where people are harmed in one way or another through no fault of their own, and it's particularly difficult where blame is not exclusive, where there is [sic] complicating factors; and since we operate on a principle of law in this country, then you almost have to define in the courts, split up where is the responsibility, do it on a legal basis and assign responsibility and the consequences. ...

I believe personally that society as a whole has a responsibility to look after those that are harmed or those that cannot look after themselves where it's beyond the law of the land ...

First of all, I don't know exactly what we've done. Nobody has told us what the consequences of our actions were.

What I'm saying is that ... the native peoples and Indian Affairs are a federal government responsibility. They have a cabinet ministry for that; and I think the native peoples have jealously guarded their special position within our society and therefore it should be handled through the channels we have in existence today ...

I'm not an expert in this area. There are experts and they should be making the judgements and they should be saying what should be done from a medical health point of view.

And I think we should never forget the people up there. They are important.

Filmed interview with
Robert Billingsley, September 1975

Minamata disease victim

Mercury-killed fish in Japan

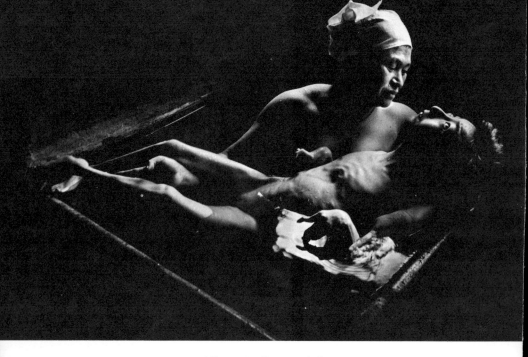

Minamata disease victim

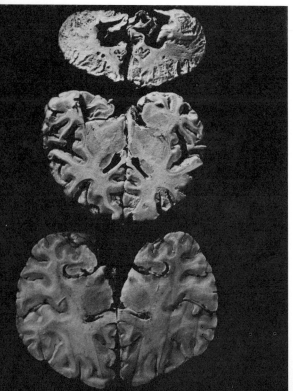

Left: The top picture of brain tissue is from a seven-year-old boy who had eaten mercury-contaminated fish for four years; the central brain was that of an eight-year-old girl who died after two years' consumption of poisoned fish; the bottom tissue is from the brain of a thirty-year-old man who did not have Minamata Disease.

Opposite page:
top: Grassy Narrows reserve
bottom left: The Wabigoon River
bottom right: Wild rice near Grassy Narro

Above: Outside Grassy Narrows schoo[l]

Left: Children of Grassy Narrows

Below: A fishing guide

The Kumamoto Study Group
visits the reserves – summer 1975

Jimmy Tanguay

Shore Lunch

Barney Lamm and poster
outside Ball Lake Lodge

Opposite page: Dryden and the mill, showing (*l.* to *r.*) Wabigoon Lake;
the dam; the main effluent outflow pipe (arrowed);
the railway bridge; the Wabigoon River.

Above: The main effluent outflow pipe

Below: One of the pits where Reed buries mercury-laden sediment

Above: The "backyard" of the mill

Below: Foam and fibre on the Wabigoon River
downstream from the Reed plant

11 "THE POLLUTER MUST PAY!"

The scepticism bred by pious statements from industrial spokesmen is matched by a growing public conviction that governments have been less than singleminded in their policing regulations and methods.

In the 6 March 1976 issue of the *Canadian Medical Association Journal* (published six years after the problem "surfaced") we read:

> The question of whether some Canadians are being poisoned by mercury is not easy to answer but there is sufficient evidence that methyl mercury is harmful and that some Canadians do have unacceptably high whole blood concentrations of mercury. Because of the possibility of mercury-induced irreversible brain damage, the current situation demands our full attention. *Action is required.* Officially, we need a mature philosophical approach to the management of environment problems of which mercury contamination is but one. ... *Canada lacks the aggressive environmental philosophy of a country like Sweden which puts teeth into its environmental legislation and muscle into the actions required.*

Writing in the *Saskatchewan Law Review*, Volume 38, of 1973/74, P.F. Rhodes said in part, reviewing environmental legislation in Canada:

> Implementation of much of the legislation by regulation or administrative action has been slow or non-existent. ... National standards dealing with pollution from mercury, phosphorous and pulp and paper plants ... promised under the Fisheries Act, have not yet appeared. A promised pollution claims fund allowing individuals to claim for water, air and soil pollution has not been established.
>
> Much of the present legislation is impotent as a result of this failure

113

... Unless the federal government is prepard to activate this legislation
one is drawn irresistibly to the conclusion that the flurry of environmen-
tal legislation was designed for political propaganda rather than to
genuinely deal with the problems at hand. ... The legislation rarely
gives the individual or a class of individuals a right to sue those who
breach it.

What the critic of current legislation did not know was that an
effort was made to establish that right three years earlier, in 1970 –
and quashed in the federal cabinet headed by Prime Minister Pierre
Elliott Trudeau. Two years after his party won a federal general
election with the slogan "The Land Is Strong," the cabinet Committee
on Legislation and House Planning (planning for action in the House
of Commons) met at 9 a.m. Thursday 17 September in the Privy
Council Chamber. Included in their agenda was "Cabinet Document
885-70," described, in the copy given the author, in these words: THIS
DOCUMENT IS THE PROPERTY OF THE GOVERNMENT OF
CANADA. SECRET.

The brief memo describing inclusion of the document is signed by
Privy Council (cabinet) Secretary J. Richard. The document itself has
the same heading as the memo, excepting the SECRET is replaced by
CONFIDENTIAL. Signed by the then Minister of Fisheries and
Forestry, Jack Davis, the three-page MEMORANDUM TO THE
CABINET outlines legislation to accomplish precisely what Rhodes
called for three and a half years later. In the passage headed
"Objectives," the memorandum says:

> The objective is to change federal law by enactment of a new statute
> similar to that already passed by the Province of Manitoba which will:
> (a)   create a right of action by the fisherman damaged ...
> (b)   provide for assignment of this right to the Crown, which can
> then sue the polluter and
> (c)   provide authority for the payment of compensation to the
> fisherman by the Crown.

Hon. Mr. Davis's memo continued:

> In the present state of the federal law it is, at best, very dubious whether
> an individual fisherman can successfully maintain an action for dam-
> ages against a polluter.

Still true. The cabinet didn't act. Six years later, on Parliament

Hill, as at Queen's Park, people with complaints about the environment or about regulation of pollution and government action to aid
victims were still, generally, regarded by public men and bureaucrats
as "guilty until proved innocent." Most such public servants had, like
most industrialists, missed the more useful principle coined by Dr.
Russell W. Peterson, ex-chairman of the United States President's
Council On Environmental Quality: "Chemicals are not innocent-
until-proven-guilty."

There was in government, from the beginning, a dichotomy
between public statements and private actions – maybe private
intentions. George Kerr and his cabinet colleagues made it clear in
1970, for example, that they expected Ontario's $35-million lawsuit
against Dow Chemical to be "settled" within eighteen months and that
actions contemplated against other polluters should await resolution of
that "test case." That intention was repeatedly emphasized in the
legislature, and on 17 March 1971, Leo Bernier, interviewed on
Kenora radio, said:

> There was some feeling that this government was in the hip pocket of
> industry. I hope that the announcement last week that turned out that
> we are suing the Dow Chemical for $35-million will remove some of this
> feeling. Mr. Davis made it plain that he means business with regard to
> the policing of the environment.

But at the end of 1976 Ontario had yet to file a statement of claim
in respect of that suit – and a court date looked as far away as it had
been six years earlier. Throughout that period the Dow suit had
surfaced from time to time as an excuse for failure to fully discuss and
disclose data on mercury dumping generally. As late as mid-June,
1974, Dr. R.B. Sutherland, now retired from his job as Chief of
Ontario's Health Studies Service, wrote to the National Indian
Brotherhood about their frustrated attempts to get any information on
health tests from government:

> I can tell you from experience that it is difficult to get ministers, or
> anybody else for that matter, to act against the advice of their lawyers,
> and that is what we are attempting to do in Ontario's case.

The temptation, in 1974, was to wonder whether having a lawsuit
as excuse to withhold data didn't rather seem to suit the political
purposes of government. Six months into 1974 the National Indian

Brotherhood was still being told that "pending litigation" kept Ontario's government from publishing data as old as that gathered in the first blood sampling program in 1970.

But at least Ontario's legislation was OK. The fellows who drafted it said so – George Kerr called it a "model" for other jurisdictions – and were even prepared to spend taxpayers' money to tell others about it. This exchange is excerpted from pages 4841-3 of the Ontario *Hansard* of 9 October 1970.

> *Mr. Nixon* [then leader of the Ontario Liberal Party and Official Leader of the Opposition]: Mr. Speaker, a question of the Hon. Minister of Tourism and Information.
>
> Did he approve, or has he even heard, the insipid and misleading promotional jingle that is being broadcast under the auspices of his department over the Toronto radio stations which claims that Ontario has the most rigid and strictest pollution laws in North America? Would he not agree that this is an ironical –
>
> *Hon. Mr. Randall:* Can the member prove we do not have?
>
> *Mr. Nixon:* – sort of jingle to be broadcast over local stations in an effort, apparently, to attract people from other countries to visit this area when the radio stations do not even have that range. What would the cost of this promotion be and how could it be justified? ... [When it transpires that the question is being addressed to the wrong department] I would like to direct a question to the Minister of Trade and Development to ask if he is aware of this advertising programme and if he approved it?
>
> *Hon. Mr. Randall:* Yes, Mr. Speaker. I am aware, and what the jingle says is exactly correct. We do have the most rigid and the best pollution control legisaltion and restrictions –
>
> *Mr. T.P. Reid:* They do not enforce them.
>
> *Mr. J.E. Stokes:* They never enforce them.
>
> *Hon. Mr. Randall:* – of any state or any province in Canada. If we have not, prove we do not have them.

Certainly, from its form and appearance, both federal and provincial legislation is promising, as is US federal and state law. So are the politicians – promising. Note the six-year time-span of the following statements.

8 April 1970. The Fisheries Minister spoke to a luncheon meeting of the Executive Council of the Canadian Manufacturers' Association in Toronto. The speech notes handed reporters bore the title: "THE POLLUTER MUST PAY! by Hon. Jack Davis." Some extracts:

This has been an expensive business. ... Our local fishermen have been prevented from starving during the winter months. But the Canadian taxpayer cannot be expected to foot this bill forever. Naturally, we are looking around for someone else to take the government off the hook. I suggest that this someone else is the polluter. The polluter, in other words, must pay. He must pay the bill in respect to mercury pollution. ...

Basically, the industry which caused the problem must solve the problem. ... It must clean up its operations and it must compensate others who have been hurt by its negligence. ...

10 April 1970 (House of Commons Debates [*Hansard*], p. 5718):
Mr. E.F. Whelan [Parliamentary Secretary to the Minister of Fisheries and Forestry]: Mr. Speaker ... We organized in Ontario a system of advances to fishermen to carry them over this unpleasant time. We are optimistic that the polluters will take care of the cost and stop polluting.

25 June 1970 (Ontario's *Hansard*, p. 4491):
Hon. Mr. Kerr: Mr. Speaker, I do not think there was any doubt at any time that in some way or another and at some time, action will be taken if there is not settlement with the Government of Ontario as far as its costs and expenses are concerned in relation to mercury contamination.

8 October 1974. Hon. Jeanne Sauvé, Federal Minister of the Environment, in a press release of a speech to the Canadian Government Affairs Seminar sponsored by the Air Pollution Control Association, said "We recognize that the 'polluter pays principle' is both equitable and economically sound."

28 May 1975. Indian Affairs Minister Judd Buchanan writing to a concerned voter, the Reverend Richard Renshaw of Toronto. His final paragraph:
... Another aspect of the problem [of mercury contamination in the Dryden area] is the need to determine responsibility for the pollution, and whether or not to take legal action against the responsible party or parties. To this end, as I said recently in the House of Commons, I have already discussed with Indians of the area the possibility of bringing an action against the company or companies involved.

17 November 1975. Judd Buchanan wrote to NDP Leader Ed Broadbent to report. Some extracts:

Thank you for your letter of September 9, concerning mercury contamination on the Grassy Narrows and White Dog Reserves. I am sorry you had to write again about this on October 14. ... We have under consideration the possibility of legal action being taken against a polluting company and have, in fact, had a meeting with the Canadian Environmental Law Association about this.

12 November 1975. (Ontario's *Hansard*, p. 484):

Hon. Frank Miller [Health Minister]. ... We have, in Ontario held to the belief that a polluter is responsible for damages caused through pollution.

20 November 1975. (Ontario's *Hansard*, p. 754):

Mr. Lewis: May I ask the Attorney General, Mr. Speaker, could he clarify what legal proceedings or recourse he is investigating that may be applied to Dryden Chemicals Limited of Reed Paper, in Northwestern Ontario, involving the pollution which may have caused, or may yet cause, Minamata Disease amongst the native communities?

Hon. Mr. McMurtry: The matter is being considered by the ministry in its broadest terms, because of course there are very difficult problems in determining just what may or may not have occurred.

8 December 1975. (House of Commons Debates [*Hansard*], p. 9799):

Mr. Malone: I have a final supplementary, Mr. Speaker. Is the federal government doing anything to assist native groups to obtain proper settlement from companies such as Dryden Chemical Company or Domtar Limited ... ?

Hon. Judd Buchanan: Mr. Speaker, this matter is being investigated. Currently representatives from the province of Ontario, who are also very much involved in this since it is their law which has to be complied with, are investigating the compensation the people should have and to see whether in fact a basis for a lawsuit does exist against the company in Dryden.

7 August 1976. Hon. Frank Miller, interviewed at Leo Bernier's annual political picnic at Eagle Lake, is reported as follows in the 9 August edition of the Thunder Bay *Times-News*:

"Mr. Miller said the real problems on the two reserves is [sic] not mercury but social and economic problems.

Unemployment leads to idle time and this leads to problem drinking. This leads to a high rate of death through violence, he said."

POLLUTION CONTROLS

Reed's Dryden mill was singled out, in an enormously detailed, unpublished Ontario study on pollution,[1] as the worst offender of twenty-six pulp and paper mills in Ontario. Ontario Environment Ministry studies say that only by dredging sediment build-ups thirty to forty feet deep in places, and by literally diverting the Wabigoon River could substantial water quality improvement be attained. A research interview with a scientist employed by Ontario's Environment Ministry revealed that there is an average flow of 50 million gallons a day in the Wabigoon at the mill site. About 17 m. gallons are used to generate hydro power; the remaining approximately 33 m. gallons (roughly, the amount of water consumed by a city of 150,000 people) go through the chemical plant and mill proper and are then fed back as "effluent," along with the untreated human sewage.

But there has been no dramatic or concerted effort by Ontario's pollution enforcement agencies to require a clean-up. In 1969 the Ontario Water Resources Commission, in a study titled "Water Pollution Survey of the Wabigoon River," recommended that Reed "... remove pulp mill wastes which have accumulated between the mill and the Wainright Dam." (3.4 miles downstream from the mill.) The report detailed the horrific state of the river and said that despite substantial reductions in waste loadings by the industry,

> annual industrial waste surveys carried out by the Commission since 1958 have revealed an effluent quality which has neither satisfied nor even reasonably approached the Commission's objectives. ... Estimated concentrations of suspended solids were in the order of 3,000 ppm whereas the Commission's long-term objectives was and is 15 ppm.

But, in 1977, the sediment was still in the river, the oxygen content and fish life indiscernible. Government policing of pollution was characterized chiefly by interminable delays and extensions of deadlines while the unpublished study made by the government showed it was vastly better economics for pulp mills to continue polluting. (See Appendix 4.)

On 22 January 1970, Domtar Newsprint Limited was convicted on one of two charges laid under the Ontario Water Resources Act. Provincial Court Judge J. Connor, in fining Domtar the maximum allowable $1,000, said that existing fines were "too low," and that the

Ontario legislation required "more teeth." Judge Connor added: "We are a little late in this country in taking a stand against pollution," and should "consider the desirability of passing down a heritage of lakes, not cesspools. ... Penalties are sometimes considered as more or less a collection, as licenced permission. They shouldn't be. They should be to deter. ... "

This oral decision is reported on page 72 of that unpublished Ontario Environment Ministry study. The study notes that none of the twenty-six mills in Ontario were living within the law as regards industrial pollution in 1974 – each of them is examined to see what improvements would occur *if the companies simply lived up to the Ontario Water Resources Commission regulations and requirements.* Couple that with the fact there were only nine prosecutions under the Act between January 1967 and December 1971. *In five years, that is, during which twenty-six pulp and/or paper mills were failing to meet standards set by the government of Ontario, only nine were charged with any breach of the law;* one of those escaped conviction. For the others, fines ranged from $350 to the maximum then allowed of $1,000. They averaged $750.

In 1970, the year that Domtar was fined $1,000, the company had a net profit, according to the Ontario government study, of $17,468,000.

In 1970 Ontario raised the maximum fine from $1,000 for a first offence to $5,000 – and to $10,000 for second and subsequent convictions. However, no charges were laid between 1970 and 1975. In 1976, in late October, the American Can of Canada Limited mill on Lake Superior was slapped with sixteen counts of emitting more mercury than permissible under the Federal Fisheries Act; even those charges, laid by Ontario, were at the request of Canada's federal environment ministry, Environment Canada.

Enforcement and application, in Ontario tend to hang on what the study described in the words:

> In practice, the government has been reluctant to utilize these powers of enforcement, preferring to seek the co-operation of the companies concerned. This approach has met with only limited success in achieving effluent control by the pulp and paper industry.

12 ALL HONOURABLE MEN

Though industry and government may appear to be in conflict over the issues raised by industrial pollution their dispute is in many respects a phoney war. A few foot soldiers may be sacrificed to the expedient need for public battle and casualties, but even those set-piece clashes are generally scheduled for office hours so that the real professionals, the "mercenaries" of both sides, will have time to change for dinner and leisure to exchange reflections on their daily scorecards and body-counts.

The differences in roles, goals and "mind-sets" between our industrial-business establishments and our politicians and bureaucrats have become ever more blurred as our political and economic mechanisms have become more complex. As the entrepreneur has given way to the corporate manager, business has moved closer to the mind-set of the cabinet minister and civil servant, substituting desire for continuing power in the place of ownership/wealth. As the partisan stump orator has been effaced by the image maker, so elected and appointed bureaucrats have moved towards the merchants' perception that stability outweighs progress; that what's believed is as valid as what is; that PR outsells fact or truth; that tradition may be superior to justice, appearance preferable to substance. To effect change, after all, requires, first, recognition of a need for it – with the concomitant of guilt-by-historical-association with the events in question. Second, change requires a reordering of priorities and resources, difficult enough for the individual, agonizing for any institution.

We don't, unhappily, have dedicated and skilled researchers in a Ministry of Political Environment turning out studies like "Alternative

121

Policies for Pollution Abatement in the Ontario Pulp and Paper Industry": " ... companies have a powerful financial incentive to continue polluting the air and water ... fines ... provide the companies with virtually no economic incentive to incur the much greater costs for pollution control. ... Hence, it is in the companies' interests to resist incurring these costs, even when this may lead to prosecution or fines." A study which translated "financial incentive" and "economic incentive" into "civil service tenure" and "political cost/incentive," might help show why government has so lamentably failed its masters, the voters, in Northwest Ontario.

For here, too, penalties are generally slight. Leo Bernier lost a few score votes at White Dog and Grassy Narrows in 1975, but still polled a plurality of 4,060 votes over his nearest rival – and a majority of 886 votes over the combined totals of his two rivals. Frank Miller, George Kerr, Marc Lalonde and their colleagues at Queen's Park and on Parliament Hill have endured some awkward questioning in their "House," an occasional tough press conference or TV interview – but nothing enduring or debilitating. Their collective civil servants held the same jobs – or better jobs – in 1976 that they'd had in 1969. Governments are rarely defeated for ineptitude or obfuscation anywhere on the scale below the obscene or ostentatious, and civil servants are rarely fired for caution. There is, on the record, powerful incentive for the government and civil service to evade every non-emergency situation; to duck every decision not forced upon them; to refuse entirely to risk antagonizing anyone by ruling on cases which can, instead, be simply thrown out of court.

A few generations – decades, at least – of that evolutionary mind-set have left most of us joining government and industry in worship of and expertise at crisis management and spasm response, forgetting that preventive medicine is cheaper and easier. The buzzword for these characteristics in 1977 is "situational ethics," and they are nowhere more evident than in the response of government to the events at Grassy Narrows and White Dog.

Then there are always jurisdictional problems – between levels of government, between departments within government, even between different branches within a single governmental ministry. A classic political ploy, for example, is for a cabinet minister to be absent from his seat when opposition critics have tough questions; a cabinet colleague may then blandly assure the House of his concern and promise to "pass the question on" to the minister concerned who may, in turn, make a brief colourless response some days later, when the venom has been sucked from the original "strike."

In Canada, as in every federal state, there are some clear-cut jurisdictional boundaries between the national and regional levels of government – and a great many more areas so amorphous that they offer politicians a virtually endless chain of escape hatches.

Commercial fisheries, to take on instance, are a federal responsibility in Canada. But recreation – and that includes the licencing and regulation of sports fishing – is in the provincial field.

Treaty Indians are a federal responsibility in Canada. But public health is a provincial field.

Food and drug safety are regulated in Ottawa, but industrial safety and environmental health are monitored by the provincial governments.

Even those artificial distinctions are diluted and blurred. For example, Ottawa has had the provincial governments "administer" the policing of the Fisheries Act of Canada; so, if an industry poisons commercial fish, it is the province which is supposed to prosecute under the federal act, although the senior government at Ottawa retains a seldom-used right to act if the province cannot, or will not.

Within either level of government the situation is as puzzling. For instance, Ontario's Ministry of Health began recommending in 1973 that the Wabigoon/English rivers be "posted" – and closed to all sport fishing; but the actual ban on sports fishing would have had to be imposed by the Ministry of Natural Resources- – and Leo Bernier saw no need.

On 1 March 1973 he was quoted by Robert Reguly in the Toronto *Star*: "Mercury pollution is not [my] problem. ... That belongs to the Health Ministry. ... [my] department is responsible for fish and non-renewable natural resources, not water pollution."

In the summer of 1974, Marion Lamm wrote to Prime Minister Trudeau about the situation. She was told that "while the federal government is having discussions with the Ontario Cabinet minister involved, the initiative will come from the Ontario government which has jurisdiction in this area."[1] A second letter from Mrs. Lamm was referred by the Prime Minister's Office to the Minister of the

Environment and the Minister of Indian Affairs and Northern Development.[2]A response came two months later:

> As you know, the Office of the Prime Minister has sent us a copy of your letter of August 27, about mercury pollution of some of the waters in the area of Kenora, Ontario. If, in fact, the Indian people are affected by this, we would, of course, like to know about it. ... [3]

There is also the matter of party solidarity and support, complicated by the fact that different parties often hold power in different provinces, and in a provincial and federal capital at any given moment. In practice:

The Progressive Conservative party held power in Ontario from the beginnnings of the mercury problem through 1977, but in Ottawa during that same period the federal PC party were cast in the role of the Liberal government's Opposition – the people most likely to unearth problems and hound the federal government for action.

The Ontario PC Party has had for three decades a vote-getting organization second to none in Canada. Dubbed the "Big Blue Machine" for the party's colours, its alliance has been regarded as essential by every federal PC leader, since no federal Conservative government has ever been elected in Canada without a powerful Ontario base of members.

So. This extract comes from an article in *The Canadian* magazine, published 13 November 1976. The author, Hazel Strouts, was formerly Press Secretary to Joe Clark, leader of Canada's PC party and Official Leader of the Opposition at Ottawa. The other man mentioned, Bill Neville, used to be, in the mid-60s, an *enfant terrible* among executive aides to Ottawa cabinet ministers. In 1975 he managed press relations for Premier William Davis's Ontario election campaign; in 1976 he handled press relations for Joe Clark's successful leadership convention bid. He worked in the federal PC headquarters offices. Here's the quote from Ms. Strouts:

> What about mercury pollution in the rivers that flow through Indian reserves in northern Ontario? Why not raise a stink over that? I suggested it once to Bill Neville. It was the morning after I'd seen a CBC Fifth Estate program on the subject. ... Bill sympathized. His wife had also been upset by the program. But as for action in the House, that was out of the question. He explained that the pollution was in the water and

water came under the jurisdiction of the provinces and those particular rivers flowed through the Progressive Conservative province of Ontario. To make a row about it would lay the party open to charges from the Liberals that it was Tory ineptitude that was to blame. ...

To do them justice, several PC Members of Parliament have raised and debated the mercury problem in the House of Commons, not heeding the backroom counsel. As an example, the House of Commons Fisheries Committee met to consider mercury pollution on 11 May 1976. Federal Health Minister Marc Lalonde was unable to attend as a witness – but sent his Parliamentary Secretary, Robert Kaplan. Mr. Kaplan was looking on the cheery side.

> I would like to tell you that we are currently, under the Health Protection Branch, doing research on mercury in pregnant monkeys, on chronic mercury toxicity in cats. The Ministry of the Environment and Environment Management Service, Inland Waters, has produced 43 publications on mercury pollution; the Wildlife Service, 24 publications; Fishers and Marine Service, 58 publications; and there are many other works in progress.[4]

Said an Ottawa research chemist, in an interview with the author: "We can't persuade the politicians it's not necessary for Canada to re-do every damned bit of research that's been done elsewhere; they seem to think Canada has more prestige if we keep repeating other people's mistakes. The most important activity in this town is re-inventing the wheel; we do it every day." Back to Mr. Kaplan:

> What can be done by the federal government has been done. ... We have an impressive record of action, I would say.

Said Arnold John Malone, PC Member of Parliament from Battle River, Alberta:

> Mr. Chairman, I think we have been fed an awful crock of crap here. ... I can just scarcely believe what I am hearing ... surely we cannot sit here, after this problem has been in front of us since 1969 ... and claim that we are still talking about the jurisdictional question of native people. ... We heard talk tonight about a nutritionist coming on in June of 1976, about repeated testing and re-testing, about more surveys, about final reports that are due to come out, and about sampling of waters. Such slowness would not occur – I am quite convinced of this – if it were to happen in a Caucasian community of Toronto, Montreal or

Vancouver because we would be doing something about the intake of mercury into their diet. We have talked about 18 publications from one section, some branches of the departments here, and 24 from another ... Mr. Chairman we can go on *ad infinitum* ... what are we doing that is significant, fast and factual about people? And do not give us that crap that we do not have the jurisdictional responsibilities – because surely with thalidomide and everything else, once the problem was discovered we did not say, well, it is a jurisdictional problem and we cannot solve it. We are a government, we have to be able to solve it. ...

Mr. Kaplan: We are reducing the levels of mercury in the environment. ... I want to reject categorically the allegation that we would do more for little white girls. ...

Mr. Malone: ... Although you may reject that there is not a lack of sensitivity towards the native people different from the others in society [sic] I do not think the government would allow this kind of condition to happen at all in the mainstream of Canada.

Mr. Kaplan: ... but what more can you do?

Mr. Malone: Close the river.[5]

In Ontario legislature debates, it's not uncommon to find a government minister responding to an opposition charge or claim in the words "That's a lie" or "That's a damn lie." George Kerr and Leo Bernier have both had recourse to that response on occasion. What custom does not allow, however, is for opposition members to charge anyone in the cabinet with "deliberately misleading" the House. Members have been expelled from the august chamber for that breach of parliamentary etiquette and required to apologize formally on their return. The tradition and custom is that all members of an elected legislative assembly are "honourable members" – as with the British military notion of officers and gentlemen. It is unthinkable that such a member would deliberately mis-state a case, mislead even an opponent; by the definition of their role, the sanctions of history, all honourable members are presumed to be above such behaviour.

The tradition is most markedly observed in the breach. In discussing and debating the mercury poisoning scandal in Northwest Ontario members of both the federal and provincial governments have resorted to misdirection as often as a two-shows-a-day stage magician. As we have seen, ministers of the Crown have, in and out of the legislatures at Ottawa and Queen's Park, had resort to exaggerated claims; they have understated real events and problems; claimed credit for non-existent programs; bragged of unimplemented policies; recited "facts" which might have made Baron Munchausen blush; answered charges with half-truths and irrelevant data apparently designed chiefly to obscure reality. Sometimes the government spokesmen have been merely retailing nonsense fed them by their staff; often the politicians have given every evidence of originating their own flight plans for take-offs on trips into fantasy.

The general lack of will to act even on avowed policy runs as a tattered thread throughout government inertia from 1969 to 1977. It is characterized most often by a simple failure to provide the resources needed, whether for legal action to recover damages to life and economic stability, or to proceed with adequate and substantive medical programs.

It grew difficult as the years passed, for an observer of government policies on mercury poisoning to avoid a conclusion that the failures of initiative had their roots, on occasion, as much in cynicism as in the bureaucratic morass of shifting priorities. On 19 November 1976, this report appeared in the Toronto *Globe and Mail*:

> Ontario fish that is deemed dangerous to health and is therefore not sold in Canada, is being sold on foreign markets – mostly in Europe.
>
> The mercury guideline of .5 parts per million, established by the federal Department of Health and Welfare, "does not relate to fishery products in the export trade," Natural Resources Minister Leo Bernier said in a letter. ...
>
> "Comparable agencies in other countries," Mr. Bernier wrote, "establish their own standards from country to country, and many are more generous than the Canadian standard."
>
> Ronald Bond of Environment Canada's fish inspection branch said that Ontario fish sold for export because they don't conform to Canadian standards generally go to Europe. He said mercury standards vary widely across Europe. "Britain has no standards. Italy has, I think, .75 ppm and others have 1 ppm. ... "
>
> Mr. Bond suggested it was not up to Canadians to say what other governments' standards should be. "Our responsibility is to ensure that fish sold for export doesn't violate any laws other countries might have."
>
> Both Mr. Bernier and Health Minister Frank Miller said in

interviews yesterday they didn't see any problem in selling fish for export. Both said it was not up to them to dictate world health standards.

"I think the receiving nation has to set standards for food," said Mr. Miller. ...

Kenneth Loftus, director of the Natural Resources Ministry's fisheries branch, said special arrangements are made for fishermen who want to sell fish that don't fall within Canadian guidelines to countries where the standards are not as stringent. He said the fish caught are funnelled through dealers with special permits who guarantee the fish will be exported.

13 GENOCIDE BY DEFAULT

The eminent North American scientist who described the mercury pollution of the Wabigoon/English river system and its effects on the local Indian populations as "genocide-by-default," commented: "If you quote me, by name, I'll deny I said any such thing."

Another scientist, this one an official of the Government of Ontario, said:

> Of course we've been acutely aware, from the start, that if we diagnosed a confirmed case of mercury poisoning up there we'd probably be opening the floodgates for lawsuits for compensation; claims against the company, claims against the government; God knows what. And of course we'd find ourselves hauled into one courtroom after another to testify as to our findings. Certainly none of us wanted that.

Nor have they got that. Yet.

Throughout the complex history of events in Northwest Ontario, the issues of legal liablility and "compensation" have been of continuing concern to officials of both federal and provincial governments. The reasons for this aren't clear; those officials are unwilling to discuss the grounds for their determination to avoid any talk of any compensation by anyone, under any circumstance.

Dr. Peter J. Connop, a specialist in occupational health, is the federal health department official responsible for all of Northwest Ontario. In an interdepartmental memo of 15 March 1973, he expressed the concern that

129

if the Provincial Government does provide any financial compensation to these communities it would be setting an extremely expensive precedent which will undoubtedly be brought out at regular intervals for every bit of smoke, bad weather or any other adverse factors which may affect the communities in the future.[1]

Bad publicity seemed to be of concern to other provincial and federal officials as well. On 2 November 1970 Leo Bernier suggested pollution experiments in the Kenora area be cancelled, as they were "adding to the adverse publicity already directed to that particular area."[2] A 1973 internal federal report on mercury blood levels in northern Canadian natives was accompanied by this comment from Indian Affairs official, R. M. Connelly:

I should emphasize that while the figures given in the report are a cause for concern they are not a cause for panic. As they may be open to misinterpretation however I would ask that you restrict circulation of the report to the appropriate members of your staff. I might add that the copy being forwarded is the only one that the Department possesses at the moment and I would therefore ask that you return it when it has served its purpose.[3]

And in a confidential internal memo of 4 December 1974, John Dennehy of the Special Assignments and Review branch of Indian affairs, told Jack Tully, Acting Director of the division:

The Department of Indian Affairs should establish a priority program to work directly with the affected communities. If there is one death from this area directly related to mercury poisoning the Indian people will break a bombshell on Indian affairs and probably receive the sympathy of the Canadian people.

According to provincial and federal health authorities, a single case of certified, *bona fide* mercury poisoning has yet to be proven. In 1971 John Munro, federal Minister of Health and Welfare, stated that "absolutely no clinical signs or symptoms have yet been uncovered following detailed and specialized examination of Indians with high mercury blood level readings" (as of September 1971 fewer than 100 of the residents of the two affected reserves had been given blood tests; none were given "specialized" neurological examination until 1973) and said "high blood levels of mercury have been found in Indians where industrial pollution is not a factor" (no such report had been published or revealed).[4] On the CBC *As It Happens* broadcast on 6 November 1974, Dr. G.J. Stopps denied that there was "obvious illness" in the reserves area that could be in any way attributed to mercury.

But, as we shall see, some people on the reserves exhibit neurological symptoms which, when combined with their fish-eating habits and blood and hair mercury levels, can only point to "sub-acute" mercury poisoning.

Moreover the circumstantial evidence points overwhelmingly to widespread "hidden effects" of mercury poisoning which have been adamantly ignored by all of the government bureaucracies involved. Research in Europe, North America, Russia and Japan points strongly to such secondary symptoms as miscarriage; increased incidence of violence; high blood pressure and heart disease; lowered resistance to alcohol and to viral and bacterial infection, and decreased physical ability to adapt to extremes of temperature. Examination of the leading causes of death in the community – alcohol-related accidents, pneumonia, miscarriage, heart disease and death by exposure in winter – makes the scholarly research into the effects of heavy metals poisoning in these areas of much greater than academic interest. A study of the research makes it irresistibly likely that many of these deaths at White Dog and Grassy Narrows came about as a consequence of mercury poisoning. (See Appendix Five.) There have been no "acute" cases yet; none of the macabre rictus, grotesque shambling gait, convulsions and assaults of pain. But the first symptoms of Minamata Disease didn't appear in Japan until thirteen years after the Chisso Corporation began dumping mercury. At the end of 1976 it was just fourteen years since the "spills" began at the Dryden Chemicals plant in Ontario. Indians in Northwest Ontario eat fish mainly in summer, unlike the Minamata fishermen for whom it was a twelve-month diet, but this does nothing to reduce the nature of the hazard nor the responsibility and need to meet and solve the problem.

What defies comprehension is that in the spring of 1977 there have *still* not been adequate studies done to identify precisely the damage to the population at risk.

14 THE DESULTORY YEARS

There are four basic methods of determining whether individuals have suffered physiologically from exposure to methyl mercury poisoning:

BLOOD AND HAIR SAMPLING AND TESTING

Mercury concentrates in the hair. Given that hair grows about one centimetre per month, hair samples can show what mercury levels were present in the system in past months and even years.

CLINICAL SYMPTOMS

Many of the neurological "signs" of mercury poisoning can be caused by other diseases, other poisons, other injuries. But when the symptoms are coincident with high blood or hair mercury levels and a history of heavy mercury intake, when the symptoms are "clustered" within family groups who eat the same diet, and, most of all, when the signs appear in certain combinations, a diagnosis of mercury poisoning can be made. No other illness produces, in combination, loss of balance, loss of co-ordination in fine "motor activities" (such as fastening buttons), sensory disturbance and constricted visual fields.

PATHOLOGICAL EXAMINATIONS

Post-mortem examinations can provide absolute and final evidence of methyl mercury poisoning. When Minamata Disease is well advanced, post-mortem examination of brain tissue reveals a classic pattern of destruction and shrinkage of cortical and cerebral brain tissue. In "milder" cases the evidence subsequent to autopsy may be ambivalent. However, post-mortem mercury levels in the brain, together with those in other organs where methyl mercury concentrates (liver, heart, kidneys, spleen, pancreas) can point to fatal or contributing effects of mercury poisoning.

Generally, with sub-acute mercury poisoning diagnosis must be based on an "educated guess" taking into account blood and hair sampling, clinical symptoms and dietary intake of mercury-contaminated fish. But there is one further means of determining whether a community has been affected by mercury poisoning:

THE EPIDEMIOLOGICAL SURVEY:

This is, fundamentally, a way of statistically establishing the presence or absence of a disease. A simple model would be that two groups would be chosen – one in an area where there was a "risk" of the disease in question, the other a group with an otherwise similar lifestyle, diet, etc. Both groups would be tested, *in toto,* for blood and hair mercury levels and both groups would be exhaustively examined for the neurological and clinical symptoms associated with mercury poisoning.

If the group exposed to mercury had higher blood levels and more symptoms, statistically it would be "proven" that the "at risk" population was suffering from mercury poisoning rather than from symptoms caused by alcoholism, diabetes, syphilis, Parkinson's Disease and birth defects. The larger the "at risk" and control groups, of course, the more exact the attainable statistical result.

ONTARIO

Blood and hair sampling and testing of the populations of Grassy Narrows and White Dog by the Ontario government began in 1970. On 3 June of that year, Leo Bernier noted that the Health Ministry's tests had revealed "urinary mercury levels ... well within normal limits in the 154 persons tested." Mr. Bernier said thirty hair samples had been tested and that those with "the higher levels" had readings equal to about half the levels at which symptoms had first appeared at Minamata. He added: "There is no evidence of any illness in Ontario from consumption of fish contaminated with mercury ... preliminary tests on some eight or ten samples show blood levels which are low and within normal range. The Department of Health is maintaining close surveillance of this situation."

Some facts to put the statements into perspective:

Urine tests are useless in testing for methyl mercury poisoning. This test method is used often in checking industrial workers for evidence of exposure to inorganic, metal mercury, which is excreted in large part through the bowels and bladder.

With regard to "maintaining close surveillance," only 113 people at White Dog and Grassy gave blood samples. Few were those most at risk. Often the commercial fishermen or guides were not sampled – a feature that persisted until 1975. Only thirty of these 113 were sampled again at any time during the subsequent five years.

As for "blood levels which are low and within normal range," "normal" blood mercury levels in people are around 5 ppb. (20 ppb is considered an upper level for absolute safety; a reading over 100 ppb gives cause for anxiety and there were identified symptoms of methyl mercury poisoning in one case at Minamata with a reading of 200 ppb.) In the 1970 samples only four of those sampled had readings under 10 ppb, seventy-one people had readings between 10 and 50 ppb; and twenty-nine between 51 to 100 ppb; a dozen tests ranged from 100 to 200 ppb and one sample was higher than 200 ppb.

The samples were taken in April – five months after most area residents had stopped eating fish at the end of the season the previous October. Given the half-life of seventy days, on average, and a passage of 150-plus days since the last substantial fish diet, one can reasonably suggest that the 1970 levels would have been four times higher had they been taken the previous October.

In 1974, Dr. G.J. Stopps told photo-journalist Aileen Smith, co-author of *Minamata*, that the first provincial blood tests had been conducted in the winter, at the time of lowest fish consumption. He himself joined the Health Ministry too late to participate in the sampling, but he told Aileen Smith that " ... the government people could only get into the reserves in the winter, because they had to fly in with ski-equipped planes – as though [she adds] he thought I wouldn't know that there were float planes in and out of those lakes every day, all summer long."

Attending a meeting of the federal Standing Committee On Mercury on 18 February 1975, Dr. Stopps is reported in the minutes as having described the timing as "due largely to happenstance." Three months later, reconsidering that reply, he telexed the committee chairman, Dr. Somers: "IT HAS ALWAYS BEEN RECOGNIZED THAT THE TIME OF SAMPLING PROGRAM ON THE RESERVES USUALLY CAME ABOUT 3 MONTHS AFTER CESSATION OF FISHING AND THIS COULD BE ALLOWED FOR IN INTERPRETING RESULTS. ... "

To Aileen Smith, who was critical of the times chosen for sampling, Dr. Stopps said, according to her testimony: "All you have to do is figure back. You know the half-life and the number of days elapsed since the last fish meals. So you can just multiply by two for every 70 days."

On that theoretically sound basis, the 1970 readings would have ranged as high as 800-plus in one case (well into the range for acute Minamata Disease) and 600 ppb in a dozen more.

Later testing by Dr. Tom Clarkson established that blood levels were highest in October, after a full summer of fish diet, and lowest in January-April, after some months of little fish-eating. The difference was by a factor of more than three.[1]

It has been suggested that levels in the range of 400 to 800 ppb in late 1969 are impossible, as no levels anywhere near those were discovered when more adequate testing was initiated in the early summer of 1975. But by 1975 people on both reserves, while still eating some contaminated fish had clearly cut back very substantially on their fish diet. Their blood levels would therefore have fallen greatly in the intervening five years.

Government spokesmen (Frank Miller and Dr. Stopps among them) have said they couldn't understand why there have not been much higher blood levels on the reserves, if people ate as much fish as they said prior to 1970. Given the foregoing, they have an answer: the levels likely *were* much higher in 1969 and before.

From 30 April 1970 until the summer of 1975, the Ontario Health Ministry program of blood sampling and testing continued in what might best be characterized as a desultory way. More samples were taken in late 1970 but, as we shall see, the results of the tests were not revealed to the residents of Grassy Narrows and White Dog for *three years.* Bureaucrats seemed to be obdurately pigheaded or simply grossly ignorant of the needs and anxieties of a people who believe that many of their number have been poisoned by mercury.

There now followed a gap of thirty-two months before more tests. It was filled chiefly with modest breast-beating punctuated by occasional bursts of rationale and apologia from various governmental officials and spokesmen.

In Ottawa, Ontario's unilateral testing program did not get in the way of some inferential self-congratulation. On 27 September 1971, Health Minister John Munro presumably dictated a letter in which he told a parliamentary colleague Canadian Indians might have "very high tolerance for mercury." He stated further:

> We are placing a great deal of emphasis on the mercury problem, and are working with other agencies to define the high risk areas across the nation. *We have a programme underway to monitor the human blood levels in these areas.* ... We need to keep a very close watch on the total situation and accumulate much more information. We will continue to give this programme a high priority.[2]

Research for this book has unearthed no federal initiatives, actions or even correspondence indicative of "a great deal of emphasis" in Ottawa as of September 1971.

Three months later, in a letter to a tourist camp operator dated 16 December 1971, Dr. Stopps was waxing both cautious and metaphorical:

> ... Our task in the Health Studies Service is to try to sift fact from fiction in looking at the health effects of mercury. This is an exceedingly difficult task because if health effects are being caused by mercury they are almost certainly very small changes and very difficult to detect. It would not, however, be reasonable to ignore such small and hard-to-find effects since cracks in an airplane wing might also be small and difficult to locate but of considerable significance for the future safety of the 'plane.

Time passed.

On 27 November 1972, Dr. Stopps wrote another letter – this one replying to a letter from the Chief of the Grassy Narrows Band:

Dear Mr. Assin:

... It was my understanding that your people had been told about the levels of mercury in the blood and hair that were taken in April of 1970 but if this is not true or the information has been mislaid I am glad to pass on this knowledge.

... the results show that the mercury levels in the blood and hair are higher than those for people like myself who eat very little fish. This is the sort of result that we expected but the results also were not high enough to suggest that anyone in your band were [sic] suffering from any illness due to mercury.

A single visit such as the one in April, 1970, is valuable but of course is much more valuable if the results obtained at that time can be compared with the results obtained at a later date ...

This comparison became possible through the blood sampling of December 1972 and January 1973. This time 123 blood samples were taken, seventy-four of which were "repeaters." Fourteen of those tested showed mercury levels above 100 ppb.

Only now did the test subjects receive any individual notification. On 7 March 1973, a "Task Force" appointed by the Ontario government to oversee and report on a study of the hazard held a public meeting at White Dog reserve. (Meetings at White Dog and Grassy Narrows were held on successive days.) Some general background on mercury poisoning was offered by Task Force members representing the provincial Ministries of Health, Environment, Natural Resources. After a perfunctory question period the Task Force headed back down the hill to their float-equipped aircraft for the trip back to their Kenora hotel. Just as they were about to board the plane, Dr. Stopps handed sealed envelopes to the Indians who had walked down the slope to bid their visitors farewell. He then boarded the bush-plane and it took off. The Indians opened their envelopes and found individually addressed form letters listing their blood mercury levels. In the description of an observer that day:

They were like a bunch of grade school kids with bad report cards; giggling, embarrassed, confused and frightened. "What did you get?" one would say, and they'd all compare their mercury levels. The people with the highest readings were sort of left alone to get used to the idea. No one really knew what it all meant.

The accompanying letter, to people having levels above those considered hazardous (100 ppb) read:

> From this measurement, and our conversations with you, there is no suggestion that mercury is affecting your health, but experts in the effect of mercury would agree that your level is somewhat too high and that, as a safety precaution, it would be wise to lower it. [No suggestion as to how one might do that – with leeches, perhaps?]

On the same day that the letters were distributed, Dr. Stopps, asked if test results would be made available to the people, responded that certainly the individual had "a right to know," but that such information was handled "on a one-to-one basis"; that it was "between the individual and the doctor." There was, Dr. Stopps told a newspaper reporter later that day, a "sort-of doctor/patient relationship between the government and the Indians" which precluded giving individual test results to the press.

In October 1975 in a research interview tape-recorded during preparation of this book, Dr. Stopps, now at the University of Toronto, was asked to recall the incident. "Probably," he conceded, "it wasn't the very best way to give them that information."

On 21 March 1973, the Ontario Task Force on Mercury urgently recommended that: "Health examinations of the population most at risk be carried out in greater depth at the earliest possible moment." But the lack of political will to move quickly and effectively could still be measured by the truncated purse strings. Wrote Ontario Health Minister Hon. Dr. R.T. Potter plaintively on 25 October 1973: "I do not, at this time, have a definite date for the re-testing to be carried out because of a shortage of manpower."

Nothing more was done until the next sampling in December 1973 and January 1974. Another set of blood tests followed in December 1974/January 1975. By the end of the fourth round the OMH had collected and tested 425 blood samples from 308 of the people in the two communities. Of this total "sampled" population, 273 were sampled only once, according to a survey done by the National Indian Brotherhood, so no extrapolations were possible in terms of rising or falling blood mercury levels. Of the total sampled, thirty-eight readings registered higher than 100 ppb. One reading, that of fishing camp guide Mathew Beaver, was 385 ppb on one occasion.

However, OMH spokesmen were happy in the knowledge that none of their tests had identified anyone in the 500 ppb-plus range – the point at which overt symptoms might be expected. None of them had heard or heeded Dr. Stopps' advice to multiply their January readings by two to learn what the levels might have been in October.

Nor had the sampling been thorough. The populations of White Dog and Grassy Narrows fluctuate greatly with the seasons and with economic changes, and it's perhaps no surprise that summer 1975 blood tests had covered only one-quarter to one-third of the people, and covered them rather less than comprehensively.

In a form letter of 16 April 1975 to Indians at Grassy Narrows and White Dog who had had their blood tested, the federal Health official most directly concerned with them, Dr. Connop, wrote: " ... there is no suggestion that mercury is affecting your health or the health of anyone else in the band who gave us a blood sample. ... " But on 25 April 1975 another letter to Grassy Narrows and White Dog residents from Dr. Connop said: "The fish in the river system around your reserve still contain high levels of mercury. There is no amount of fish that can be considered safe to eat. The more fish you eat, the greater the danger to your health. You are strongly advised not to eat any local fish at all. ... "

The shortage of manpower referred to by Dr. Potter was presumably one factor – but only one – which frustrated plans for the lengthy and complex process of an epidemiological survey. Such a survey was on the drawing board in Ontario in 1971; begun then, it could have been completed and the definitive results known by late 1973 or early 1974. The people with the highest mercury levels, the worst symptoms, could have been identified and persuaded, at least, to eliminate fish from their diets. But the funds were never given the Ontario Health Ministry.

Various statements by officials of the Health Ministry who have left since 1971 and people still employed in the Ministry emphasize the lack of government action. Paraphrasing their various recollections:

"There really was no support for such a study within the government or at the cabinet level. ... There was no shortage of money then.... But all the senior officials of government could see coming out of such a survey was bad publicity, I guess. ... Those plans were made by Dr. Stopps; he had them complete and ready to go by the fall of '71. ... There was some delay while we made sure we had or could get adequate lab facilities, but certainly the study could have gone ahead."

So far we have left aside the question of post-mortem examinations. Some concerned officials in the Ontario Ministry of Health were attempting to manage events in the best interests of the people at risk from the beginning, but their numbers were small and their clout less than overwhelming. In a research interview in late 1976 a senior official said, "There were numerous reports and recommendations made but you'd never get a 'yes,' or a 'no.' If we'd even had a 'no,' we'd have had something to complain about; but everything disappeared into a vacuum. Then you'd send up a memo saying 'Do we or don't we do so-and-so?' and that one's not answered, either." He also said:

> We knew at the beginning ... in 1970 ... we were going to need tissue samples and brain histologies. So one of the first things they [Health Ministry people] asked for were tissues and brain histologies, requesting that Dr. Peter Pan co-operate in this matter as he was the pathologist in the area. [Dr. Pan, a private practitioner, is the only pathologist in Kenora, where deceased from White Dog and Grassy Narrows would be taken. Dr. Pan was the only man able to obtain and supply the needed material.]...
>
> Dr. Pan refused, point-blank, to help us. ... No reason for the refusal was ever given to us. ... But in the face of the refusal there was nothing we could do. ... We had no legal authority to order him to do the work for us.

By the end of October 1976, only seven "acceptable" brain samples had been received by Ontario Health Ministry staff in Toronto from White Dog and Grassy Narrows. Many of the thirty-five brains taken for sampling had been incorrectly sampled, incorrectly treated, kept without refrigeration too long before shipping or sliced into sections too tiny to be usable. Five of the twelve useful brains were from populations outside the Grassy Narrows and White Dog reserves. No results were publicly available from tests of those seven brains taken from reserve residents. One Ontario government scientist in conversation with the author, added yet another entry to the litany of reasons why information isn't always made public expeditiously: "You can have any *old* data that's here. But *I'm* going to be the first person to publish *my findings. This is my research, my data.*"

Added a colleague: "This sort of data is scientific and complex; the proper place to publish this information is in the scientific journals. *... The press and the public can too easily misinterpret this sort of data.*"

But at least the brains are now being efficiently collected, preserved and studied. Well, sort of. The best available method of preserving and shipping the tissue samples is by refrigeration. Since Ontario Ministry of Health officials confess, privately, to having little confidence in testing facilities in Winnipeg, the samples must be shipped to Toronto.

Until August 1975, no one in the Ontario Health Ministry was "really carrying the ball," as one employee put it, to arrange for collection and shipment of the specimens. In that month Dr. Lesbia Smith joined the Ministry and was given the responsibility. The first "fresh brain" shipped and refrigerated to her specifications, arrived in Toronto from Kenora exactly a year later. The delay had been caused by the need to make arrangements and obtain specimens.

For example, the samples are placed in plastic bags – the kind used to store sandwiches in household refrigerators. These bags are then placed in a styrofoam cooler – the kind used to cool beer on picnics – together with a freezer pack – the kind bought in any sporting goods chain store. The cooler is then placed in a cardboard carton, sealed, and shipped the 1,200 miles, by bus, from Kenora to Toronto.

The precise size of cooler desired by the Ministry of Health for the purpose wasn't immediately available when the program was instituted. For whatever reason, it was decided no other size of cooler would do and *it took four months* to find and buy the insisted-upon size; no "fresh" brains could be shipped until those coolers had been delivered to Toronto, then trans-shipped to Kenora.

There were still other problems in late 1976 with "legal authority." Post-mortem examinations are normally only carried out in four circumstances: on order of a local coroner, in cases of violent death (automatic in Ontario); on request/demand of the Provincial Attorney General; and on request of the deceased's immediate family.[3] At the end of 1976, six years after Ontario Health Ministry researchers first attempted to get brains for histology from Dr. Pan, only those from cases of violent death were being obtained for study. This is because first, no order had ever been made by Ontario's Attorney General for more general post-mortem examination following deaths of people from Grassy Narrows and White Dog (nor had officials of the Ministry of Health, including the then Minister of Health, Frank Miller, ever asked for such an order). Second, no one from any government agency or Ministry had ever suggested to the people of White Dog and Grassy Narrows that they had the right and, in view of the circumstances, a substantial interest, in seeking post-mortem studies.

Therefore it seemed the brains and other organs being shipped to Toronto in 1976 were being "taken" without legal authority. All violent deaths in Ontario are, automatically, "coroner's cases," and the remains are evidence for the coroner's jury. It's likely that the scientists engaged in those few post-mortem mercury studies being done are all guilty of a breach of law and open to potential prosecution.

Health Ministry officials are evidently "stealing" the evidence of coroner's juries in the hope of getting some data, their sample selection based simply on the availability of the cadavers which, in cases of violent death, end up in the hands of Kenora's coroner, assisted by a now co-operative Dr. Pan.

A final irony. On 26 January 1973, a coroner's jury in Kenora, deliberating on the death of Thomas Strong, an Indian from Grassy Narrows, recommended: "That a Grassy Narrows or White Dog Reserve resident of a known high mercury content become a Coroner's Case upon death."

That recommendation, like all such, was forwarded to Ontario's Attorney General, who did *not* act upon it. There have been no inquests into deaths from the area intended to probe the possibility of mercury poisoning since the Strong case.

It wasn't only the Ontario Health Ministry who wanted autopsy specimens of area residents made available for testing. In spite of repeated efforts between March and December 1975, the Federal Standing Committee on Mercury in the Environment (which included representatives of the federal Departments of National Health and Welfare, Environment and Indian and Northern Affairs) failed to obtain samples of autopsy tissue via either Dr. Stopps or Ontario's Chief Coroner.

In early January 1977, the author wrote letters to Robert

Billingsley and key Ontario cabinet ministers, asking if they had any fresh thoughts on mercury poisoning "for the record." The following response was received from Leo Bernier just one day before he was made Minister of Northern Affairs:

> ... My position and that of the Government of Ontario from the beginning has been that it is the Government's responsibility to ensure that all medical scientific information which could possibly be gathered should be made available to the public, and to those affected by mercury contamination. This we have done. As well, it is the Government's responsibility to ensure that all relevant scientific data wherever it is to be found in the world, should be assembled and made available to the public of Ontario. This has been done. It is the responsibility of the Government to ensure that its decisions are based upon scientific evidence and this we have always done, and we will continue to do. When additional scientific information is available to us from our advisors in and outside the Government, it will be made available to the public and appropriate decisions will be taken based upon the evidence available to us.
>
> As you are aware, there is a great deal of research taking place in Canada and in other countries of the world on the question of environmental and health hazards resulting from industrial natural pollutants [sic]. You will appreciate that this information is constantly being assembled and policy revisions are taken regularly to ensure that the Ontario Government maintains a policy in this respect which is in conformity with all the facts established by the scientific community. This has always been our stance and it will always be the case.

OTTAWA

Meanwhile what was happening on the federal front?

The 14 October 1975 statement by three federal cabinet ministers said: "The Department of National Health and Welfare began to monitor the levels of mercury in humans in Northwestern Ontario ... in 1971." Simply untrue. The only blood-hair tests done prior to summer 1975, were undertaken by the Health Ministry of Ontario.

However, according to the unpublished federal task force report of 1973 the Federal Health Protection Branch was carrying out animal studies in 1973 to determine the effects of mercury. Researchers in Ottawa fed some cats fish from the water system below Reed's mill at

Dryden, Ontario. The cats contracted Minamata Disease and died; brain tissue studies showed they had died of mercury poisoning.[4] The fish contained levels of mercury similar to those in fish eaten by the populations of White Dog and Grassy Narrows.

The cat study results, made available to the task force in 1973, weren't published until 1975, when visiting Japanese specialists in mercury poisoning forced disclosure in testimony before a parliamentary committee. The data, like so much in other "unpublished" studies, wasn't even transmitted between different agencies at the same level of government. Both Ottawa and Ontario failed to act on their own data, or that of the other level of government. As an illustration of just how difficult it was for colleagues at other levels of government to keep abreast of events, witness this declaration, from an internal memorandum of 28 November 1974 (file number 487/3-8) in the Department of Indian Affairs and Northern Development. Telexing the Operations Director of the department to report on programs at Grassy Narrows and White Dog, Ontario Regional Director Howard B. Rodine summarized the state of federal intra-governmental communications as succinctly as anyone could: "ACTIONS TAKEN BY THE DEPARTMENT OF NATIONAL HEALTH AND WELFARE UNKNOWN."

Information flow between the two levels of government was at least as sparse as between the departments within each level – but officials at both Queen's Park and Parliament Hill were blessed in that they had one another to blame. For instance, a senior Ontario Health Ministry official said, in a research interview for this book, that efforts for full-blown and adequate neurological and epidemiological testing

> ... would have been in the federal camp and I was too far away from that to know what was going on – and I didn't meet anybody much above my level who was in a position to do anything.
>
> When we chatted at my level they agreed there was a problem; I don't think they were quite as enthusiastic about it as I was – but after we left nothing happened. But why – why it didn't happen – I have really no idea. I'm as mystified as anybody as to what went on in the federal government.

As soon as Ontario's 1972/73 blood level results were correlated, Dr. Stopps sent a copy to Dr. Connop. He was clearly hoping the federal authority would initiate the epidemiological survey he had blueprinted two years earlier. In his 13 March 1973 letter to Dr. Connop he said:

> ... As we discussed the other day, I feel that it is very important if the two levels of government are to maintain their credibility with the Indian Bands that follow-up measures are instituted as soon as possible. ... My own personal feeling is that it would be important to follow up as quickly as possible with neurological and ophthalmological examinations of those persons with blood mercury levels above 100 parts per billion.

The feds offered free neurological examinations, at a hospital in Winnipeg to the sixteen Indians who had registered over 100 ppb. They were not pressed to take the tests, nor were the tests made available to them in their own communities. The wonder is that six of them accepted the offer and made the five or six hour journey to and from Winnipeg. Said Premier William Davis of Ontario, in a letter of 13 January 1975: "Sixteen were notified, eight accepted. No cases of abnormalities were identified."

Leo Bernier, by the way, went one better than Premier Davis. In an interview filmed in the summer of 1975 he said: "I understand that there were at least thirteen taken to Winnipeg, and neurological tests were done on them. ... There was no problem at all. This is the information that was referred to me as a politician."

On 14 October 1975 the three federal cabinet ministers most directly involved in the problem, Health Minister Marc Lalonde, Environment Minister Jeanne Sauvé and Minister of Indian Affairs and Northern Development Judd Buchanan, made a joint statement to the House of Commons and the Senate in which they said, "A ... group from Northwestern Ontario was investigated in Winnipeg. ... No findings specifically attributable to methyl mercury excess were found. ... The results of these tests were reported to the persons concerned and made public in summary form."

What was "made known," and "reported in summary form," was a statement that there had been absolutely no symptoms of mercury poisoning found. Dr. Stopps in a conversation with the author also said all six were free of symptoms. But in the *Canadian Medical Association Journal* of 6 March 1976, Dr. David E.A. Shepherd says:

> It is beginning to look as though there may indeed be mercury poisoning

in Canada. ... One of six Indians examined in Winnipeg in 1973 has known whole-blood mercury concentrations of 126 and 55 ppb, together with occasional numbness and shakiness of his hands and arms, vestibular function – consistent with, but not diagnostic of, a cerebellar lesion, and evidence of borderline peripheral neuropathy. It is by no means clear what the cause of these abnormalities was, but the findings demand our attention today.

Dr. Connop did get some specialists into the reserves two years later, in the spring of 1975, when he funded and commissioned a "research" project. It was to be undertaken by an ophthalmological specialist from Waterloo University – a man used by the federal Health people to study vision problems among the Indian populations of other parts of Ontario. This time, however, there was a caveat: the specialist was required to pledge to Dr. Connop that he would never reveal or publish the findings. He agreed, and proceeded to test in the communities for the defects of vision symptomatic of methyl mercury poisoning. The results were ready in the spring of 1975 – ready for Dr. Peter Connop. The investigating scientist kept his word. Not even the people studied were told what the tests showed. They will read here of those findings for the first time.

A total of seventy-four people, ranging in age from eight to eighty-three were examined. There were fifty-two men and twenty-two women in the test sample; about one third from White Dog and two thirds at Grassy Narrows. (It's as though the sample was chosen to search out the highest-risk elements in the communities since the people of Grassy Narrows eat substantially more fish than those at White Dog and since men, many of them fishing guides, are more likely to have high mercury readings than women.)

"Constriction of the visual field" (tunnel vision) is a classic symptom of Minamata Disease – a clinical sign often demonstrable in sub-acute cases before more acute and dramatic symptoms appears. *Of the seventy-four individuals studied, forty-five were found to have "visual field losses."*

Nor were the cases of constricted vision a symptom of aging or of the diseases of the elderly: one in four of those under 20 had the symptom, one in three of those between 20 and 30 showed visual field loss, between 30 and 40, the percentage dropped to 17 per cent, then to 11 per cent between 40 and 50. In those over 70 the symptom appeared in only one person-per-decade of age.

The Waterloo University scientist could not evaluate his findings fully in terms of risk to those he examined since he was not told the blood mercury levels of the people. Nor were these seventy-four "guinea pigs" tested for any of the other neurological signs of mercury poisoning. Nor were their fish-eating habits correlated. The scientist did find, however that eight of those tested were suffering from "lens sclerosis," a loss of transparency of the lens tissue in the eye. The condition, similar to the development of cataracts, seems unique to victims of mercury poisoning.[5]

In the civil service exercise described by some as "covering your ass," bureaucrats take elaborate pains to reassure their masters, the elected politicians, that everything is under control. A classic example occurred in an internal memo written to federal Health Minister Marc Lalonde by his Deputy Minister, Dr. J.L. Fry on 14 March 1975, just before the arrival of the Japanese team mentioned earlier.

The memo, "an up-to-date report on the problem in Northwestern Ontario, with our evaluation of the present situation and information on our current activities," starts with a brief review of the history of mercury poisoning and of the area. Then the Deputy Minister moves on to actions initiated "in late 1974 to up-grade the surveillance over the health of residents of Grassy Narrows and White Dog Reserves." These steps included designation of "a branch co-ordinator and a mercury consultant ... at headquarters and an additional nurse was taken on staff at the Kenora Health Unit." That is, two existing staff members in Ottawa were presumably given extra duties co-ordinating and consulting, and one nurse was hired. This person was responsible for:

> obtaining blood and hair samples from all residents of both reserves ... clinical examination of all persons found to have blood mercury levels of 100 parts per billion or more and of any individuals complaining of symptoms possibly attribuable [sic] mercury intoxication ... the maintenance of a special register of those "at risk" with provision for a three-monthly review of health status and annual clinical examination.

Simple tasks for any nurse able to drive from Kenora daily and work there twenty-six hours a day. In the event the implicit assumption, that all residents would now be tested, that those "at risk" would be given full neurological examinations, that three-monthly checks would be made and annual clinical examinations guaranteed was mainly honoured in the breach. But there was more in Deputy Minister Fry's report "on our current activities":

PATHOLOGY WORK

Arrangements were made with the pathologist in Kenora for reporting to Medical Services of pathological findings when autopsies are done on persons from the reserves ...

FURTHER ACTION BEING TAKEN

The current program, including surveillance of mercury levels in humans and fish, monitoring of the health of residents including clinical examinations, and study of available information on the problem will continue.

All of which, for Hon. Marc Lalonde, must have been extremely reassuring: all the right things were being done. Sort of. By one nurse with a car.

15 NEEDED–
A DEAD INDIAN

In 1975 the federal Department of Health approached Dr. Tom Clarkson, asking him to mount a comprehensive and continuing program of blood tests and hair sampling among the people of Grassy and White Dog.

Dr. Clarkson agreed. He lived at Grassy Narrows, with his family, throughout the entire summer of 1975 and August of 1976 and his most skilled laboratory technician stayed on the reserve from July 1975 until September 1976, when she was replaced by two other technicians from Rochester University.

Originally Dr. Clarkson was asked by the federal Health officials simply to "collect samples" in the communities. These blood and hair specimens, he was advised, could then be shipped to Ottawa or Rochester for analysis. When he suggested that, to gain the confidence and respect and co-operation of the local people, the tests ought to be done on site and the results and technicians available for discussion with the people directly affected, he was told not to cause logistical problems. After a period of stonewalling by the Ottawa bureaucrats, Dr. Clarkson finally refused to carry out the program unless it was built around a full testing system *on the reserves*, with full and convenient disclosure to the population at risk.

The federal bureacracy relented; a trailer equipped with complex lab equipment was taken to Grassy Narrows, towed by Dr. Clarkson behind his family-filled station wagon. In fairness to Dr. Clarkson it should be noted that the anecdote above, confirmed by three disparate sources– one of them with the federal Health Department – did not

150

spring from his "indiscretion." He will be as surprised to see the story in print as those who couldn't comprehend the logic of his demands.

The October 1975 joint statement by three federal cabinet ministers said that, "Dr. Tom Clarkson, an international authority on mercury toxicity, has been engaged by National Health and Welfare and is conducting an epidemiological assessment of the problem on the reserves in Northwestern Ontario." Dr. Clarkson would be among the first to deny that even the most comprehensive program of sampling and testing blood and hair represents an "epidemiological assessment" of the entire population. Such a study must range over long periods and include a massive complex of tests and studies.

The statement continued: "The Department of National Health and Welfare is sending in medical specialists – neurologists and ophthalmologists to assist the health team on the reserves in screening for signs of mercury toxicity." The "health team on the reserves," Dr. Clarkson and his single lab assistant aside, comprised that one federally employed nurse with the aid of one native assistant in each of the communities. As for the medical specialists and the impression of a stream of carefully co-ordinated tests and examinations, up until the time of the statement, federal efforts in this direction had been limited to the Winnipeg tests and the still-hidden study of visual defects. Even an *ad hoc* survey of those who happened to be available for neurological tests was still, as this statement was tabled, six months in the future. Then there was a virtuous peroration:

> Ministers indicated that the highest priority is being given to assisting those people who are affected by the mercury problem, and to prevent further occurrences. They stated their determination to pursue effective action on the problem and to take whatever steps can be taken to control pollution and to protect the health of those exposed to mercury contamination.

Between August and November of 1975 Dr. Clarkson arranged the collection of 587 hair samples and 158 blood samples from Grassy Narrows and White Dog. Findings from his interim report[1] brought little reassurance:

> Adult males working as guides at fishing camps have the highest intake of mercury. Five guides out of eleven that were sampled had blood levels in the range of 100 ppb to 330 ppb. Analysis of hair samples from the

guide having the highest blood concentration (330 ppb) revealed that the peak mercury concentration had occurred two months prior to the collection of the blood sample. This peak value in hair was close to 150 ppm equivalent to a blood concentration of 500 ppb [a level where symptoms were unmistakable in both Japan and Iraq].

The fishing guide who had the extrapolated level of 500 ppb was Mathew Beaver, the Grassy Narrows man who has consistently had the highest readings among those sampled in his community. In August 1975 I filmed for the CBC a neurological examination of Mathew Beaver, made by Dr. Masazumi Harada, Professor of Neuro-psychiatry at the Institute of Constitutional Medicine at Kumamoto University. Dr. Harada probably has a broader experience in the diagnosis of Minamata Disease than any physician in the world.

During the examination he identified the following symptoms of Minamata Disease in Mathew Beaver:

i)   Constricted visual field (tunnel vision)
ii) Tremor (when attempting to hold his hands steady)
iii) Romberg's sign (inability to balance with feet close together)
iv) Glove and stocking syndrome (loss of feeling in the skin of the extremities)
v)   Loss of sensation around the mouth
vi) Reduction of normal hearing (Mathew was unable to hear a stop watch held about 18 inches from his left ear – yet CBC microphones easily recorded its ticking from a distance of approximately eight feet)
vii) Abnormal reflex responses

Mathew was employed as a fishing guide by the Hohnsteins. He told the author that he ate shore lunches which he prepared for the guests of Grassy Lodge, because to refuse to eat might scare the guests away. No guests meant no work, and Mathew had no other job. He was concerned about his wife and children, so he'd stopped bringing fish home for them, and tried to avoid fish meals for his family. As for himself, he was, "a little bit afraid, I guess," but "there is no other work, now."

He was examined a few months later by a neurologist employed by the government, who said in a research interview that men like Mathew were very sophisticated, good at faking symptoms. Mathew had shown no signs of mercury poisoning at all, said this man, and had probably been drinking the day he was filmed with a tremor. Dr. Harada didn't agree. Neither did the evidence of the film, nor the observations made over a period of more than a year, of Dr. Peter Newberry, the Quaker doctor who lived at Grassy Narrows in 1974-6.

There were other findings in Tom Clarkson's report:

> The wives of the guides tended to have higher blood levels than other females on the reserve. Children usually have lower blood levels than their parents but younger children tended to have higher mercury levels than older ones. A matter of serious concern is the continued exposure of pregnant women to methyl mercury. One example is described of a newborn infant with a hair concentration of 30 ppm, equivalent to a blood concentration of 100 ppb.

Mercury levels at Grassy Narrows, where more fish is eaten, were approximately 50 per cent greater than those in adult males at White Dog.

When older children in a family were found to have lower mercury readings than younger brothers and sisters, investigation revealed the older children had been "not resident in White Dog, but were attending school in Kenora." Seasonal variations in three children from the same family followed a consistent pattern as all had similar diets. (The Japanese research demonstrated that a pattern of high levels within a family unit was one strong indication of mercury poisoning.) Ominously, Tom Clarkson found that "in this particular family consumption of mercury and therefore presumably of fish, *has been increasing in recent years* as compared to what appears to be a very low intake of mercury about two years ago."

The evidence that Indians who did, generally, reduce or eliminate fish meals after the first alarms of 1970, are now eating more fish again should surprise no one. After all, the Ontario government had not banned fishing in the waterways. Moreover with a failed economic base and the inroads of inflation on subsistence diets between 1970 and 1976, other protein foods are, more and more, beyond their reach. Government failure to deal with the economic crisis on the reserves and government reluctance to acknowledge the gravity of the hazard are, inexorably, bringing on the very situation most-feared by thoughtful bureaucrats and alert politicians: more fish eating, more mercury ingestion and, if the situation goes on, an inevitable death or series of deaths.

Here are Tom Clarkson's recommendations, published in 1976:

> 1. ... Discussions should be held between the guides' employers and responsible Health Authorities as to the most effective means of controlling [guides'] exposure. A resolution of this problem should, in turn, lead to a reduction in exposure of the members of the guides' families. Surveys should be made of guests and other residents for exposure to methyl mercury, with emphasis on regular guests and long-term residents in fishing camps and lodges in areas having high methyl mercury in fish.

Neither of these recommendations had been acted on eighteen months after receipt of Dr. Clarkson's report. The only survey of fishing camp guests was the *ad hoc* attempt made by Dr. Clarkson himself, (see p. 72). There was some effort to reduce exposure of the guides. All fishing camps traditionally supply a box to each fishing party, containing tea, the ingredients for frying fish at shore lunch, and some tinned food against the improbable failure of the group to catch their lunch. In the summer of 1976 one fishing camp instituted a system of charges for guides who ate the non-fish canned food in the box. The guides were not told they had to eat the fish at the shore lunch, only that they must pay $1 each if they ate the alternate food, which consisted of either a can of pork and beans or a tin of luncheon meat. But they could only eat one tin, and if it was shared by two guides, or three, each was charged a dollar. The guides opted to eat the fish.

> 2. The present programme of surveying neo-natal exposure should continue and be further developed.

No further development had occurred six months after the recommendation was printed. An Ontario Health Ministry researcher told the author the government had found "fairly high" mercury levels in three infants, of whom one was "OK" – but added that the Ministry had "lost track" of the other two.

> 3. High priority should be given to the expansion of the clinical programme for which plans are now underway.
> 4. The Health Education Program instituted in the last year on the two reserves should be vigorously continued. This program has undoubtedly

helped to dissuade excessive fish consumption on the Reserves and may still be useful in reducing exposure of the guides.

5. ... the mercury problem may continue for some time. From the point-of-view of long-term plans to deal with the environmental health hazard from methyl mercury and other pollutants, it would seem highly advisable to establish a National Center in Environmental Health. Such a Center, consisting of a multi-disciplinary team of scientists and physicians would help detect and deal with potential threats long before they emerged as a national problem.

From scores of research interviews and communications with federal and provincial officials it's clear no such development is in the works. Conditioned by a history of spasm response and crisis management, these governments will be as ill-equipped to deal with the next crisis as they have been in Northwest Ontario and Northwest Quebec.

There were two other sets of tests run in 1975. The first was by Dr. Masazumi Harada, and three other Japanese doctors from Kumamoto University. The team came at the invitation of the band councils, their trip funded by concerned Japanese. Later they made a formal report of their findings, from which these extracts are taken.[2]

... As a beginning we collected materials which had already been made public there. Those data were fragmentary. ... Then we went to the locality where mercury pollution was severe, and conducted epidemiological and clinical surveys as well as analysis of hair for mercury content. ... Most of the inhabitants of the reservations refrain from eating fish but there are some who are still eating it regularly. Also, it has become known that bread is baked with fish roe in it. ... Our analysis of the bread showed 0.44 ppm of mercury, a dangerous amount because such food is taken more regularly than fish.

At one point Kumamoto University researchers report on a cat fed fish from a lake near White Dog, which their pathologist Dr. Takeuchi destroyed and examined in February 1975, after other kittens from the same litter, and one adult cat, had died with Minamata Disease symptoms. Says the report: "Symptoms of these cats were exactly the same as those observed in cats in Minamata which were found to be suffering from methyl mercury poisoning."

The Japanese team, doing clinical testing in the communities themselves, surveyed eighty-nine people, ages six to eighty-four:

... The subjects of our survey were relatively healthy people ... those who were hospitalized or bedridden at home were excluded. [The invalids of the reserves had still to be tested by anyone at the end of 1976.] Clinical study consisted of routine neurological examination and examination of visual fields. ... Many neurological symptoms were found. It cannot be concluded that all of these symptoms resulted from methyl mercury. Neurological symptoms caused by other diseases should be distinguished carefully. *However, symptoms observed frequently in Minamata Disease – sensory disturbance, impaired hearing, contraction of visual fields, tremor and inco-ordination – were immediately recognized.*

A table describing the symptoms they found is reproduced below, from their published findings.

Clinical Symptoms (89 cases)

		Number of cases
Subjective symptoms (complains)	Numbness	28
	Pain in limbs	40
	Convulsion of limbs (Crampus)	16
Neurological symptoms	Disturbance of eye movement	19
	Nystagmus	3
	Impaired hearing	40
	Sensory disturbance	37
	(glove and stocking type)	(15)
	(perioral area)	(5)
	Abnormalities in visual field	16
	(para-concentric contraction)	(9)
	Tremor	21
	Hyporeflexia	20
	Hyperreflexia	15
	Muscular weakness	16
	Ataxia	8
	(when walking straight line)	(8)
	(adiadokokinesia)	(16)
	(dysmetry)	(7)
	Dysarthria	5
	Fainting-fit	2

"Glove and stocking" sensory disturbance is, like "disturbance of eye movement," one of the most characteristic symptoms of Minamata Disease, but one which can also result from alcoholism and diabetes, and so must be noted in conjunction with other symptoms. Cases of ataxia (unco-ordinated walk) and dysarthria (slurred speech) "are important symptoms of Minamata Disease in its acute or serious stage."

Finally, these summary excerpts from the report:

The present situation of Canada is exactly like that of Minamata before the mass outbreak of the disease. ... Although there are differences between Japan and Canada in the ratio of morbidity, severity of symptoms and other factors, *there is no essential difference.* ...

It has become clear that non-typical, mild cases vastly outnumber typical and severe cases. In some patients, symptoms were so mild that only sensory disturbance was observed. Unless typical cases were found among family members, or mercury pollution was proven, diagnosis could not have been conclusive. ...

It is a mistake to ignore the effects of methyl mercury until typical [severe] cases of poisoning are found ... Even though typical cases may be absent, methyl mercury poisoning must be suspected whenever there is a high incidence of contraction of the visual fields, and sensory disturbance, especially when the same symptoms are prevalent in families. ... Glove and stocking sensory disturbance – 15 cases – and paraconcentric contraction of the visual field – 9 cases – were found among those with high values of mercury concentration in blood or hair, and in some cases some symptoms were found among their family members. In such cases the influence of methyl mercury is suspected. It is necessary to conduct immediately a more detailed examination. ...

When the Japanese team came to Canada, Leo Bernier was interviewed by an area radio station and asked his reaction. He described the research team as "a bunch of troubadors." (He is later said to have apologized, after much adverse publicity resulting from the remark.)

Ontario Health Minister Frank Miller sent a team to Japan and Iraq in the winter of 1975-6, to benefit from the experience in those jurisdictions. But a year after the Japanese clinical testing at the reserve Mr. Miller told a reporter (at Leo Bernier's political picnic) that he had learned Dr. Harada was a "psychiatrist, not a neurologist," and was (like the minister) "politically active."

In 1976 the federal Ministry of Health arranged a set of clinical tests. The Minister, Hon. Marc Lalonde, had said in Parliament on 13

February 1976: "In each area involved, doctors regularly perform intensive tests."

But this was two months before the first-ever clinical tests arranged by his Department. Mr. Lalonde did have an explanation for the incomplete nature of the still-to-be-conducted "intensive tests" being "regularly" performed: "We asked for the co-operation of the population ... everywhere there seemed to be problems. Most of the times, we are dealing with a nomad population hard to get in touch with but all best possible efforts are being made. ... "

This second set of clinical tests was done in March and April of 1976 by a Canadian team headed by Dr. John Stobo Pritchard, MD, FRCP, a pediatric neurologist at Toronto's Hospital for Sick Children, a Professor at University of Toronto's Faculty of Medicine, and a member of the team sent to Japan. Dr. Pritchard's team studied eighty-seven Indians in all – only thirty-six of those at Grassy Narrows, where more high blood levels and higher fish consumption have been documented. He found that of fifty-one people examined at White Dog, twenty-three showed symptoms of neurological abnormality and eighteen of these had symptoms consistent with mercury poisoning.

At Grassy Narrows, twenty-three of the thirty-six cases studied showed neurological signs – and it was estimated that thirteen of these were consistent with methyl mercury poisoning.

So 35 per cent of those examined, in the late winter of 1976, had symptoms which "could have" resulted from Minamata Disease. Dr. Pritchard's findings were released in the Ontario legislature by Frank Miller on 1 June 1976, just weeks before the Health Minister told a Kenora *Miner and News* reporter: "We don't want to come out and say there isn't a problem, but we say it has been greatly exaggerated."

Dr. Pritchard eventually returned to Toronto, having promised those tested he would "come back and explain the results to you." On 24 May 1976, he dictated an individually addressed form letter to those tested. In the case of those who had been observed to have symptoms "consistent with mercury intoxication," the letter read, in its entirety:

> Dear_____
>
> We found some minor neurological signs when we examined you recently. These can be caused by mercury poisoning as well as from a number of other reasons. They are not serious and you should not worry

about them but please do not eat any of the fish from your local contaminated waters.

I will be glad to send a more detailed report to you or your family physician if you wish.

Yours sincerely,
John Stobo Pritchard,
Professor,
University of Toronto.

The letter sowed confusion and anxiety at White Dog and Grassy, and local people deluged those they trusted with pleas for clarification. Some went to the National Indian Brotherhood in Ottawa where Alan Roy, a researcher long-involved in studying mercury poisoning, tried to help. Roy wrote Dr. Brian Wheatley, the federal Department of Health official given the task of co-ordinating all Ottawa programs related to mercury hazard in Northwest Ontario. Roy explained the fears of the Grassy and White Dog populations and pointed out the need to have knowledgeable people visit the settlements and explain the meaning and ramifications of the tests.

Dr. Wheatley replied to the Roy letter with a lengthy, defensive document explaining that Mr. Roy's complaints were groundless and assuring the NIB researcher of "the importance I place on communication."

In late September 1976, in a tape-recorded interview conducted during preparation of this book, Dr. Pritchard acknowledged that he had not yet been back to the communities to discuss the findings with those tested. (The fact that none of them have "family physicians" wasn't mentioned.) When asked about his promise to return to the reserves and explain the results of his tests, Dr. Pritchard said: "There was an air-strike the Saturday I was to go – no planes were flying." Not that Dr. Pritchard had given up, four months after mailing his ambiguous letters: "I'd still hope to get out there. ... Of course, it's very difficult, with all the international travel I've been doing this year [to Iraq and Japan] and my responsibilities at the University and the hospital. ... But I still plan to go back out there, if they'd like me to." They would, Dr. Pritchard. They would. They are afraid.

In August and September/October 1976, Drs. Wheatley, Stopps and Pritchard gave interviews to the author.

"The Japanese data is suspect, you know. ... On a scale of one to five I'd put the probability that any of the symptoms we found were related to mercury poisoning between one and two," said Dr. Pritchard. Asked how he could differentiate tunnel vision or sensory loss caused by alcoholism, diabetes or syphillis from the same symptoms caused by methyl mercury, Dr. Pritchard waved at a line of autos on a nearby street and replied, "The same way you can tell those aren't cows – from experience." (At that point Dr. Pritchard's experience of Minamata Disease victims included all those he'd seen while in Japan and Iraq.)

All three men cast doubt on the Japanese research; none acknowledged the "hidden symptoms"; none mentioned the still-suppressed federal ophthalmological study.

Of course there was not enough evidence at the beginning of 1977 to "prove" Minamata Disease at Grassy Narrows or White Dog. But there was a considerable body of evidence available.

Even so there was still no costing or planning for, let alone implementation of, an epidemiological survey aside from Dr. Pritchard's small pilot project. What there was, at the end of 1976, was a request from the federal Ministry of Health to the University of Toronto, asking the University's medical school to study the feasability of undertaking such a survey under contract from the Ottawa government.

Experts at the University, assisted by Dr. Stopps, who went there after leaving the Ontario civil service, expected to decide in early 1977 whether they would agree to accept the commission, and on what terms. If the University's terms are agreed to by the federal funding agency, the survey could get underway in the spring of 1977 – if a control community can be found by that time. It's estimated that the survey will take at least eighteen months and analysis of the results from six to twelve months; then the "findings" must be extrapolated, correlated, written and published. The findings, which could have been available in 1974, will not likely be known to the people of Grassy Narrows and White Dog much before January of 1980.

In early March 1976, Dr. Peter Newberry, the Quaker who had provided the only local medical service to the two communities since mid-November 1974, announced that he had encountered a case which might be one of congenital Minamata Disease. The patient, three-and-a-half-year-old Keith Papasay, son of a Grassy Narrows fishing guide and commercial fisherman, had been living in an institution for retardates since shortly after birth. The author travelled to Thunder Bay to film Keith and his parents, who travelled to that city to visit the child. Dr. Newberry accompanied us.

Keith exhibited symptoms of "cerebral palsy." He was uncoordinated with jerky, spastic movements; he was unable to speak and evidently had poor sight and hearing; he had never been able to feed himself, stand unaided, be toilet trained. Keith also clearly suffered from profound intellectual impairment. Said Dr. Newberry: "One can't say, short of an autopsy, that Keith has congenital Minamata Disease. But what's vital is that we realize that this is what it looks like, this is what we're going to see more of, if these people don't stop eating contaminated fish."

In March of 1976 Ontario Labour Minister Dr. Bette Stephenson was also acting Health Minister. Responding to press reports about Keith Papasay, this physician and former President of the Canadian Medical Association made the following points, which were accepted uncritically by reporters at an impromptu press conference: Keith Papasay had, not Minamata Disease, but cerebral palsy; the child had suffered probable brain damage because of a lack of oxygen at birth; he had been tested and found to have very low blood mercury levels.

What was not pointed out was that Minamata Disease in infants is a form of cerebral palsy, the latter merely describing any case of infantile brain damage. Also the Japanese have found that while disturbance of intelligence is rare and slight among most cases of cerebral palsy, it is common among victims of congenital Minamata Disease. Their studies showed a deterioration in congenital Minamata Disease victims from birth onwards, a situation utterly unlike that of most victims of cerebral palsy.

In addition, Keith Papasay's blood mercury levels at age three were utterly irrelevant to a possible diagnosis of congenital Minamata Disease; it was his blood levels while in his mother's womb and immediately after birth that mattered. With a 70-day half-life, even massively high levels of mercury in Keith's blood would have been dissipated long before he was tested in Thunder Bay.

We know that in the year that Keith Papasay was conceived, his family ate a heavy and regular diet of fish from the poisoned waterway.

In March 1976, Keith Papasay's sight and hearing were impaired but had some function. In December 1976, eight months after Dr. Stephenson's dismissal of the question with the announcement that he had very low blood mercury levels, Keith Papasay was reported to be both deaf and blind. In April 1977 a hospital official described the boy's condition as "unchanged."

In the summer of 1976, Dr. Newberry reported that an Indian youth, Jimmy Tanguay, had symptoms of Minamata Disease. Jimmy, 23 in 1976 and a fishing guide for seven years, was subsequently taken to Winnipeg from Grassy Narrows and examined by a neurologist at the St. Boniface Hospital. He found Jimmy had no signs of Minamata Disease. He said this in a report to the government, not to Jimmy, who was never given the results of the tests. Politicians and their civil service doctors were soon telling reporters that Jimmy had gotten drunk, slept on his arms in the bush, causing them to "go to sleep," and "conned" Peter Newberry into diagnosing a "sensory disturbance" related to mercury poisoning.

Jimmy was given a welding course by a helpful government so that he wouldn't have to guide anymore. Here's what he said to the author in an interview at Grassy Narrows in late August of 1976 His words echo the sentiments of many people at White Dog and Grassy Narrows. The question is whether his final comments must serve as an epitaph for those two formerly happy communities or for a moribund government policy.

> I was guiding for about seven years. I'd still guide; I need a job; there's nothing else to do. ... I'm having a pretty hard time right now trying to know what to do. I can't see enough for the welding; the bright light is too hard on my eyes – they're getting worse, I think; I don't see good enough for it now. ... When the doctor examined me at the St. Boniface Hospital he didn't tell me anything; just examined me. Nobody tells me anything; the government hasn't told me anything; they don't care about me. It doesn't do any good to talk. I went, when we went to Ottawa to talk to them. They didn't listen to anything we asked, anything we wanted to say; all they did was change the subject. Talk is no good; TV cameras don't help; stories don't help; nobody listens. The government doesn't listen. Nobody cares.
>
> What the government is waiting for is to get a dead body. They

don't care. They won't admit anything. They won't say anything until they have a dead body – a dead Indian. Nothing else will do any good.

16 MERCURY IN QUEBEC

There are two chief differences between the incidence of mercury poisoning in Northwest Ontario and an outbreak in Northwest Quebec. First, the Indians of Northwest Quebec are chiefly Cree and Algonquin rather than Ojibway. Second, government in Quebec has acted even more slowly than government in Ontario, amazing as that may seem; and the federal government's inertia has matched that of the provincial administration at Quebec City.

The mercury contamination in Quebec is centred in an arc ranging from Poste de Mistassini, roughly 350 airmiles north of Montreal, westwards to Matagami which lies about 350 miles northwest of Montreal and southeast of James Bay. Until 1969 Cree in the area were commercial fishermen, selling up to $400,000 worth of fish annually through their company, Matagami Indian Fisheries. In 1969 the firm which bought Matagami's catch refused to buy, citing contamination. The federal government followed suit by banning commercial fishing. But the local people, white and Indian, were not warned of the personal hazard in their fish diets.

In the summer of 1971 the federal government began testing area Indians and whites for blood mercury levels. The tests continued each summer, but those sampled were given no information; until 1975 they were not even provided with results of the tests. Nor, until 1975, were the people at risk warned to avoid eating the contaminated fish. This in spite of blood readings (in two cases) over 500 ppb and, in one case, of 649 ppb.

In 1972 the Quebec government and the federal Ministry of the Environment undertook a study of the problem, which recommended

164

area residents be warned against eating mercury-contaminated fish and waterfowl, and reported fish mercury levels of from 3.65 ppm to 4.88 ppm, between seven and nearly ten times over the safe maximum. *But the report went unpublished for three years and the people were not warned.* One would expect the cover-up of such information, in private life, to lead to charges of criminal negligence. Not so in government.

In early 1974, five years after the commercial fishing in the area had ended, a biologist employed as a consultant by the Cree heard of the 1972 report and requested a copy from Ottawa. Wrote Dr. John Spence:

> One study of particular interest to native groups that we have not yet been able to obtain is that on mercury in the Bell River, Matagami, and southern James Bay region that was carried out in 1972 for Environment Canada.

Dr. H. N. Hill of the environment protection service of Environment Canada responded:

> In reply to your request for a copy of the report of the mercury investigation in northwestern Quebec, I regret that I am unable to make a copy of this document available to you.

That "document" said, among other things, that a chlor-alkali paper mill on the Quevillon River, operated by Domtar, used and spilled mercury and that "emissions were excessive" during early years of operation. The mill, built in 1967, was later estimated to have lost at least seven tons of mercury into the river by 1975. Emissions into the air were never estimated but probably equalled those into the waterway. In September 1975 the Montreal *Gazette* quoted federal environment protection service chief Dr. Leo Buffa as saying the estimate could be higher than seven tons, "but no one knows except Domtar." Buffa told the *Gazette* his attempts to document Domtar's mercury loss at Lebel-sur-Quevillon before 1971 had been "consistently rebuffed by the firm's officials." The Environment Canada study, meanwhile, was finally released by Ottawa in 1975, in the face of heavy political pressure. It was only then, six years after the hazard was first known, that people still eating the poisoned fish were publicly informed that their diet might not be such a good idea after all. And it was only then that the Quebec government moved to initiate some blood tests and neurological examinations of those with the highest blood mercury levels.

But reassurance was as easy to come by. Writing to a federal Member of Parliament on 2 September 1971 (two years after the end of commercial fishing) the province's Minister of Tourism, Fish and Game noted happily:

> While commercial fishing has been prohibited in waters where mercury content has been recorded, sport fishing is permitted.
>
> Moreover, biologists ... reveal that the actual damage caused by this particular pollutant is, all told, much less extensive, in Quebec waters at any rate, than the original cries of alarm would lead one to believe.
>
> Trusting these few thoughts on the matter will prove beneficial to you, with my best wishes and kindest regards, I remain,
>
> Yours faithfully,
Claire Kirkland-Casgrain
Minister

The occasional "slip" in recording, book-keeping or whatever was also treated with substantial complacency. On 9 October 1975, for example, the federal government revealed there was a small matter of some eight-or-so tons of mercury evidently "missing" from Domtar inventory. Barely a year later Ottawa Environment Minister Jeanne Sauvé had an answer for her parliamentary colleagues. As reported, in the fall of 1976, by the Toronto *Star*:

> Eight tons of mercury missing from a Domtar Limited plant in northwestern Quebec may have evaporated ... Domtar cannot account for more than 16,000 pounds of mercury used in its plant in the last three years.
>
> Mrs. Sauvé said in the House of Commons that distilled mercury, which costs about $20 a pound, is extremely volatile and evaporates easily, especially in warm temperatures.

All of which may help, somewhat, to explain the "high background levels" of mercury in the area described by Domtar and government apologists, not to mention the very high ambient air levels of mercury on the Domtar parking lot recorded downwind of the plant by Environment Canada.

Domtar itself seems little troubled. This from their vice-president of research and environment technology, G.H. Tomlinson II (in the Montreal *Gazette* of 30 September 1975):

> ... the natives who have fished these waters consumed mercury-containing fish long before Domtar started its operation in 1967.
>
> Domtar has not denied that mercury has been emitted to the Bell River from its Quevillon operation. However the amount is small in relation to the amounts involved in the total environment. [Said Dr. Louis Azzaria, a Laval University environmental geologist: "Keep in mind that when you have an area where there is already a high natural background of mercury in the rocks, any addition can be very hazardous."]
>
> We believe that the suggestion that Domtar's activities can result in another Minamata disaster is unwarranted ... Although it was established in Sweden that mercury ... can be converted to methyl mercury by micro-organisms, the rate has been found to be very slow, of the order of one per cent (per) year. Thus the concentration of biologically methylated mercury could never reach high levels. [Only nine-plus times safe levels in fish, and 649 ppb in humans.] ... Industry has a responsibility to respect the environment and Domtar is endeavouring to meet this responsibility.

Researchers working with the Domtar plant union reported one instance of Domtar "respect" to the author. The plant workers are given regular urine tests, a measure of inorganic mercury absorbed at work; the metallic mercury accumulates in the system during the work week and is partly excreted via the bladder and bowels. But the catch, they said, is that Domtar allows no specimens to be taken after 12 noon each Wednesday. Toxicologists say that readings would be highest during the latter half of each work week.

The Quebec government, too, felt that things were largely under control. Said Environment Minister Victor Goldbloom, in August 1976:

> You can't wave a magic wand and solve all the problems. ... [The companies] do not appear to have done anything illegal. There is no evidence of any violation of environmental laws. ... There has been a ninety-five per cent improvement.

The new government elected in November of 1976 may view things differently. What the previous government did was set aside over $7 million: $5 m. to assist Domtar and Noranda Mines (the other major mercury polluter) to clean up; $2 m. for a survey of mercury pollution in Quebec; about ½ m. to assist the 2,300 or so affected Indians to rebuild their lives and livelihoods.

Then there is the bottom line, as they say in industry. Ignoring the experience that Minamata Disease may strike ten or more years after exposure to the poison, these comments from the 1976 report of the study group headed by Montreal neurologist Andre Barbeau:

> ... the present nutritional study is evidence that ... nourishment of the populations studied ... favour(s) a new episode of the Minamata variety.
> ...

> *We conclude that at least 6 Indians and possibly 25, of the 49 examined at the time of the medical team's visits show signs and symptoms of organic mercury poisoning.*

> The investigation demonstrated for certain that several individuals living in northwest Quebec show objective signs of neurological poisoning by methyl mercury.[1]

On 11 May 1976, the diagnoses were confirmed in Ottawa by Dr. Lyall Black, director-general of programs management for the Medical Services Branch, Federal Department of Health and Welfare. Testifying before Parliament's Standing Committee on Fisheries and Forestry, Dr. Black said, " ... as far as Dr. Barbeau's qualifications are concerned, the department holds him in high regard as a very well-qualified and competent neurologist, and we certainly accept his findings."

Said the Barbeau team's report:

> Taking into account the difficulties we have met during our investigation, it is important to insist upon the principle of non-confidentiality, as far as data connected by the different ministries and organisms involved is concerned. These data concern the public and belong to the public.[2]

Dr. Barbeau's group recommended that all mercury emitted by industry be banned, that all such industries be given a five-year maximum deadline to comply. Quebec's government declined to act.

In September 1976, a researcher for this book wrote to Health and Welfare Canada for data on surveys and tests underway and completed in Northwest Quebec. L.A. Monty is Assistant Regional Director for the Quebec Region of Medical Services for Health and Welfare. He replied in part, in respect of those 2,300 Indians at risk, "In so far as our nutritional survey is concerned the number of interviews that were conducted is limited: a total of 18 families were surveyed."

This seven years after the threat was known and the commercial fishing industry was shut down. And still no prosecution of Domtar or Noranda, no compensation for the victims, no move to restrict game fishing, no recognition of any fault by a federal government that for three years and longer buried blood test results and study recommendations that fish-eating be discouraged.

It doesn't inspire confidence.

17 MERCURY IN THE ENVIRONMENT

Most government and industry apologists would have us believe that contaminants in our environment, like mercury, may come from "background" sources – natural mineral deposits simply not noticed in earlier decades. To prove their point they note that heavy mercury levels are found in areas remote from mercury-using industry, and that's true. Since Arctic Eskimos have begun showing blood mercury readings above accepted safe levels, we may assume that the industrial poison is capable of getting to any of us, anywhere. We may not eat the seal livers in which that Arctic mercury has been concentrated, but we must breathe, eat, drink water; and there's some of the quicksilver poison there, wherever we live.

To take a small instance first, a study prepared in late 1976 for the Science Council of Canada (unpublished) estimates there are 8,800 pounds of mercury just in thermometers in use in Canadian hospitals. Extrapolating from population figures and hospital beds, that translates into 80 tons of mercury in hospital thermometers in industrial societies – and any nurse can tell you that most of them eventually get broken. Incinerated in garbage or left to evaporate, the mercury finds its way into the air and thence, through rain and fallout, into the soil, the aquatic food chain and, eventually, the human consumer of fish.

Another bizarre airborne mercury hazard has been exaggerated by an equally bizarre combination of events in modern society: mass advertising, which fosters a universal desire to have "good-looking" teeth, combined with the rising cost of grave lots and an increasing preference for cremation.

In 1971 there were more than 160 million teeth filled with a mercury amalgam metal in the US alone. So here's an extrapolation of the macabre hazard left to us all by those who die each year:

Given an average of five fillings in the mouth of mature adults, most of us are carrying (quite safely) 1.875 grams of mercury around in our bridgework.

Eight of us in every 1,000 in the western industrial nations die each year – that's 4,500,000 deaths annually. During cremation, the mercury in those fillings is vapourized and goes into the air through the crematorium smokestack. In 1976 thirty-five per cent of us were cremated. If these people averaged five fillings containing 1.875 grams of mercury per mouth, this means 2,953,125 grams of mercury in the air over crematoria each year. That last figure translates to approximately 6,509 pounds of mercury, in the air, from the fillings of cremated teeth, every year.

Certainly all the world's crematoria pump less mercury into the air than one chlor-alkali plant. But this is more than a laborious exercise in black humour. Most governments, in setting emission standards, *do not take overall emissions into account; they simply decide, considering only the isolated situation of each polluter, how much may be spewed into water or fired into the atmosphere.* (So a chlor-alkali plant, for example, may be told how much mercury it may dump in relation to tons of chlorine produced – but that regulation takes no account of the fact that another mill may be dumping a similar amount upstream or downstream.) It's only when our environmental caretakers survey data on *all* sources of contamination that "safety regulations" will be based on rational standards. Such bases for regulation have rarely been considered, let alone implemented, although environmentalists have been making the point for two decades.

In the early 1970s, a team of US researchers studied mercury levels in the Greenland ice sheet. Said Dr. Frank D'Itri, in an interview with a reporter for *National Geographic* in 1972, "They found mercury levels in the atmosphere remained stable from 800 BC until the 1950s. Since then the levels appear to have doubled – a result, it is believed, of industrial pollution. ... "

At the end of the 1960s there were fifty-two chlor-alkali plants in the United States and Canada. Studies by Canada's federal Environmental Protection Service demonstrated, in July 1973, that such plants emit between .0585 pounds and .350 pounds of mercury into the air for each ton of chlorine produced, depending on the efficiency of their equipment and their emission controls. Most of these plants, producing an average of 100 tons of chlorine daily, were therefore pumping from five to thirty pounds of mercury into the air daily. In the sixties, when both US and Canadian environmental and health officials were turning aside suggestions that mercury emissions might be dangerous, one can estimate those mills fired *949,000 pounds of mercury* into the atmosphere; that is, if their equipment was up-to-date and well-operated and their emission controls efficient – and many had *no* emission controls. Using the higher figure of .350 pounds, one arrives at a total loss of 5,694,000 pounds of mercury "lost" into the air over ten years. This may be too high to be fair – but a median estimate of from two to three million pounds, 1,000 to 1,500 tons, is probably conservative.

In a research interview during preparation of this book a scientist who has worked for Ottawa's National Research Council noted that mercury, once in the air, can literally circle the globe twice before it is all leached out of the air by rain, snow and "fallout" on the dust particles to which it often clings. It can, that is, go anywhere.

The release of mercury vapour by chlor-alkali plants and hydro installations is a hazard for everyone on earth; but far the greater risk is created for those living near such installations.

The Canadian study of this matter was prepared for the Air Pollution Control Directorate of the federal Environmental Protection Service – a public watchdog if ever there was one. That study was printed in July 1973, for *internal* use. The public, never having seen results of the studies, wasn't told – then or since – that "the results of our survey indicate that the level of mercury in the ambient air in the vicinity of the chlor-alkali plants studied frequently exceeded 1,000ng/m³."[1]* The significance here is that the US Environmental Protection Agency (EPA) has estimated that *only* air having mercury levels lower than 1,000ng/m³ can be "sufficient to protect the public health from illness due to inhalation of mercury." Even this level has been challenged, in studies in Wisconsin in 1972/73, and by the

---

*"ng" means a nanogram, one-billionth of a gram; "m³" represents a cubic metre of air.

Canadian report, cited above, which states: "although an ambient air level below 1,000ng/m³ may be sufficient to protect public health, it should be noted that very little data are available on the effects of low-level continued exposure to mercury vapour, as would be experienced in the vicinity of chlor-alkali plants." The Wisconsin study recommended that "a zero level standard for emission of mercury to the air from this facility" be enforced.

So how often were samples made by the Canadian team above "safe" levels at sites in Quebec and New Brunswick? At Beauharnois, Quebec, 2.7% of the samples were above the red line; at Shawinigan, Quebec, 38.4% of the samples were too high "to protect human health"; at Dalhousie, New Brunswick, 70% of the air sampled was beyond the US-set safety firewall. Nor were the high sample "just a bit" over that threshold. One reading at Shawinigan was more than eight times higher (8,529.81ng/m³). At Dalhousie, samples frequently showed mercury levels five, six and seven times the accepted safe level; one sample was more than ten times above – it registered a record (for this survey) of 10,855ng/m³.

In plain language, a government agency charged with protecting the public knew in 1973 that the health of people downwind of several chlor-alkali plants was at hazard from mercury poisoning. Those people weren't told; the data printed here is the first public account of the risk; moreover similar risks have very probably occurred at the sites of most such plants in the world and may be occurring today.

We don't know, will never know, whether there were illnesses, deaths-by-spontaneous-abortion or other results of mercury poisoning in Shawinigan or Dalhousie – or in your community. But we do know the public wasn't told about the danger to which it was exposed. One government-employed scientist who assisted in gathering some of the material above – anonymously, for obvious reason – said:

> In the public service, you don't score any brownie points for raising problems. ... Then there's the possibility you might be held accountable by the public – even taken to court for not blowing the whistle soon enough. ... Some of these people are close to retirement or bucking for a bigger job. ... And then you must remember that the politicians, the Ministers, are not much known for "taking falls" for their deputies or people farther down in the pecking order. ... And deputy ministers very seldom like to tell their Minister that they can't handle something in

their department, or that something has gotten out of control or out of all proportion. ... Nothing happens, usually, in these cases, because none of the people with the information see anything to gain in their own careers by trying to bell the cat – but they can always see a lot to lose. People who cry wolf aren't popular in the civil service, but people who are good at protecting their own ass usually are good survivors ... and survival is the name of the game.

Another major source of airborne mercury vapour is the burning of fossil fuels by industrial processes. Coal and petroleum have substantial amounts of mercury which are "released completely into the atmosphere" during combustion. In a paper published in 1971 in *Science*, O.I. Joensuu estimated that 3,000 tons of mercury are released annually in the US by coal burning alone – much of that from coal-fired hydro plants.

A series of research projects in 1971 found mercury content in coal samples ranging from .18 ppm to as high as 300 ppm in coal from "mercuriferous" belts of the United States. The coal samples were tested simply by burning, with the exhaust gases passed through mercury vapour detectors.

In one project, sampling 36 different American coals, mercury content ranged from .07 ppm and 33 ppm. The average mercury component of all the coal tested was 3.3 ppm. Joensuu's figure of 3,000 tons of mercury released annually from coal – fueled fires, was arrived at by using a figure of 1 ppm of mercury – allowing a "safety" factor of more than three from the sampling average.

Ontario Hydro is also in the coal burning, and hence mercury, business. In a research interview for this book a Hydro official said that in 1975 the Ontario government's energy corporation bought and burned approximately 7.5 million tons of US coal in its fossil fuel-fired generating stations. Taking that 3.3 ppm average, that would mean Ontario Hydro pushed 49,500 pounds of mercury into the atmosphere in 1975 alone; even at the "conservative" figure of 1 ppm, the mercury loss would have been 15,000 pounds – or 7.5 tons – during 1975.

What may be critical is that coal-fired hydro generating plants, unlike pulp mills, tend to locate near concentrated centres of population and industry. Their mercury emissions, therefore, are added to the other industrial pollutants of the urbanized area; and no one yet knows about the additive or "multiplier" effects of, for example, simultaneous exposure to both mercury and lead fumes. Both are heavy metals, both toxic, both attack similar neural and physiological functions. Their properties are so similar that most chemists and toxicologists try to avoid dealing with both on any one day, to avoid confusion in their own minds.

What's known is that there has to be some such additive effect; what's feared by chemists and researchers generally is that the effect of two or more such industrial pollutants is probably expressed as a multiplier.

Scientists in Washington and in Ottawa know they must tackle the Pandora's box of additive and multiplier effects in our ecology: they are terrified by the complexity of the problem – almost equally fearful of the potential economic impact of the results they suspect will be revealed.

> What is our society going to do [asked one in a research interview] if we find we have to scrap every single regulation on pollution? We may very well find that putting ten units of lead into the atmosphere – which is OK given no other industrial pollution in that area – has to be cut to 1 unit, or 1/100th of one unit, because somebody else is pumping out a little bit of selenium, or mercury, or some substance we haven't even heard about yet. And maybe we are told, OK. But these six factories will have to close; these nine industries will have to shut down, because ... we can't operate and stay in business without losing at least three units of lead, no matter what we do. What do we do then? It's a nightmare. And if we have that kind of disruption, you know who'll get blamed: the scientists.... I can see a day, pretty damned soon, say within ten years, when we'll have to monitor our entire population for pollution poisoning the way we give school children vaccinations now. We'll probably take a demographic sample, like a pollster; then these people in the sample will have to be tested say once a year, twice a year. They'll be the mine canaries* for the rest of us. When problems show up in the sample – maybe five per cent, ten per cent of the overall population, we'll know we've got a problem. Hopefully, then, we'll have the time, the resources to act. And the political will to act. ... I'm not hopeful about the resources. Or the will.

---

*Miners used to carry canaries into the coal shafts to warn them of the presence of deadly gas; if the canaries became unconscious the miners would run for the surface, knowing they'd blundered into a pocket of the colourless, odourless killer.

A very few researchers are cautiously nibbling the edges of these additive/multiplier effects. When brain tissue samples from Grassy Narrows and White Dog are tested in Toronto for cell damage and mercury content, they are also checked for selenium. According to one Ontario Health Ministry official, "We're not sure whether the presence of selenium would be significant or not; but it could have an effect and we think we should start keeping some records, at least, against the day when we have more data."

In Ottawa, a National Research Council chemist wondered whether anyone had checked mercury-threatened residents of Northwest Ontario or Northwest Quebec for lead contamination. (No one has.) "There's nowhere on this continent, anymore, where there isn't some lead present," he said. "And you can bet, if there's very much, that the risks to those people are even greater than they are being told so far."

The fact is that no one is monitoring hydro plants for mercury "spills" into the atmosphere; nor are those emissions being studied in concert with other poisons fed into the same air by other industries. No one, so far, is even asking the pertinent questions. For example:

Heavy metals attack the human liver, heart of man's immunity system. Does industrial pollution contribute to rising incidence, in crowded, urban environments, of influenza, colds, pneumonia?

The liver's capacity to deal with alcohol may be impaired by lead/mercury poisoning, even at low levels. Does spiralling alcoholism, with all its attendant problems, have any relationship to industrial dumping?

Heart disease is our major killer – along with cancer – and Soviet studies imply a direct link between mercury poisoning and heart disease. Are our coal-fired hydro generating plants contributing to a rising incidence of fatal cardiac arrests? Are industrial poisons, together or singly, carcinogens?

Mostly because we haven't asked yet, we don't know the answers. Scientists haven't yet been funded or prodded by governments even to begin marshalling a list of appropriate questions.

18 NO SAFE PLACE

Turning from Ontario and Quebec to other industrialized regions of the world, one is struck by a sense of *déjà vu*. The lessons seem to be that:

Governments and their spokesmen and agencies lie when truth is embarrassing; at the least they dissemble, delay, confuse and hide information – that "currency of a free society," in Ralph Nader's felicitous phrase.

Industries also exaggerate or minimize when it's in their most pragmatic and intimate interests to hide error and duck culpability.

Citizens unaware of the damage they may be suffering at the hands of the environmonsters will go on in ignorance if they depend exclusively on government industry/regulatory agencies for help. Often these agencies fail through inadequate resources, political will, resolve and candour. None are likely to move far without the spur of an informed, even angry, public constituency.

The remainder of this book glances at five recent histories of industrial poisoning and government inertia ranging from Brazil to New Brunswick – all of them startlingly reminiscent of what we have seen in Northwest Ontario. Considerations of space have excluded many more stories. Indeed there is probably no sizeable area of the industrialized world where similar stories couldn't be developed. Someone once asked where one would begin to catalogue such hazards. The answer is numbingly simple: step outside your front door and take a deep breath – or run a cold glass of drinking water in your kitchen.

177

HOT AND COLD RUNNING CANCER

A link between cancer death rates in US cities and industrial pollutants in drinking water was first reported in the New York *Times* on 8 November 1974. The story cited a study directed by Dr. Robert Harris for the Environmental Defence Fund, which found that Louisiana had "hot spots" – nine counties which ranked among the forty-five American counties and cities with the highest reported deaths from cancer among white males in the United States. The research team found carcinogens in the drinking water at New Orleans, Cincinnati, Washington, San Francisco and Evansville, Indiana, as well as in the nine counties mentioned above. In Louisiana the suspect water came from the Mississippi River, the known or suspected cancer-producing agents including chloroform, benzine, carbon tetrachloride, phenols, cyanides, mercury, arsenic, lead and cadmium.[1]

Prodded by a lawsuit, the US EPA began looking at the drinking water supplies in eighty-three cities of six states. They discovered carcinogens in "most of them," as reported in mid-1975.

In Canada, five months after publication of the Louisiana data, the Ontario Environment Ministry reported that only one of a dozen Ontario community water supplies tested *higher* in chloroform than New Orleans. Ministry spokesman W.H. Dodds said the tests would continue. He gave no data on cancer death rates in the city with a higher reading than New Orleans – Belleville, Ontario (144 parts per billion of chloroform to New Orleans' 133 ppb) – nor on Brantford (129 ppb). Dodds reassured reporters and citizens of Belleville and Brantford by claiming that someone using a non-prescription cough-syrup with a chloroform base and brushing thrice daily with a 3 per cent chloroform "whitening" toothpaste was already getting as much of the carcinogen as a Belleville resident drinking more than 450 gallons of water. Mr. Dodds did not say whether his careful calculations would require a permanently sore throat combined with the habit of swallowing one's toothpaste, nor did he mention the utter lack of scientific knowledge about chloroform's effect over a lifetime of exposure.

In 1976 Ohio residents whose drinking water came from the Ohio River or from Lake Erie were found to have an 8 per cent higher cancer death rate than other Ohio people whose water came from somewhat less polluted sources. Dr. Harris announced the results with Nancy A. Reighes, a researcher at Ohio State University's Department of Preventive Medicine. They found that eighteen of the chemicals present in drinking water in Ohio and Louisiana were known cancer-causing agents. Much more chilling is the disclosure that those eighteen carcinogens are among about 50 of the more than 360 organic chemicals present in most urban drinking water which have been tested for carcinogenic effects so far. Nobody knows whether the remaining 300 or so are cancer-producing agents or not. Nor have the ways in which these chemicals work in combination been assessed. Neither do we know the long-term effects of the poisons in our water.

The commonly accepted catalogue of "most dangerous sub-stances" in the drinking water of industrialized nations now numbers at least sixty poisons and carcinogens which are particularly lethal. Yet it took a series of four lawsuits launched by US environmentalist groups just to force the EPA to develop rules governing their emission. Enforcement of those rules, after the lawsuits were settled in late 1976, was still years in the future.

The sheer volumes of air and water besieged by industry surpass comprehension. In the State of New York alone industry accounts for more than a billion gallons of water every day — and figures around the world are rising. It was calculated in mid-1975 by the US Geological Survey that US mining and manufacturing industries were using enough water per year to flood an area the size of Vermont or Wales deeply enough to cover fifty-storey buildings. And the same study said the US, even with multiple recycling, would require twice as much water within 20 or 25 years.

Nor is the problem restricted to the industrial west. Professor A.N. Voznesensky of the Soviet Academy of Sciences Institute on Water Problems reported to the Supreme Soviet in May 1971 that Russia's industrial use of water was going to double by 1990 – and suggested vast diversions of water systems from Western Siberia into the agricultural and industrial areas to the south. In Poland, a year later, published studies showed one-third of the country's entire water supply to be unusable, with a further 33 per cent seriously polluted. Poland has since learned, along with Canada and the US, that banning use of its most ubiquitous pollutant, DDT, didn't bring the instant relief it had anticipated.[2]

To take just one carcinogen, no one was quite sure, at the end of 1976, exactly how chloroform was "created" in municipal water lines. The source, however, was known – the chloroform, through some chemical process, is an end-product of the chlorine purifiers which have been the disinfectant-of-choice in drinking water for 100 years. Researchers are still trying to find out what other substances in the water react with the chlorine to produce the chloroform. That may take awhile. But we do know that chloroform is a cancer-causing agent.[3] Chlorination has virtually eliminated the risks of bacterial infection from water, as DDT virtually wiped out malaria through the destruction of disease-spreading mosquitos. But with chlorine, as with DDT, the apparent saviour may be sorcerer's apprentice after all.

Many cancer researchers now believe that as much as 90 per cent of all cancer may be triggered by pollutants in the environment. People asking why the cancer death-rate is so much higher in modern society might begin by looking to the 2.5 million industrially used chemicals. Of these, at least 600,000 chemicals and compounds are known to have some risk associated with them, yet fewer than 500 are regulated. Between 1974 and 1976 alone 2,000 new chemicals were developed and marketed. If those chemicals were deliberately intended to be drunk, eaten or inhaled, their makers would have to test and prove their safety before they could be sold. But knowing they are ultimately destined for our air, our drinking water, our food chain, the day they leave the chemical factory gates, we go on presuming them innocent. The problem, say some researchers, is that people die too slowly from most industrial poisons to generate the dramatic, public outcry needed to force adequate safety regulations and enforcement. Those Great Lakes poisons identified in the drinking water of Ohio are likely to go on killing people, slowly, for a very long time. Lake Ontario needs eighty years to flush its water down the St. Lawrence and renew itself; Lake Superior, which is much deeper, has a complete "turnover" of its water only once in every 200 or so years.

Cancer is the leading cause of death after heart disease, taking 147.9 of us per 100,000 of population every year according to the most recently published figures. That's 369,750 cancer deaths every year in North America alone. If just 1 per cent of them related to pollution (rather than the 50 to 90 per cent suspected by some researchers), we'd be killing off about 3,697 people a year.

A BLIZZARD OF FOAM

For a combination of reasons, the globe's less industrially developed nations are likely to provide the next decade with its most macabre and dramatic tales of industrial pollution. Newly industrialized states have far less legislation, regulation and policing than their richer neighbours – and we've seen how limited those mechanisms are in the best of all existing worlds. Hungry for industry, jobs and export trade, the countries of the southern hemisphere are particularly vulnerable to the industry refrain that "to clean-up means to close-down." Forced to clean house in their home states, many industries find they can use their environmentally obsolete equipment and processes in less carefully regulated countries.

Towards the end of September 1975, the River Tiete, flowing through the Brazilian town of Santana do Parnaiba, was suddenly covered with huge crests and flakes of waste-inundated foam; the foam was blown from the surface of the river, drifted and descended over the town, and was gathered in the arms of laughing children. Within minutes, their arms were covered with chemical burns.

The sudden blizzard had been caused by a release of water, after a very dry summer, from a hydro dam operated by a Canadian company called, in Brazil, LIGHT. The water stirred the industrial waste in the sediment and dry bed of the river – especially the phosphate detergent wastes, which sucked up the chemicals emitted by the 33,000 industries upstream of Santana, in the São Paulo area, and swept them through the town.

Brazil has virtually no prohibitions regarding industrial wastes – a problem becoming so acute that there have been serious government discussions concerning the possible total evacuation of the capital city of 10 million, São Paulo, by 1978. So when detergent manufacturers got into trouble by using phosphate-based cleansers in North America and Western Europe, Brazil seemed to be one of the jurisdictions where the old technology could still be used for the balance of its economic life. Even after the horror of Santana, the Brazilian government failed to get rough with Unilever, Orniex and Colgate-Palmolive

– all three, it was argued, had made major contributions to Brazil's industrial miracle. When Brazil's minister of public works and environment met with representatives of the detergent manufacturers, he explained that there was no need for them to change over immediately to soaps which were biodegradable in water. His logic was irresistible:

a) The only non-polluting soaps are those which are broken down and "degraded" in rivers and lakes.

b) Rivers cannot biodegrade any materials without the chemical actions dependent on the presence of oxygen.

c) The phosphate detergents, along with other pollutants, had already destroyed all the oxygen in Brazil's hardest-hit rivers, so the process couldn't occur, anyhow.

The soap makers agreed with the flawless reasoning, and went back to producing and marketing their phosphate cleansers. Santana resigned itself to the continuing pain of life on a river with no marine life, where water cannot be drunk and where children cannot swim.

A BREACH OF INTEGRITY

When in September of 1975 the New York State Conservation Department suggested General Electric would be prohibited from dumping any further PCBs into the Hudson River after 30 September 1976, General Electric declined to accept the deadline. It would, said GE spokesmen, be a breach of integrity to commit to zero loss by that date, since it was not feasible. It would also have been lousy economics, as the state agency was asking for a $2 million performance bond which GE would have had to forfeit if the deadline had been exceeded. In the event the date was extended to 1 July 1977, the bond left unposted, the PCBs left to continue trickling into the Hudson.

PCBs are "polychlorinated biphenyls," a virtually indestructible group of industrial compounds first commercially developed in 1929. In North America, PCBs have been made only by Monsanto Industrial Chemical Company. The "wonder" compounds have also been made in the UK, France, Germany, Japan, USSR, Spain, Italy and Czechoslovakia. They have been used in the manufacture of specialty inks, paints, plastics, paper coatings (carbonless-carbon paper) and as the "working fluid" in hydraulic systems and heat transfer systems.

Virtually all of those uses of PCBs were banned, in the US and Canada, in the early 1970s. The only remaining commercial use of the toxic compounds has been as insulating fluid in electrical transformers and capacitors, most notably by General Electric.

Capacitors, sandwiches of alternate layers of electricity-conducting foil and non-conducting layers of PCB-impregnated paper, store electricity and feed it at a uniform rate, making enormous power savings available in equipment as big as huge power generators and as small as the toaster in your kitchen. PCBs make the most efficient "dielectric" or non-conductor ever devised. Alternatives to PCBs are being developed, most notably by Dow Chemical. Canadian and US authorities have allowed the continued use of PCBs in transformers (as a heat transfer agent, carrying heat away from the coils, to prevent fires) and in capacitors, as they are "closed systems" in which the PCBs, sealed within equipment, will presumably not leak into the environment. Not that it works quite that way: New York State Department of Environmental Conservation wildlife pathologist Ward Stone found PCB concentration as high as 18,000 ppm in soil around the base of hydro poles which had fallen and spilled the toxins from broken transformers.

Because PCBs just don't break down, "biodegrade" or disappear once made, they have become ubiquitous. Canadian polar bears have been found with double the body burden of PCBs allowed in commercial fish, as have Antarctic penguins. It's now estimated that more than 40 per cent of all Americans have more than 1 ppm of PCBs in their body fat, where the compound concentrates are stored. Some of the Arctic and Antarctic PCBs are probably courtesy of the GE plants at Hudson Falls and Ford Edward.[4] As for effects on the food chain, PCBs have been shown to concentrate from 40,000 to 75,000 times in marine plants and fish.

All of which matters because PCBs are known carcinogens – they can produce liver cancer at sub-lethal concentrations; are known to cause miscarriages, menstrual disorders, the birth of abnormally small children; are known to cause skin disease and nervous disorders; are known to kill. In Japan, in 1968, sixteen people died after PCBs were accidently mixed with rice oil – there were miscarriages and many births involving underweight infants. In September of 1976 it was revealed that seven of ninety-two factory workers exposed to PCBs in a Mobil Oil plant at Paulsboro, New Jersey, between 1953 and 1958 died of industrial poisoning – PCB poisoning. (General Electric admits to sixty-five cases of worker illness which might have been related to PCBs over fifteen years, but says they involved only minor skin irritations and cleared up when workers were transferred to other jobs.)

US EPA chemist Thomas E. Kopp estimated in November 1976 that American industry and society were losing 10,000,000 pounds of PCBs into the environment annually through leaks, spills and vapourization. GE was contributing about thirty pounds daily towards that total until the company reduced emission from its plants on the Hudson River. The unchallenged guess is that General Electric poured about 458,000 pounds of PCBs into the Hudson and that all of it, barring some vapourized and some already in the Atlantic Ocean, is still there. Which is why most commercial fishing was banned in the Hudson, in 1976.

Scientists first became aware of the hazards of PCBs in the mid-60s. By 1970 the dangers were clearly known and understood although long-term hazards and multiplier effects are still not understood. But, in 1970, warnings about PCBs in the Hudson were adamantly ignored by the New York State Department of Environmental Protection as well as by the US federal EPA. Until late 1975 the GE plants actually had a federal EPA permit, endorsed by the state, allowing them to dump up to thirty pounds daily of PCBs into the Hudson River. As early as 1971, faced with the possibility of forced closure following federal research, Monsanto "voluntarily" began limiting PCB sales to users of "closed systems." (Before 1971, PCBs had even been sprayed on country roads, as a dust inhibitor.) But GE was still getting new dumping permits from Washington as late as 31 December 1974.

The US Food and Drug Administration (FDA) imposed a limit of 0.5 ppm in commercial fish. (In Canada, not following the US numbers game blindly, for once, permissible limits were set at 0.2 ppm; that meant, in 1976 and 1977, that Lake Ontario smelt having higher levels than could legally be sold in Canada were being exported for US consumption.)

At the University of Wisconsin PCB tests were run on rhesus

monkeys, the animals closest to man. Eating food with the FDA permitted level of PCBs, only one female monkey in eight was able to give birth to a normal offspring. After birth the infant monkeys, continuing to ingest PCBs from their mother's milk, increased the level of PCBs present in their systems at birth by 100 times. In the summer of 1976 the EPA revealed results of a survey of American nursing mothers in ten states (Maryland, Virginia, Michigan, North Carolina, New Jersey, Alabama, Florida, Georgia, Pennsylvania and South Carolina). Fifty samples of mothers' milk were tested; there were PCBs in 48 of the samples – with an average measurement of 2.1 ppm – higher than would be allowed in commercially sold milk in Canada. The US FDA "provisional tolerance level" for commercially sold milk is 2.5 ppm. Said John R. Wessel of the FDA: "We're considering lowering these tolerances."

In Canada, a research scientist employed by the Canadian Wildlife Service became concerned about alarming decreases in the populations of ring-billed gulls and terns around Lake Ontario. Identifying the culprit as PCBs, Dr. Michael Gilbertson found, in 1973, that only one gull nest in ten was producing a live bird as opposed to a norm of one live birth per nest. Dr. Gilbertson and his colleagues found evidence, too, of mutation and genetic distortion: sixteen gull and tern chicks found had bills which were crossed or couldn't meet – all of those fated to starve to death; one chick was born with four legs; another had toes growing out of the area around its knees. A further twenty-six chicks they found had died; they had become immobilized and helpless after their leg tendons simply slipped off their leg bones.

At hearings in November 1975, it was revealed that a single eel, caught downstream of the GE plants, contained so much PCB that one meal from it would have given a human more than the lifetime safe limit envisaged by Canadian "safe" standards for fish. GE provided an expert witness of its own, Gerald Lauer of Ecological Analysts, Inc., who denied high PCB readings in Hudson River fish. Lauer had difficulty with cross examination, agreed a Tennessee lab had screwed up some fish tests, and withdrew in confusion. GE withdrew his testimony but stood by the defence that it had acted legally, with permits, and, therefore, properly. There was one further and fascinating disclosure at the hearings, as reported in the New York *Times*

Magazine of 24 October 1976, by Peter Hellman:

> ... even before the PCB problem became public, GE already had
> determined that further significant discharges could be eliminated
> without much difficulty. PCBs entered the river primarily via waste
> waters used to wash off the castings of capacitors that had been
> submerged in a PCB bath. This water could easily be contained and the
> PCBs destroyed by ultra-high-temperature incineration.

What next? Well, General Electric, after many months of
negotiation, and reminding everyone that it admits no culpability or
liability, has agreed to pay New York State $3 million to help
"restore" the Hudson River, if that proves possible, and a further $1
million to aid in research into pollutants. The state's Department of
Environmental Protection will add $3.5 million to the kitty, belated
recognition of its own failure to act on data it had for at least five years
before it blew the whistle. Ogden R. Reid, the "new boy" who, as DEC
commissioner for New York State finally broke into the old files and
forced GE to ease up in a year when his boss, Governor Carey, was
promoting industrial development and jobs, got his predictable reward:
he was fired. Monsanto said it would stop making any PCBs at all, as of
November 1977. Commercial and sports fishermen along the Hudson
River and the Atlantic coast were being deprived of 22 million pounds
of striped bass every year; but in Lake Ontario, where 80 per cent of
salmon tested contain PCBs in excess even of FDA "safe" limits, New
York State continued to express its confidence in happy endings by
promising to fund a $10 million salmon hatchery. Ontario Resources
Minister Leo Bernier agreed. Said he, on 27 October 1976 (Legislature
of Ontario Debates, Supply Committee, page S-2246):

> I just want to make it very, very clear that we are making great strides
> with regard to commercial fishing in the Great Lakes. ... We read where
> they [the State of New York] are planting X number of thousands of
> rainbow and cohoe and trout in Lake Ontario. ... I think ... we can look
> to some real improvement with regard to the fisheries, particularly in the
> lower Great Lakes. I say that with a great deal of enthusiasm.

Ontario Hydro meanwhile is exporting the problem it used to
stockpile; the scrap transformers with their deadly PCB burden that
used to be stored in oil drums in Ontario are now shipped to Chem-trol

Pollution Services Ltd., at Model City, New York, where they are "stockpiled."

Pcʙ manufacturing hasn't stopped in Europe; it probably won't. West Germany, Italy and Spain have been identified as the most flagrant offenders against human safety by the Organization for Economic Co-operation and Development which also noted, in January 1976, that if the US had lived up to a commitment signed by it and the organization's twenty-three other members in February of 1973, GE would have been stopped, that year, from dumping more pcʙs into the Hudson River.

For the rest of us, the problem will continue. pcʙs from the adhesives in safety glass, from ceramics, adhesive tapes, putty, rayon, concrete and asphalt, from waterproof canvas and plastic bottles, from fluorescent tubes and old transformers will continue to leach into soil, atmosphere and water. And the FDA, still undecided, will decide whether to suggest to mothers whose breast milk contains enough pcʙs to make it illegal for sale as commercial milk in a Canadian supermarket, whether they ought to go on nursing their infant children.

GE's north-of-the-border subsidiary, Canadian General Electric, had a little bad PR of its own, when, in late 1977, research for this book revealed the manufacture and distribution of washing machines with a built-in fire hazard. It was only after the author released an internal company memo detailing the consumer risk that CGE reluctantly revealed the serial numbers of the faulty machines. (See Appendix Eight for details.)

FLAME-PROOF BEEF

Some time in the summer of 1973, as nearly as can now be guessed or reconstructed, a quantity of from 500 to 1,200-or-more pounds of a fire retardant trade-named Firemaster was delivered by its maker, the Michigan Chemical Corporation, to a farm feed company distributor, Farm Bureau Services, Inc. The Firemaster was in fifty-pound brown paper bags, its name stencilled on the sides. It was delivered along with (and in mistake for) a feed additive, magnesium oxide, trade named Nutrimaster and also manufactured by Michigan Chemical. Firemaster, which is "polybrominated biphenyl," is a five-times-more-toxic cousin of the PCBs, and is nicknamed PBB. The PBB sent to Farm Bureau Services was then presumably mixed into feed for cattle, hogs and poultry and delivered to feed stores and farms throughout Michigan.

By the beginning of 1977 over 30,000 Michigan cattle had died or been destroyed as a direct results of poisoning by the PBB; so had 4,534 hogs, 1,371 sheep and an estimated 2,000,000 chickens. Tons of butter, eggs, milk and cheese were condemned and buried, with the sacrificed herds, in a remote part of Kalkaska County in central Michigan. Ninety-six per cent of nursing mothers tested in 1976 had PBBs in their breast milk; nine of them had more PBBs in their breast milk than is allowed in commercial milk – and the US FDA had already admitted that permissible PBB levels in food had been first set on the basis of what amounts could easily be analysed rather than according to how much was "safe." (There is reasonable cause to suggest zero consumption of PBB as the only "safe" level, as the alleged carcinogen is never expelled by the body and is never broken down or "metabolized" by the human system; it simply accumulates.) Dr. Thomas Corbett of the University of Michigan School of Medicine, speaking of mothers who have PBB in their breast milk and go on nursing their infants, said, "You are subjecting children to a possible cancer risk. You're taking a chance on jeopardizing their health and welfare for the rest of their lives." (NY Times, 2 January 1977.)

By January 1977, Michigan Chemical had paid out over $35 million in out-of-court settlements and still had several hundred law suits pending. Michigan state officials were putting the agricultural losses from PBB in the range of $150 million. No one knew about human losses – there had been no formally diagnosed cases of illness in the farmers and their families, nor among the consumers of PBB-contaminated beef, pork, eggs, milk, butter or cheese. (No one, by early 1977, had even considered other possible victims such as the pets fed on bone meal made from PBB-poisoned carcasses.)

PBB can cause cancer of the liver in mice (studies by Dr. Corbett at Michigan's medical school). Stored indefinitely in body fat the artificial chemical can pass through the placental barrier in pregnant women as well as being transmitted, later, in breast milk. PBBs cause skin sores, swollen and arthritic joints, thyroid, liver and nerve damage and abortion brought on by abnormalities in pregnancy. Loss of appetite, fatigue, digestive problems, loss of hair and lowered resistance to infection were also observed in affected livestock before they died or were shot.

Michigan farm families complaining of similar symptoms between 1973 and 1976 were often told by their family physicians the ailments were psychosomatic; some were referred to psychiatrists. None were compensated for illness and most hid the symptoms from friends; the PBB epidemic had become a matter of embarrassment – farm mothers interviewed for this book spoke of being shunned at Home and School meetings because their cattle had .been slaughtered, of being told neighbours' children had been warned not to play with "those kids" whose dairy herds were poisoned; some mothers reported threatening telephone calls. Said dairy farmer Clyde Clark at Vogel Center, Michigan (Toronto *Star*, 24 March 1976):

> They [his slaughtered herd] fed our family, they supported us and they sent 2,500 quarts of milk to town a day. How do you ever replace that? It's a hell of a way to end a dairy career – poisoning people.

In late 1976 Dr. Irving Selikoff and a team from New York's Mount Sinai Medical Center undertook the first stage of an epidemiological survey of affected farm families. A study of all Michigan births since 1973 was also planned to look for statistical changes in birth defects. (A large proportion of the women with PBB in their breast milk were not farm mothers, merely consumers of Michigan foods.)

The first severe symptoms of cattle poisoning were noted by dairyman Frederic Halbert in late September 1973. Possessed of a master's degree in chemical engineering and three years' work experience with Dow Chemical, Halbert suspected chemical contamination of his cattle feed. But it took him over six months and $5,000 of his own money to track the killer down. At one point analysts at the National Animal Disease Center at Ames, Iowa, were pulled off their study of Halbert's feed by a Washington order reminding them that the centre's research funds were committed to other purposes. PBB and its industrial source, Firemaster, was finally identified, entirely through Halbert's initiative and tenacity, on 29 April 1974.

In May 1974 the FDA established "action levels" for "safe" intake of PBBs in beef, pork, etc. Six months later, noting that some farm animals had overt symptoms of the poisoning at levels below those it had set for *human* consumption, the FDA lowered the permissable amounts. Moreover the "hedging" was such as to make one wonder greatly about the degree of protection afforded consumers. First "limits" for meat and dairy products, for example, were 1 ppm. A dairy cow might have higher readings than that in its flesh, but the milk was still commercially saleable, for example, at 0.999 ppm. The same sort of standards applied, six months later, when the limits were dropped to 0.3 ppm.

As early as the 1960s E.I. du Pont de Nemours and Company had abandoned the notion of using PBBs in the manufacture of flame-resistent clothing after learning that the toxin caused enlarged livers in rats. But PBB wasn't studied or banned by the FDA – not until late 1974 when US federal studies showed that the chemical caused "dramatic alterations in normal biochemical and physiological processes." (*Science*, vol. 192, p. 242, 16 April 1976.)

The State of Michigan did not order the contaminated animals destroyed; it simply "quarantined" the livestock. As explained by Dr. Charles Cole, chief of Michigan's Animal Health Division in the Department of Agriculture, a state statute (Michigan State Act 181, passed in 1919) permits the government to condemn herds, but requires the farmers be compensated at "appraised value." The state couldn't have raised the money to pay the 540 farmers whose premises were quarantined, said Cole. So the farmers were left either to go on feeding and maintaining livestock they couldn't sell (much of it already dying, all of it a financial burden) or to "volunteer" the animals for slaughter and burial in the hope the PBB corporate producer might eventually be forced to pay compensation. In July 1974 the state legislature passed a new act to permit state-ordered destruction of livestock without compensation; the new statute was ruled illegal.

As for the State of Michigan's efficiency in protecting the consuming public from the contaminated beef, milk, eggs, poultry, pork and cheese, it took more than eighteen months simply to locate the most heavily contaminated herds and impose a quarantine on the meat and by-products.

A sidelight for Canadian readers: evidently there were no tests for PBB on agricultural products imported into Ontario from Michigan.

One report, unconfirmed as this book went to press, is that PBB-poisoned cattle were shipped into Ontario from Michigan for processing in Canadian packing plants; that some died en route to Sault Ste. Marie, Ontario, but that the remainder were imported, processed and sold on the Canadian market. What is known is that Canada imported 67.8 million pounds of processed meat and 57,000 head of beef cattle from Michigan in 1976 alone. None of that meat was tested, in Canada, for PBBs.

To researchers attempting to elicit details of the outbreak in Michigan the muffling effects of fear, cover-up and stall were monumental. Government officials denied knowledge, cited "incomplete studies," described jurisdictional difficulties. Industrial spokesmen denied responsibility, refused to speak in the face of impending lawsuits, said data requested weren't available or didn't exist. Farm families approached were afraid of the response of neighbours, afraid of losing markets for their products, afraid that their attempts to get compensation for livelihoods destroyed might be jeopardized by publicity.

Michigan is not an isolated case. The United States Department of Agriculture says there were twenty-four cases of livestock and/or poultry being affected by chemical contaminants (poisons) in twenty-eight of the American states between 1968 and 1976. Damage to lost livestock alone from those "incidents" is estimated at $97,000,000.

Have there been birth defects, miscarriages, in Michigan or anywhere where mothers ate PBB-contaminated Michigan produce? No one knows. Will infants ingesting PBBs at their mothers' breasts in 1976/1977, when *they* reach maturity, produce defective second generation infants or aborted fetuses from the PBBs stored permanently in their bodies from infancy? No one knows. Does PBB act in concert with other toxins to trigger exaggerated response to infection? We can't say, although the answer is a qualified "yes." One neurologist, Dr. Sydney Diamond, has reported an unusually high incidence of disorders of the central nervous system among Michigan farmers (NY *Times*, 9 November 1976). He is trying to learn whether there is a link to PBB.

We can be certain there will be more Michigans. Not every industry is as cautious as was Du Pont with PBB; nor will industry or government need to be more painstaking until we require that chemicals used commercially be pre-screened as we now test and screen additives to foods and chemicals used in medical treatment.

In the meantime those Michigan families who have children suffering from aching joints, weight loss, chronic fatigue and irritability, failing memory and skin sores are hoping the symptoms may soon be as remote as the sympathy and help extended them by their governments in Lansing and Washington.

When government and polluter are one and the same, as in our final story, the hope of regulation diminishes almost to vanishing point.

"I DON'T LIKE TO SEE PEOPLE DYING ... "

The airplanes carrying spruce budworm spray over New Brunswick could hardly do more damage to the province if they were enemy air forces dropping nuclear bombs ...
> Dr. A.G.B. Fairchild,
> Entomologist

I don't like to see people dying. This is one of the things I really wouldn't like to see. But at the same time, knowing the forest as it is, my decision will have to be with the forest and with the future of New Brunswick.
> Hon. Roland Boudreau,
> Minister of Natural Resources,
> Province of New Brunswick

The spruce budworm attacks and destroys stands of softwood, principally balsam, that are the favourite woods of pulp producers. The budworm appears cyclically, affecting chiefly "mature" trees and those past maturity. Once infested, the trees must be harvested within about eighteen months or they die and rot. In the past the insect was regarded by foresters as a natural means of maintaining balance in a forest. If not interfered with the budworms tend largely to disappear between their cyclical appearances.

But in 1920 New Brunswick developed a pulp industry and, as the industry grew, its operators began to be impatient with the natural cycle. The budworms, they reasoned, were killing trees not in the harvesting plans for the subsequent eighteen months. So, as technology made it apparently possible to attack the budworm, large-scale chemical defences were mounted. New Brunswick began spraying forests assaulted by the budworm in 1952, and the insecticide chosen was DDT.

Between then and the end of 1975 $75 million was spent in the spraying program. While there is substantial doubt as to whether the program has significantly reduced the depredations of the budworm, it has clearly been effective in other areas. Researchers for Environment Canada found in 1973 that test areas sprayed by New Brunswick had 40 per cent fewer pairs of birds and 35 per cent fewer bird species than other areas in the province. It's estimated that the 1973 budworm program killed 12 million songbirds. Studies by the Canadian Wildlife Service indicated an even heavier bird kill in 1975.

The chemicals sprayed over NB forests are also lethal to honey bees, with the result that pollination of some plants has been virtually eliminated in areas near those sprayed. On 14 June 1976, Justice J. Stevenson awarded damages of $58,499.16 to an NB blueberry producer whose crop has been destroyed through precisely that chain of circumstances. Apples are a $40 million annual crop in Canada, and New Brunswick contributes significantly to that total. But in 1975 the NB Fruit Growers Association reported unusually low apple yields in areas near those sprayed for budworm despite "excellent bloom and ideal pollinating weather." Many orchard operators are also bee-keepers; the NB honey crop can bring in as much as $100,000 in a good market year.

Then there is a possible threat to potatoes. Those grown in the province in 1972 sold for $45,548,000. Mitchell Franklin, a NB woodlot operator, reported in the autumn of 1976 that a senior provincial official told him the spruce budworms were beginning to attack potato crops (perhaps after being driven from the forests by the spraying).

The spraying began in 1952, with joint funding by the provincial government and New Brunswick International Paper Company. In 1953 a non-profit corporation, the Forest Protection Limited Company, was founded, in which the province joined with four pulp and paper companies. By 1976 there were eight private companies involved, the province holding 160 of the 180 outstanding shares in the corporation.[5]

The companies pay one-third of the costs of spraying. Until 1968

New Brunswick recovered 50 per cent of its two-thirds share from the federal government in Ottawa; but in 1968, sensing political trauma, Ottawa opted out. Since then the NB government has paid a full two-thirds portion of the costs.

DDT was used until 1969. Then the NB government shifted to Fenitrothion, a "broad spectrum" insecticide first developed during World War Two as a nerve gas. The new pesticide was not then licenced by Ottawa's regulatory authorities but Forest Protection Limited used it anyway – on 3,109,650 acres that first year with some of that acreage sprayed three times over.

In 1970 the National Research Council established a committee to develop some ground rules for the measurement of pesticides in humans and in the environment. Following the standard governmental practice (in environmental matters) of operating on the theory that the best hen-houses would be designed by a fox, the NRC appointed, as committee chairman, Dr. G.S. Cooper. Dr. Cooper was a well-known advocate of chemical spraying; he was, in 1970, Managing Director of Cyanamid of Canada, manufacturers of Fenitrothion.

When it was first "registered" by Canada's Department of Agriculture on 3 June 1969, Fenitrothion was described in a departmental memorandum as *"Hazardous by inhalation, skin contact or swallowing. Repeated inhalation or skin contact may, without symptoms, progressively increase susceptibility to poisoning."* The pilots engaged by Forest Protection Limited take the warnings seriously; so seriously they are not allowed to land an airplane until all the Fenitrothion has been dumped. (It's alleged that this safety regulation for pilots has led to nerve gas "dumps" over and near homes, farms and school playgrounds on days when wind conditions keep pilots from spraying in their assigned areas.)

As for the efficacy of Fenitrothion, a professor of zoology at the University of California, formerly at the University of New Brunswick, testified in 1973 that there was evidence the budworm population had doubled in a second year of spraying as compared with unsprayed woodlands. A noted entomologist, Dr. A. G. Bell Fairchild, said the spray program, while destroying nature's checks and controls against the budworm, would eventually make the province "a desert." Also, although the budworm traditionally pretty well disappears for thirty-five years following its cyclical appearance of from two to five years, it is not disappearing in New Brunswick. Some biologists now suggest the spraying program has hastened a system of natural selection, producing a strain of budworms who love Fenitrothion. Meanwhile, those budworms who don't like the nerve weapon and survive it, move to less lethal areas.

At low levels, symptoms of Fenitrothion poisoning are headache, fatigue, nervousness and nausea. At moderate but non-lethal levels they include blurred vision, cramps, a feeling of constriction in the chest and throat, vomiting, difficult breathing, mental confusion and diarrhoea. Detailed tests haven't been run on Fenitrothion, but many of its close relatives among the organo-phosphates also cause both birth defects and genetic mutation of future generations.

At least nine New Brunswick children have been diagnosed as having a mystifying illness known medically as Reye's Syndrome – and five of them have died of that illness. At the end of 1976 no one could definitely prove they died as a direct result of the spraying. But the circumstantial evidence was of a sort to make fear a staple in the lives of New Brunswick parents near the "spray blocs."

The illness, first identified by R. D. Reye in Sydney, Australia, in 1963, is characterized by a relatively minor illness or infection. A child develops some normally innocuous illness, perhaps chicken pox, measles or flu. But before recovery more violent symptoms appear: vomiting, high fever, mental and emotional disturbance, convulsions, coma. Fifty to eighty per cent of those children affected die; many of those who survive suffer permanent brain damage. An evidently "new" disease, its causes are still unknown; but its victims suffer clear degeneration of the liver – home to the body's system of immunity. Best theories so far seem to be that some substances in the environment, singly or in combination, make children susceptible. The nine who contracted Reye's Syndrome in the winters of 1971-2 and 1972-3 all lived adjacent to areas which had been repeatedly sprayed for spruce budworm.

Dr. J. F. S. Crocker, of the Izaak Walton Killiam Hospital for Children in Halifax, conducted experimental studies with mice at Dalhousie University which were reported in 1974.[6] When he first theorized a connection between the spraying and Reye's Syndrome he approached the province's Natural Resources Ministry to get samples of the spray, so that he could analyse its chemical composition. He was told the material was "classified." Co-operation of any sort was denied him.

Dr. Crocker, through meticulous and massively laborious analysis, then identified Fenitrothion in a sophisticated study of tissue from the disease victims. He asked the National Research Council in Ottawa to confirm his results. They refused. He then approached Cyanamid, manufacturers of Fenitrothion, for 50 ccs of the insecticide, so that he could compare his analysis with the commercial product. Cyanamid told the doctor they could not supply him with 50 ccs – enough to fill a large hypodermic syringe – as they sold the nerve gas only in carload lots; he couldn't afford to buy a railway car filled with the poison. Eventually an NB Health Ministry official supplied Dr. Crocker with the sample he needed.

One claim made for Fenitrothion is that since it disintegrates so quickly in the atmosphere (within ten days) it is not even hazardous if it coats young fruit and vegetables.[7] But the Crocker study group found that Fenitrothion may endure much longer in the human system than on leaves in the forest. Children exposed to the spray in New Brunswick (and in other Canadian provinces) may be "storing" the nerve gas in their bodies for slow release. If they are, what will be the effect when they are exposed to chicken pox, or swine flu? Nobody knows, nor has any testing been done to find out.

The reassuring noises made by Cyanamid of Canada and the governments of Canada and New Brunswick are postulated on the notion that Fenitrothion landing on the trees and crops nearby will simply rest on those surfaces until total disintegration occurs. But a 1972 study by Crocker et al[8] indicates the toxin is absorbed by plants as it was designed, during World War Two, to be absorbed through the skin in humans. Are we getting Fenitrothion in our apple pie? Nobody knows, because no one has done any studies.

There are many ramifications to the spraying program. Fenitrothion, insoluble in water, is mixed with an "emulsifier" in order to make a sprayable liquid; some studies indicate that the emulsifier, formerly thought to be chemically inert, may have greater effects than the nerve gas itself in building exaggerated response to bacterial or viral infections. New Brunswick says it has changed emulsifiers since 1972

– but as all such products come in job lots with their component chemicals unidentified, the change is, at best, an empty gesture.

This whole question could eventually become a major horror story for vast areas of the world. If the emulsifiers have, in themselves, the property of triggering killer responses to mild infection, the problem extends far beyond such substances as DDT and Fenitrothion to literally thousands of sprays which use an emulsifier because the active substances are insoluble in water.

Forest Protection Limited makes a great virtue of its care to avoid spraying over populated areas. But the fact remains that a wind of 5 mph would spread half the material sprayed from a height of 1,000 feet five miles from the spray zone. A 10 mph wind would cause *all* of the spray to be blown at least five miles from its intended target. With over half the province covered by two applications of the spray in spring 1976 (which itself raises the image of a man attacking a mosquito biting his scalp by striking himself on the head with a 16-pound sledge hammer) and with the closeness of forest to every settled community in the province, it's not hard to imagine some "settling" of the nerve gas anywhere in New Brunswick. Even if the toxin is sprayed precisely on target on perfectly windless days, it is still likely to remain accessible to honey bees which normally forage up to 2½ miles in search of nectar and sometimes go further.

In April 1976, the NB government appointed a six-member panel to study the issue, chaired by Dr. W. G. Schneider, President of the Canadian National Research Council. (It was Dr. Schneider who had hired Dr. Cooper, the Managing Director of Cyanamid.) NB Premier Richard Hatfield and his Natural Resources Minister needed quick answers; the 1976 spraying program was scheduled to begin in May. The panel met, as they reported on 27 April 1976, for three days in Fredericton. Following that marathon study and in a report which appeared just twelve days after their last hearing, the panel said " ... that it was unable to find evidence linking the occurrence of Reye's Syndrome in New Brunswick to the forest spraying program and to Dr. Crocker's experiments on baby mice." The panel recommended that future studies be conducted, since "a number of questions are left unanswered."

A favoured technique of all apologists is the metaphor or parable.

Robert Billingsley of Reed, for example, told the author, in 1975, that headaches were a symptom of Minamata Disease – and that a lot of Torontonians and New Yorkers suffered from headaches. A much more sophisticated fable came, in July, from Mr. E. R. Houghton, Chief of the Control Products Section of the Federal Department of Agriculture. In a "Memorandum of Information" sent to New Brunswick MP Gordon Fairweather, Mr. Houghton pointed out that a full two ounces of Fenitrothion are needed to provide a lethal dose for an average man. But 12,000 mg of caffeine would entail the same risk, he adds, and so would 105,000 mg of aspirin. In other words, concludes one of our public guardians, anyone who drank 80 cups of coffee at a sitting, or took 324 aspirin, would be at as great a risk of dying as someone exposed to two ounces of Fenitrothion. Having decided that a man in a forest being sprayed would receive only 10.5 mg of Fenitrothion, Mr. Houghton then postulates that Fenitrothion is "forty times as safe as drinking one cup of coffee and ten times as safe as taking one adult-sized aspirin."

That few of us have a bladder capacity to handle 80 cups of coffee at a single session, and that not too many headaches tempt one to ingest 324 aspirins at a go, that few of us absorb caffeine or aspirin through our skin or by inhalation, or store those substances in our body fat, are only four of the many factors missing from Mr. Houghton's appraisal of the comparative hazards.

There have been one or two tiny public acknowledgements of risk. Said NB Health Minister William Cockburn: "I wouldn't stand outside and let them spray anything on me."

But that hasn't happened to the Hon. Mr. Cockburn, or his children. It did happen on 21 May 1976, to Dr. and Mrs. Abram Friesen. They and their eleven-year-old son were sprayed by planes which made four repeated passes directly over their home near Fredericton. All three suffered symptoms of Fenitrothion poisoning (bees in nearby hives died). On that same day thirteen-year-old Eric Helmuth was sprayed while riding his horse – his vomiting, dizziness and diarrhoea lasted four days. Four-year-old Massey Walton suffered the same symptoms that night; so did Mrs. P. Geddes, sprayed while driving her car towards Fredericton – all of these instances, and many more, just three weeks after the expert panel published its report.

On 4 January 1977, the author spent the evening with Premier

Hatfield who said there had been no cases of Reye's Syndrome "for several years," and that, anyway, the province had "changed the emulsifier we were using." "It's all under control now," he said. "There haven't been any more illnesses or deaths."

There have, though. Fern Amos had died ten weeks earlier on 20 October 1976 and Douglas Falconer was dead less than a month later, on 27 January 1977. Both were grade four pupils in the Hampton Elementary School. The following is from the 2 February 1977 edition of the New Brunswick *Plain Dealer*:

> Three children in Hampton have been stricken with various forms of encephalitis since August 1976. Two died. One has mostly recovered, but still periodically has severe inflammation in the cornea of both eyes. [Eye problems are typical symptoms of insecticide poisoning.] The three cases occurred in the Hampton Elementary School. On May 28, 1976 an aircraft sprayed pesticides in an area close to the school, and some of the spray drifted over the school yard where about 1,000 children were playing during morning recess. ...
>
> Encephalitis is an inflammation of the lining of the nervous system. Fenitrothion, according to Canadian government publications, affects the nervous system. A recent report ... indicates that Fenitrothion can be stored in the fatty body tissue and affect a person's health months or years after the original contact with the poison. ... [9]
>
> Dr. R. W. Tooley, Director of Public Health Services, said that Reye's Syndrome was considered by medical experts, but was ruled out after considering all symptoms. ... Dr. Tooley said that encephalitis, "is not an uncommon disease; three cases in one community in seven months is not remarkable." However he also said his department has no precise figures on the number of cases since they are not routinely reported. He said the disease has "a great many causes, and is really a great many diseases." Chances of recovery are usually good.

Not, however, for Douglas Falconer and Fern Amos. Nor are all medical specialists as sanguine as Dr. Tooley. Tissue samples from the dead schoolmates are being examined for traces of Fenitrothion by Dr. Crocker in Halifax. Certainly Fern Amos and Douglas Falconer, several months after being exposed to Fenitrothion spray, had fatal ailments which were variously diagnosed by different medical spokesmen as encephalitis, meningitis and meningoencephalitis. What is as extraordinary as the recent deaths and the less-than-alarmed response of NB government and health spokesmen is the lack of attention paid the story by Canada's national press and media, apart from the CBC network TV program *Ombudsman.* Perhaps the nation's journalists are simply accustomed to the spray program. After all, as far back as 1971, a full 43 per cent of all the insecticides sprayed anywhere in Canada were being deposited on New Brunswick. While 105,522 acres of NB farmland went out of production in five years, the volume of acreage sprayed against the budworm has been steadily increasing – from 3,109,650 acres in 1969 to an estimated nine million acres in 1976. The 1976 program covered 50.52 per cent of New Brunswick's entire area at a time when most jurisdictions have been reducing their aerial spraying. Neighbouring Nova Scotia, for example, cancelled its program "for health reasons." Nor does Newfoundland spray; instead, that province spends money on access roads to allow early and easy harvest of trees attacked by budworms.

In January/February of 1977 the Nova Scotia government, following a marathon series of ten cabinet meetings – two called expressly for the purpose – reconfirmed its decision to ban all spraying. Newfoundland's government, under heavy pressure from the forestry industry, agreed in February 1977 to a very small, experimental pilot project.

Government statements of reassurance echo rather thinly, when measured against the following brief confidential memorandum sent to every New Brunswick hospital administrator on 10 May 1976 by the Health Department's Director of Public Health, R. W. Tooley. The memo was unearthed by *Ombudsman* research staff.

> As in previous years, the budworm spraying program will be carried out shortly and this memo is to draw your attention to possible health hazards associated with chemicals used in this operation.
>
> Essentially two groups of chemical compounds – Organophosphates and Carbamates – will be used. For the information of physicians and emergency room staff in your hospital, a summary of composition, effects and toxicity management of these chemicals is attached.
>
> Every precaution is being taken at the operational aspect of the spraying but we want to ensure that immediate medical assistance is made available in the event of accidental poisoning with these highly toxic chemicals.

New Brunswick's spraying program uses World War Two vintage aircraft, often manned, it's said, by pilots unable to get any work other than the dangerous job of sitting atop 600 gallons of deadly nerve gas at tree-top height. Sometimes they crash; oftener it's alleged, they lack even commercial flying licences. In the winter of 1976/77, *Soldiers of Fortune*, the newsmagazine published exclusively for mercenaries, carried the following recruiting blurb: "Canada is looking for TBM jocks with low-level formation experience for a six-week project next spring. Excellent pay plus expenses. Contact Forest Protection, Ltd., Fredericton, NB, Canada."

Soldiers of Fortune is widely and avidly read by unemployed Viet Nam veterans among others; presumably experience in low-level defoliation there could suit a pilot for work in New Brunswick.

The budworm control program is a monument to ineptitude. The history of the spraying is a chapter from *The Silent Spring*. If it continues the province may well become North America's first coniferous desert.

CONCLUSION

It would take 100 books to catalogue just the cases of industrial poisoning and pollution revealed in the past decade. It's enough to know that those hazards, now scattered by wind and water, penetrate every cranny of the earth and its food chain, from the Greenland ice cap to Alaska seal livers and Antarctic penguin; and to your water tap, food cupboard.

Some of the lessons of Northwest Ontario and the parallel examples we've examined are obvious: the crying need for major, publicly financed environmental/occupational health centres with the staffs, legislative muscle and resources to move, instantly and effectually in future cases. (There will be a case near where you live, the day you read this page – check your newspaper.) We need real, enforced requirement that chemicals be proved safe before they are unleashed on us; we must have real, enforced requirement that polluters clean up after themselves, pay all of what it costs to remedy their assaults on our community. Industry used to say, eighty years ago, that it would have to shut down if required to live with safety regulations, if forced to reduce the twelve-hour day, if prevented from employing children in sweat shops. That wasn't true, either. There's a remarkably simple test, for example, of industrial boasts that their effluent water is "good enough to drink." Simply require them by law to recirculate it, continuously, through their plants, adding only what's lost as steam. Hey presto. No effluent.

The key lesson of Northwest Ontario is that we can't accept the reassurances of government or industry at face value. So we need, too, more "sunshine laws," more statutes guaranteeing freedom of information. The public's safety is the public's business. Mushrooms thrive in the dark. Societies don't.

But mostly, however banal it may seem, we need simple participation. Any television journalist knows and will confess that twenty individually composed letters to an elected official have more impact on public policy than an hour of network television. Politicians don't respond perceptibly to notions of philanthrophy, gratitude, kindness and charity. But they all know that most elections are decided by that crucial 12 per cent-/or-less swing vote, the ballot-booth nod of the not-quite-sure folk. It's from the letters and calls, not the posturing of critics, journalistic or otherwise, that they get their input and their inspiration.

And politicians, like industrialists, and like the lawyers from whom both get much of their advice, are very big on tradition, on experience, on precedents. And on the record, from Minamata, Grassy Narrows and White Dog, Michigan, Brazil, New Brunswick, Quebec, New York and most other places, we don't care much. If we did, they couldn't go on getting away with it, could they?

Maybe it's because of the money. ... I can't understand why they won't get after the company. ... I'm scared for the future. ... Government is so big. ... People ... don't care.
Josephine Mandamin

Appendices

APPENDIX ONE
WILD RICE

Many of the community at One Man Lake were away in Kenora, Minaki and at White Dog on the day they were flooded out of their homes; others were on trap lines a distance away. When the waters rose there was such heavy piling of ice from spring break-up on the shoreline that fleeing residents were unable to carry their belongings over the frigid barrier to the lake.

Hydro promised them "new housing" at White Dog. Eleven families from One Man Lake eventually got tar-paper shacks, but some of the families, forced to wait several months for the "alternate housing" which no one at Hydro (or the federal Department of Indian Affairs) had considered preparing *before* the old houses were flooded, moved into tents with their children. Some, not provided even with the frame and tar-paper buildings before fall freeze-up, spent the entire winter of 1958-9 living in tents pitched at White Dog.

A few individuals received token compensation payments for the loss of some possessions. Two individuals were compensated for the loss of their homes – one got $400 and the other $800. But no general compensation had been negotiated by Hydro at the close of 1976; not for homes, furniture, clothing, tools, trapping and fishing equipment; nor for the large family vegetable gardens now under forty-four feet of water.

When trees had been clear-cut around the area to be flooded, Hydro work crews had simply left them where they fell. When the dam was closed, the lake was filled with trees, bark and dead-heads that made boat travel almost impossible. The resulting pollution instantly ended the commercial fishing and fishing for food that had helped make One Man Lake residents economically independent. It wasn't possible to resume fishing in the lake until 1969 – just as the provincial government was closing it again because of the mercury poisoning. No compensation for the lost income from fishing in that eleven-year period was ever discussed or paid. Only in 1973, with the waterway long since closed to commercial fishing, was it announced that Ontario Hydro was willing to clear the flood-damaged timber.

Local residents had realized their cemetery would be flooded and had insisted that Hydro arrange agreeable disposal of the graves. Some were relocated to higher ground by Hydro. Those not moved were soon and increasingly threatened by flood erosion. When Hydro was told that some graves had literally been washed away, coffins and remains exposed and dispersed, there was no response. In a confidential internal memo Mr. J. Dennehy, a Special Assignments and Review Officer of the federal Department of Indian Affairs, warns senior department officials of the need to act on the mercury pollution-related problems of the area.

> When Grassy Narrows and Islington [White Dog] reserves were relocated due to Hydro control measures, the communities were promised electrical power for their homes. This was never completed. The communities also had to undergo a social adjustment change to their environment. ... *There was the floating coffin incident at Islington Reserve.*

In June 1976 the White Dog Band decided to block the road running through their reserve. The plan was to give tourists pamphlets describing the mercury poisoning at the fishing lodges. The roadblock was to be initiated on 10 June 1976. On June 7 the provincial government asked the White Dog band council and representatives of Indian Affairs to a meeting with the province, and with Ontario Hydro, in Kenora, on the 9th. No agenda or reason was given. The band council representatives and those of Indian Affairs went to Kenora only to find that the meeting had been "called off by Toronto."

The Indians decided to launch a lawsuit to force Hydro to build a coffer dam around the remaining graves. Said Bruce Crofts, a successful Toronto insurance executive who has worked with the White Dog and Grassy Narrows communities as an unpaid consultant on economic development since 1975:

> The government had apparently tried to call the June 9 meeting to forestall the road blockade, which was causing them political embarrassment. But someone in Toronto, at Hydro, called Natural Resources and said Hydro wasn't prepared to offer the Indians anything; so the meeting was cancelled to avoid having to admit there was no offer ready. Then the government, with the fishing camp operators all over its back because of the road blockade at White Dog, put some real heat on Hydro to negotiate with the band about the burial ground.

In the late fall of 1976 the "heat" had paid off; Hydro was busy building the coffer dam around the remaining burial sites.

There were, at the end of 1976, still some other unresolved problems dating from 1957/58. Ontario Hydro, having made loose arrangements for the construction, on reserve property, of one dam, a road, and a transmission line, had built a second dam at the west end of Goshawk Lake, two access roads more than announced in advance, and two boat landings; destroyed some existing access roads during their construction activity; cut and used timber in areas not discussed with the band council; and used large amounts of gravel and fill without arranging that use with the owners of the land, the people of White Dog. Compensation for those acts was not even at the stage of active discussion twenty years after that sequence of events was begun.

As for the wild rice, it has always been a staple of Ojibway diets. Nowadays middle-class North Americans happily pay $5 per pound for the chance to stuff their Rock Cornish game hens with succulent wild rice dressing. In the 1950s and 60s the Indians were paid about 20 cents a pound by processors and packagers. At the end of the 60s the local Indians formed the Man-O-Min rice co-op and were, a year later, being paid 60 cents per pounds. That price escalated to as high as 90 cents by 1975. But there was no crop at White Dog in 1975.

By 1959 the extra forty-four feet of water stacked behind the Goshawk dam had submerged eight upstream wild rice locations while "releases" from the dam in spring had begun destroying five locations downstream. (In June/July, when Hydro releases large volumes of water from the dam, wild rice, growing in shallow, marshy areas on the shorelines of waterways, is in its most critical "floating leaf" stage; flooded at this time, the plants die.)

There have been periodic complaints from provincial officials (including Leo Bernier) and private packagers that Indians don't harvest the rice efficiently; that proper marketing is impossible to organize because Indian indolence and inefficiency preclude guaranteeing the steady supply demanded by food distributors and retailers. But a glance at the White Dog production figures and at personal incomes from rice harvesting, generally an all-family activity, answer the charge. One man, in 1973, earned $3,000 in thirty days at White Dog, rice picking. Here are some White Dog production figures:

1963– 1,393 pounds	1970– 4,908 pounds
1964– 6,471 pounds	1971– 14,454 pounds
1965– no records	1972– 154,834 pounds
1966– no recorded crop	1973– 187,472 pounds
1967– 358 pounds	1974– 1,669 pounds
1968– 26,713 pounds	1975– no crop
1969– 7,468 pounds	1976– 200,000 pounds

The sites below the dam were chiefly on lakes and tributaries feeding into the Winnipeg River, but one-shot, massive releases of water from the dam would back up into these tributary systems, flooding out the other spring crops. In 1972 the White Dog rice harvesters beat the system. They built an earthen dam four feet high and about sixty feet long to prevent the Hydro releases from backing up into White Dog Lake, source of half the remaining local crop. The dam had a crude, homemade wooden control gate designed by community carpenters. And it worked; crop figures in 1972 and 1973 attest to its value. Then, in the spring of 1974, without warning, Hydro released a wall of water that washed over the top of the White Dog Lake dam, tore out the control gate, crumbled the entire structure and destroyed the spring crop in White Dog Lake, along with most of the area's wild rice. The 1974 harvest for all the rice in the area was equal to 0.89 per cent of the 1973 crop. In 1975, with no dam to protect the rice, it was *all* destroyed. 1976 brought better fortune; the relatively light snow burden of the winter and the dry spring kept river levels at record low levels, so that Hydro releases weren't sufficient to damage the rice. 200,000 pounds was harvested at White Dog alone, with prices ranging from 80 to 90 cents per pound.

So, in October of 1975, Indians from White Dog met with Leo Bernier and asked for an engineer from his Ministry to make a feasibility study for an effective dam. The Grassy Narrows Band asked for similar help at a meeting in Kenora on October 31. At that meeting four Ontario cabinet ministers were present including Leo Bernier and George Kerr.

By December 1975 there were no responses from Queen's Park to the requests made in the detailed briefs prepared by the two communities; no sign, yet, of that engineer from Natural Resources. In January Natural Resources was reported to be "promising action." On 26th February, Rene Brunelle, now Provincial Secretary for Resources Development, visited the reserves and promised "a reply to the request in your briefs." By mid-March the engineer still "hadn't made it" to the reserves, but a comprehensive answer from Mr. Brunelle was promised by March 31.

On March 31 a group of officials from government ministries met representatives of the two communities in Kenora; there ensued an embarrassed explanation to the effect that Mr. Brunelle's letter couldn't be seen yet after all; it was being "re-drafted" they said, as some provincial public servants had been "embarrassed" by a "lack of depth" in the draft reply and by the "inadequacy of the proposed responses." However it was promised that an engineer would be found and sent.

On 6 April a Natural Resources engineer flew to White Dog from Thunder Bay. His feasibility study occupied less than two hours on site and led to a brief report recommending the dam be rebuilt, using proper metal fittings and controls. The fittings were even ordered from a Manitoba firm.

However, as of the end of 1976, the final fittings hadn't been delivered. At Grassy Narrows, at the close of 1976, residents were still waiting for "their" engineer to come; a Natural Resources "generalist" had looked briefly. Neither community was optimisitic about the 1977 crop.

Mr. Brunelle's letter was dated 8 April 1976. In the section dealing with wild rice, this "re-drafted" response said, in part:

> ... An engineer from the Ministry of Natural Resources has been in recent contact with you to discuss the problems of the dam and pumps on Whitedog Lake.
>
> When his report becomes available, it will be examined to determine the most appropriate course of action to correct present deficiencies in the dam and pump system.
>
> With respect to the overall increase in the wild rice harvest, I am advised that only a small portion of the known rice reserves are presently being harvested ...

Said Bruce Crofts of the Brunelle letter: "It was the most cynical document I've ever seen. ... It's also a bit hard to understand why it took Leo Bernier over six months to get an engineer to spend two hours at White Dog, when he could send an OPP inspector to Grassy the same day he was embarrassed by spoiling fish – so he could find out about a 13-year-old boy throwing stones. That says a lot about where this government places its priorities."

APPENDIX TWO
THE GREAT FREEZER DEBATE

The OPP investigation showed that although a 13-year-old admitted breaking into the Grassy Narrows freezer and damaging the fan on 22 May 1976, the fish were already unfit for human consumption by that date. There was no proof of a previous act of delinquency.

On 8 June Stephen Lewis asked Mr. Bernier to recant the charges he had made:

> *Mr. Bernier:* Mr. Speaker, I'm particularly pleased that the Ontario Provincial Police inspector's report exonerates totally members of my staff. As you know, there were indications that we were negligent, that we were not doing our job on behalf of the Grassy Narrows Indians. I'm particularly pleased that it has been clarified. ... With regard to my comments, I indicated yesterday that I was looking into this matter further and I have no further comment to make at this time.

> *Mr. McClellan:* Shame!

> *Mr. Deans:* Are you serious?

> *Mr. Lewis:* By way of supplementary: What further matters does the Minister have to examine? ... Wouldn't it serve relationships between his Ministry and the very difficult problems on those reserves in the Northwest much better were he to stand and simply say, "This is clearly not deliberate sabotage; and I'm sorry I implied it in the first instance"?

> *Hon. Mr. Bernier:* Mr. Speaker, as I said just a moment ago, I have no intention of continuing this discussion; it's not in the interests of those people.

> *Mr. MacDonald:* Is that right?

An Hon. Member: You mean it's not in your interests.

An Hon. Member: You're not for real.

Mr. Deans: Have you ever heard the words, "I'm sorry"?

And so on. Later that afternoon the minister reaffirmed to reporters that his officials "knew nothing" of the freezer problems until reading of Mr. Lewis's visit in Toronto's *Globe and Mail.* He reiterated his pleasure in the "exoneration" of his officials in the matter.

Reporters telephoned OPP Inspector Civil and two officials of the federal Department of Health and Welfare, Assistant Deputy Minister Charles Caron and David Eckhart, an environmental health officer in the area. Said Inspector Civil: "I'm convinced there was nothing more to it ... than a boyish prank." Referring to Mr. Eckhart's visit to the reserve on May 18, Inspector Civil said the federal official had "found the fish were soft, and their juices were running."

But at a May 20 meeting, according to his boss, Charles Caron, Mr. Eckhart reported that "the fish were OK but the freezer temperature should be lowered." (This statement was confirmed by minutes, kept by the Indian representatives who met that day with representatives of a dozen federal and provincial agencies.) On June 7, Mr. Caron said, "I was told verbally that the fish looked reasonably all right, although there was some seepage." He added that Mr. Eckhart had, however, told the band not to eat the fish. "Tests on the fish showed that bacterial counts were within safety margins," said Caron, although "the fishes' appearance was not good." Nor their odour.

A final piece for the freezer-sabotage jig-saw from an interview transcript with Dr. Peter Newberry:

> People working inside the freezer noticed it was getting warm [in early May] and they called Natural Resources in Kenora to tell them. There was no response. Natural Resources frequently got calls from the reserve which they considered frivolous ... , so apparently they just ignored this call. Two weeks later, at a meeting with government people in Kenora, the Indians reported that the fish were now rotten. The minutes of that meeting *contained a pencilled-in addition inferring that the phone call had been received on the same day as the fish were reported rotten.*
>
> I got in touch with several of the other people who had been at the meeting and asked them if any such statement had been made at the meeting. None of them could recall it. The man from the Provincial Indian Secretariat, who had prepared the minutes, seemed very embarrassed about the pencilled-in addition. ... [The addition, subsequent to

the meeting, was apparently made after the issue blew up in the Ontario Legislature.]... No explanation was made. Some of the Indian people said someone must have been ordered to cover-up for the Natural Resources people, since Mr. Bernier was so anxious to prove sabotage with the policy investigation.

On May 31 in the legislature the following exchange took place:

Mr. Lewis: Doesn't the Minister think he needs to find an alternative policy to those he has undertaken, rather than to engage in some kind of prosecution on Grassy Narrows and undermine what little credibility he has left?

Hon. Mr. Bernier: Mr. Speaker, I can't accept the comments that there is a breakdown between the Grassy Narrows and the White Dog Indian Band in relation to this particular Ministry. I would have to say to you, sir, that we have an excellent working relationship with that band, as we do with all our native peoples in the northern part of the province.

Mr. Lewis: Oh, wonderful.

Mr. Warner: They love you up there.

Hon. Mr. Bernier: And I'm sure, sir, in your position as speaker of this Legislature today, you will agree with that particular statement, having complete knowledge of the excellent relationship and working field we have with the native people of this province.

Mr. Lewis: They speak warmly of you, Hon. Mr. Bernier.

Hon. Mr. Bernier: I have to say to you, sir, that there is a certain amount of onus and responsibility on the native people.

APPENDIX THREE
CHECKS ON RESEARCHERS

In 1970 Norvald Fimreite obtained a federal permit to catch birds to test for mercury content, and a provincial permit to catch fish for the same purpose, in the Wabigoon/English water system. Fimreite told the then Ontario Ministry of Lands and Forests of his plans and invited local officials of the Ministry to meet with him and, if they wished, send a game warden to accompany him. Fimreite got no response to his offer.

While he was staying in a motel in Dryden, Fimreite was visited by a Lands and Forests official who said he'd heard that Fimreite had "collected" an eagle. Fimreite confirmed the rumour and showed the official the bird he'd taken under terms of his federal permit.

"I wouldn't do any more of that," advised the Lands and Forests man, "if I were you."

On Dr. Fimreite's return to Kenora a few days later, he was visited again, this time by a member of the RCMP. The officer demanded to see Fimreite's federal permit, asked questions about the eagle, and declared himself unsatisfied. Fimreite suggested the Mountie wire Ottawa about the validity of the permit. The Mountie did so, received confirmation, and ended the interrogation.

Another scientist who has undertaken considerable research in the area is Dr. Frank M. D'Itri, Director of the Institute of Water Research in the Office for Research Development at Michigan State University.

On 18 August 1972, Professor D'Itri, alerted by the Fimreite studies, wrote to Mr. Douglas Roseborough, Director of Sports Fishing for Ontario's Natural Resources Ministry: "I am actively engaged in research relative to the environmental mercury problem with special interest in the accumulation of mercury in fish."

Professor D'Itri said he hoped to collect approximately sixty specimens

213

each of walleye, northern pike, bass, whitefish and lake trout from the Wabigoon/English systems. He would analyse the fish tissue at Michigan State University and provide results of his tests to the Ontario Ministry as soon as they were completed. "I would very much appreciate permission [to collect the fish]", he said.

Ontario's Ministry of Natural Resources was not enthused about this offer of freely supplied research data. By 25 August 1972, Mr. Roseborough had developed a file number (4045.2.1) for Dr. D'Itri – and a reply:

> Dear Mr. D'Itri:
>
> Your request for a permit to collect 60 each of the walleye, pike, bass, whitefish and lake trout creates a number of difficulties and I am consulting with our field staff to see whether these can be made available to you through some other means than your own fishing activity.
>
> Before we could supply fish or before we could issue a permit, however, we would require from you some further details of the purpose of your study, how it became initiated and how it is financed. This considerable detail is made necessary because of our practice of not issuing permits under normal circumstances to non-residents of Ontario. Since I will not be in the office for the next few weeks, I would appreciate you providing this information in letter form at your earliest convenience.
>
> Yours very truly,

One other reason was later given the researcher by Natural Resources officials: that he hadn't applied for his permit "early enough."

Dr. D'Itri was not about to forsake his project. And Natural Resources officials did explain that he was perfectly entitled to purchase an out-of-province non-resident's angler's licence, so long as he fished with a rod and took only his allowable daily limit. So he did. The Director of Michigan State University's Water Research Institute flew into the affected lakes by float-equipped aircraft and, having bought his angler's licence, trolled and cast for the game fish he wanted to study. He was careful not to keep more than his daily angler's limits.

APPENDIX FOUR
REED AND PAINT

Mercury is the preferred preservative for commercial paints – and Reed, through its subsidiary in Vancouver, General Paint, manufactured and sold 1,936,000 gallons of paint in 1975 as well as 5,140 tons of pigments manufactured at two Reed plants – in New Toronto and Ajax, Ontario. The red ink used around the world and made, in part, from Reed pigments, has a base of vermilion, the colour constituent of cinnabar, from which mercury is refined.

Mercury compounds are used in paints as anti-fouling (in marine paints) and mildew-proofing agents as well as being added to give the paints a longer shelf-life by inhibiting bacterial attack. Once the paint is applied to any surface, the mercury evaporates out of the painted surface entering the environment. In interior paints, it's believed all mercury will vapourize out of paint within two years, depending on temperature, etc. In exterior paint, where higher mercury concentrations are generally used, about half the mercury leaches into the soil and, eventually, the water table; the balance, not "washed" into the earth by rain, becomes airborne vapour.

There have been a number of cases of mercury poisoning – some fatal, following the application of mercury-treated paint (as reported by Brown and Kulkarni, 1967; see also p. 11). Most documented poisonings have occurred only where mercury-bearing paint has been used in poorly ventilated rooms.

The Science Council of Canada reports that, of 156 paint factories in Canada, only that operated by Canadian Industries Limited (CIL) abstains from the often less expensive mercuric compounds in use since the late 1930s. That data was given to the Science Council (as reported on 29 September 1976, in the unpublished document "Three Perspectives on Mercury in Canada," pp. 17-18) by the Canadian Paint Manufacturers' Association, which declined to tell researchers for this book how much of the estimated

77,708 pounds of mercury used annually by Canadian paint producers was used by which companies. Nuodex Canada Limited, maker and distributor of most mercury-based "paint fungicides" used in Canada, also declined to provide "confidential customer data," but was generous in supplying research material and general background.

It's believed CIL's elimination of mercury fungicides from their paints resulted from difficulties in exporting to the US. In their action of 15 May 1975 to have "mercurial paint biocides" banned, the US EPA noted: " ... in this procedure the risk of using mercurials in paint outweighs any benefit of such use ... and preferable alternatives exist" (docket no. 246). The EPA then listed twenty-one separate fungicides sold in the US and containing no mercury (several of these marketed in Canada).

Applying, in 1975, for the "cancellation of all uses of pesticides containing mercury," and specifically those used in paints, the US EPA concludes in an action against the Chapman Chemical Company et al (pp. 252-6): "All mercury used in pesticides eventually enters some environmental medium... can eventually be converted to the deadly poison, methylmercury. ... Fortunately, effective substitutes for all uses of mercury pesticides contested in this proceeding are currently available. ... The social, economic, and environmental costs far outweigh any benefits to be gained from the continued use of mercury pesticides."

Persuasive argument, bought by CIL, but not (by the end of 1976) by any other of Canada's paint manufacturers, Reed included. However, Robert Billingsley was able to tell his employees, truthfully, in his 29 October 1976 memo: "Reed does not use mercury or mercury compounds anywhere within our *pulp and paper-making operations* in Canada."

The Reed paints are called General Paint, Monamel and Breeze. Reed paints and pigments are also likely used in the manufacture and printing of the large line of wallpapers – Sunworthy, Sanderson, Lloyd, Boxer and Stauton – sold through Reed's own stores and franchise operations in Canada and the US. They are marketed chiefly in Western Canada from the Vancouver plant. With total sales of over $90 million in 1975, the "Decorative Products Group" of Reed companies was second in financial importance only to Reed's forest products businesses. In 1975-6 Reed expanded its operations further by buying several wallpaper retail outlets in the US.

APPENDIX FIVE
REED AND FORESTS

Reed's main business in Canada is forestry products, and as 1976 ended the company was moving into the eye of a fresh political hurricane over plans to develop a 19,000 square-mile tract of boreal forest north of White Dog and Grassy Narrows – in an area where many conservationists and foresters said growth cycles were so slow because of soil conditions and extremes of cold that the small trees would never regenerate, once cut. (Boreal black spruce need up to 150 years to fully regenerate.) At the year's end Reed had something called a "Memorandum of Understanding" with the Ontario government, under which it had, in effect, first refusal on the vast tract of timber and agreed, in return, to undertake an environmental impact study and submit to public hearings before the Environment Ministry's Environmental Assessment Board.

The "memorandum," signed 26 October 1976, two years-plus after the deal/proposal was first announced, commits Natural Resources to complete a "forest inventory" for which the Ministry will be reimbursed by Reed "if and when a licence is granted."

The overall project would entail, by Reed estimates, a $400 million development including a new pulp and paper mill near Ear Falls, Ontario, and 1,200 new jobs. The objections to the plan are two-tiered:

a) Critics of the scheme, spear-headed by professional foresters and conservationists, say the development would destroy Ontario's last-remaining massive stand of boreal forest, effectively destroy the habitat of wild game and end the current lifestyle and economic base of several thousand Indians who hunt, trap, fish in the area. These critics are also unimpressed with Reed's record of forestry "management," as well as with Natural Resources' record of reforestation. (Leo Bernier blames tight budgets for the fact that only

217

about half the trees required for adequate reforestation are planted in Ontario, with only one-third to one-half of those surviving.)

b) Critics of Reed and the Government of Ontario say the deal is made – that plans for hearings and studies are only window dressing, that anyhow the final say rests legally with the Minister of Natural Resources. In a public meeting at Ear Falls on November 6, reported in the *Globe and Mail* November 8 (page 8), there was this paragraph concerning the then Minister: "Mr. Bernier warned about the possibility that Reed 'might just walk away' from the project because of recent criticisms. 'Let's hope it doesn't happen,' the minister is quoted as saying."

Certainly Ontario's Housing Corporation and the Ministry of the Environment seem to have begun expecting big things for the 1,200-strong community of Ear Falls as early as 1974, when the tiny town was in the grip of an economic recession. Doug Turner of the Ontario Housing Corporation told a researcher for this book, in November 1976, that a subdivision for 116 new homes had been "laid out" at Ear Falls and that sixty of the building lots were serviced with water, sewer and hydro in 1975. The decision to go ahead, said Turner, was made in 1973. There are also eight empty homes at Ear Falls, he said, built by the provincial government's housing corporation but unsold. Turner said he didn't expect the rest of the houses to be built "for at least another year ... until there's a definite decision that Reed are to go ahead." Of the first sixty serviced building lots, ready since early summer 1976, one had been sold by November.

On 17 October 1976 reporter Robert Reguly broadcast a report on the proposed Reed expansion on the CTV program W-5. Reguly interviewed Reeve Stan Lesschuk of Ear Falls, one of two possible sites for a new paper mill.]

Lesschuk: We are ready to roll with Reed whenever they want to go.

Reguly: Aren't you personal friends with Mr. Leo Bernier, the Minister of Natural Resources, and with Mr. Tom Jones, the vice-president and Mr. Billingsley, the president of Reed?

Lesschuk: I am a personal friend of the Honourable Leo Bernier and I've worked on his campaigns. I am a close friend of Mr. Jones. I know Mr. Billingsley through our meetings with the township, and I think we have a close relationship.

Reguly; You've taken part in fund-raising for Mr. Leo Bernier and others in the provincial cabinet.

Lesschuk: Yes. I certainly do. I take an active part. And like I told you before, I don't hide my colours. It's true, whenever I make a public statement where

I stand within my political life here, as I do here in Ear Falls. [Reeve Lesschuk was defeated in that subsequent election.]

At this point in time, Ontario government funds had provided a $4 million grant to Lesschuk's small community to provide water and sewer facilities for that new housing sub-division. Across from the serviced-and-ready building lots accommodated by that $4 million dollar grant was a sign in a large, empty field which read: PHASE TWO.

At the "Public Co-ordination Branch" of the Environment Ministry, Maurice Sacco spoke with a researcher for this book about the installation of the water and sewer services. "In 1974 there was talk of Reed coming to Ear Falls," he said. "The projected population increase was 5,000 people by 1995. Facilities had to be planned ahead to service that increased population."

On 7 March 1974, announcing plans for "preliminary studies" in Ontario's Legislature, Premier William Davis said, "The government intends to ensure that sufficient serviced housing lots are made available in the communities affected." And he added, "Close co-operation between Anglo-Canadian [Reed] and the Ontario Government will be maintained to ensure that all necessary efforts are made to protect the environment."

However, two years later in late 1976 the Premier, along with Leo Bernier, was denying that there was any deal; everybody said no decision would be made until after all the studies, at least two years later.

But there were indications of attitudes – witness three comments from a Toronto *Star* report of 28 August 1976. Jim Keddie of the Timber Sales Branch of the Natural Resources Ministry: "Our indication is that there is enough wood in the proposed area to supply Reed with their needs. We did an initial quick study in co-operation with Reed. As a forester, I think the other arguments, the environmental ones, are invalid. Yes, of course I'm biased in favor of logging." R.M. Dixon, head of the Ministry's Silvaculture Section: "Based on my experience, there is no need for a major environmental impact study. Perhaps we study too much." And in contrast the president of the Ontario Provincial Foresters' Association (representing 700 foresters, half of them civil servants): "We need more information but it's damned hard to find out. ... Based on past experience ... good management has never been done so far. ... "

Then there is this extract from a brief prepared by J.R. Cary, the Natural Resources Ministry Forest Manager who has been in charge of existing timber limits leased to Reed, and disapproves of their clear-cutting practices. "If Dryden [Reed] is a representative microcosm of Ontario's coniferous forests, the awesome spectacle of huge acreages going out of production annually must alarm all foresters." And this extract from a confidential internal memorandum of 6 July 1976, written by A.G. Appleby, Senior

Environmental Planner, Environmental Assessment Section, and sent to D.P. Caplice, Director of the Environment Ministry's Environmental Approvals Branch:

> The Cabinet submission considered ... last December recommended that the government make no commitment to the Reed proposal until the company had ... made its environmental assessment public, and assessed public reactions and concerns ...
>
> ... Dr. Reynolds, Deputy Minister of MNR [the Ministry of Natural Resources] indicates that agreement in principle is a long way off and might never be reached. In fact we have a letter on file from Mr. D.P. Drysdale, Director, Timber Sales Branch, MNR, indicating that MNR has made an offer for licencing timber to Reed, and that the proposal offered reflects the MNR final position very closely. ... It would seem to us that an offer – which in fact has the force of an agreement – by the Provincial Government to licence timber to Reed, is a major commitment to further the proposal. It therefore appears to contradict the Cabinet resolution.

And from D.P. Drysdale, on 3 May 1976, in a letter to D.P. Caplice: "An offer by this Ministry for licencing timber in northwestern Ontario is still being considered by Reed Limited. As far as we are concerned, the proposal being offered reflects very closely our final position."

This, from M.D. Kirk, of the Environmental Assessment Section in an internal government memorandum of 26 April 1976, to an Environmental Planner:

> ... The Ministry has failed to secure adequate regeneration in a large portion of licenced timber limits, and has failed, by in-house consensus, to control or mitigate logging and road-building practices by the industry. ... Clear cutting and high grading by Ontario's forest industries, according to MNR foresters, are out of control. Many clear cuts are so extensive that regeneration is poor or non-existent ... the extent of forest not restocking increases annually. ...
>
> So extensive is the lack of actual knowledge in the management of the boreal forest that foresters find themselves practicing without adequate information. Canada spends much less on research than any developed forested country. The results are showing.

APPENDIX SIX
POLICING POLLUTION

On 26 November 1976 Reed was charged by Ontario's Environment Ministry with ten counts of causing "pollution dangerous to the environment and possibly hazardous to human health," at the Dryden plant. Reed, with Abitibi Paper Co. Limited (charged the same day), thus joined a very short list of companies charged under Ontario's 1971 Environmental Protection Act. Both firms were charged for failure to clean up pollution at their paper mills.

Ministerial orders for Reed to reduce its punishment of the Wabigoon River date from 3 December 1970. Yet in 1970 Reed was dumping 25 tons of suspended solid waste into the Wabigoon daily; in 1975 the daily average was 24.9 tons. (The Ministry "guideline" [voluntary] allowed daily loadings of 8 tons.) In 1970 Reed was dumping 24 tons of organic waste every day (voluntary "guideline" 5 tons). In 1975 Reed was fouling the Wabigoon with 46.2 tons of organic waste daily.

The 1970 order, delivered to Reed on 16 January 1971, required a clean-up by 31 October 1974. Reed asked for time – and got it – until 31 December 1976. In November 1976 the Ministry decided, and announced, that Reed couldn't have the required primary and secondary treatment facilities on stream by the deadline.

If the 1976 charges were proceeded with, *if* the company failed to get yet another extension, *if* the full weight of the law and the maximum penalties were brought to bear – a lot of "ifs" given the less than rigorous record of prosecutions in Ontario – Reed stood to face a fine of $200 daily after 1 January 1977, in the worst of all worlds. Extended over a full year the fines would total $73,000, probably not enough to fuel Robert Billingsley's executive jet on its regular trips to Atlanta. No one, though, in early 1977, was holding very large stakes on bets that the prosecutions would proceed either vigorously or expeditiously.

Moreover, on Wednesday, 5 January 1977, George Kerr told the Toronto *Star* in an interview that his ministry, " ... had decided not to prosecute Reed for not meeting a pollution control order deadline of December 31, 1976." Emphasizing that his ministry was not "letting Reed off the hook," Mr. Kerr allowed that, "We've been aware for sometime that Reed couldn't possibly meet the deadline on time."

Adds the *Star* story: "A Reed spokesman told the *Star* last month the installation of the treatment equipment had been delayed by a lengthy strike at the Dryden mill last year. Kerr said the government began negotiating a new clean-up deadline for Reed "some months ago, and take it from me, this time there'll be no extensions."

A CBC radio newscast of January 5 quoted an official of the Ministry of the Environment as saying the new deadline was to be three years from the 31 December 1976 cut-off date.

On 29 October 1976, Robert Billingsley, in a memo distributed to Reed employees, said: "Overall, this company has a strong commitment to environmental protection. ... " The quotations which follow are from Copy No. 20 of "The Ontario Pulp and Paper Industry" Alternative Policies for Pollution Abatement... (prepared in 1973, printed in 1974, but never, as of November 1976, publicly distributed by the "Special Studies Section" of the Ministry of the Environment, although a "summary" version was revealed and published about sixty days after the original was made available to the author):

> Summary of Environment Effects if Mill [at Dryden] Meets Ministry of Environment [Ontario] Water Quality Objectives:
> No improvement because river flow too small relative to mill discharge.
> Effects if Mill Closes Permanently:
> Massive sludge deposits would continue to ... affect bottom flora and fauna for many years. ... Accumulations of sludge and fibre are so extensive in the Wabigoon River that even closure ... would not result in short-term restoration of satisfactory water quality (pp. 281 and 287).

> ... there appear to be few additional benefits that could be gained by closing a mill which could not be achieved through some kind of currently available waste water treatment. *Except for the Wabigoon River, it would not be necessary to close any of the mills* listed in Table IV-5 in order to restore most of the potential uses which can be made of the respective receiving water systems. *Even in the case of Wabigoon, a restoration of water quality and water uses could be achieved without mill closure, but this would involve large capital expenditures for dredging or rerouting the river* (p. 306).

In principle, the Ministry of the Environment is able to enforce its policy for pollution control by using the provisions for fines, stop orders and control orders that were established by the Ontario Water Resources Act. ... In practice, the Ministry has been reluctant to utilize these powers of enforcement, preferring to seek the cooperation of the companies concerned. *This approach has met with only limited success in achieving effluent control by the pulp and paper industry* (p. 327).

In September 1976, in a "Summary and Update" of the same document:

The Present Approach Assessed. Continuation of the present policy has the advantage of being understood by Government and industry and it will avoid open conflicts between Ministry officials and industry representatives. However it is essential to realize that, in the present economic and legal context, *companies have a powerful financial incentive to continue polluting the air and water.* Firms seek to minimize their costs wherever possible. Pulp and paper mills have traditionally been able to use the air, lakes and rivers to dispose of their wastes free of charge. Waste treatment, waste recovery and proper disposal techniques are generally very costly to companies even when half the costs are borne by government through the tax system. *Hence, it is in the companies' interests to resist incurring these costs, even when this may lead to prosecution and fines.* Between 1968 and the present, only twelve convictions under the Ontario Water Resources Act and five convictions under the Environmental Protection Act have been obtained against pulp and paper companies. The fines for water pollution averaged $812 per conviction: for air $1,400 per conviction. *Fines of this magnitude provide the companies with virtually no economic incentive to incur the much greater costs for pollution control.* This is especially the case in the pulp and paper industry since there have been no convictions for water pollution by these mills since 1971, and only two for air pollution, both in 1974.

Continuing the present policy approach is, therefore, unlikely to achieve the Ministry's abatement objectives over the next ten years. Furthermore, it is inequitable in that some mills have spent large sums of money on pollution abatement while *those who still pollute excessively have not been penalized.*

This situation will not be remedied by an even greater share of the costs of pollution control being shifted to the Government as has been proposed by representatives of the pulp and paper industry. *The primary deficiency lies in the lack of an adequate penalty to induce companies to abate their pollution to the desired levels.* (pp. 57-8)

APPENDIX SEVEN
HIDDEN EFFECTS

Methyl mercury works savagely in its invisible assaults on the body. In 1928 a German scientist, S. Lomholt, reported that mercury could be detected in the stillborn fetuses of women who had been treated for syphilis with mercury medications ("Quecksilber, Theoretisches Chemisches und Experimentelles," Berlin).

Research conducted between 1950 and 1971 was to demonstrate, in the words of Claes Ramel, that "the dosage at which methyl mercury interferes with chromosomal segregation is evidently very small. This should be considered in view of the fact that chromosomal disorders usually are estimated to cause around a third of all spontaneous abortions." Methyl mercury, which concentrates in the testes as well as such organs as kidneys, liver, heart and spleen, also causes "effects ... on germ cells ... irregular c-mitosis. ... This leads to errors in the distribution of single chromosomes ... [which means, in plain language] an increase of congenital disorders like mongolism." (Chapter on the genetic effects of mercury in "Mercury In The Environment," 1972.)

So add another killer and another crippler to the list: miscarriage and congenital idiocy-mongolism. In Ontario there had by 1977 still been no studies to determine whether rates of miscarriages and of congenital retardation were abnormally high at White Dog and Grassy Narrows – no formal studies. But on 1 March 1973, W.P. McKinley, Director-General of the Food Directorate of the federal Health and Welfare Branch, told Robert Reguly of the Toronto *Star*, speaking of possible consequences of mercury poisoning in the area: "We get a considerable amount of abortions and a very high level of malformations– the thalidomide type of thing." Ottawa bureaucrats were less forthcoming about such matters after 1973. European research in 1970 showed that "mutagenic effects" from methyl mercury could produce about double the number of genetic defects found in nature. (Overall infant deaths at Kenora are double the Ontario average according to Dr. Frank D'Itri.)

With genetic effects, there is a further shadow, still unresolved, in the impact of methyl mercury on DNA and on the "somatic" cells which we carry through life. Says Claes Ramel (*op. cit.*, p. 181): "With regard to ... the genetic risk of mercury exposure ... [to] somatic as well as germ cells ... the consequences of genetic changes in postnatal life are quite obscure, although *a connection with carcinogenesis* [the creation of cancer] *may be suspected.*" Ramel's studies proved mercury to be 1,000 times more potent in causing genetic damage than any other known agent. For the populations of Northwest Ontario and Northwest Quebec it is fear of the invisible symptoms that destroys sleep and peace for expectant mothers and fearful parents.

As described by the Canadian Federal Task Force in its 1973 "Final Report" the symptomology of methyl mercury poisoning also includes: " ... inability to concentrate, lack of interest at home and at work, weakness, apathy and extreme fatigue ... emotional instability, with fits of anger, depression or rage."

Said a worker who was employed in the Dryden Chemicals plant, in the years it was using mercury, of another worker – a slight, soft-spoken and friendly man: "George [not the man's real name] developed an insane temper, not long before they moved him onto a job outside, painting, to get him away from the mercury. He'd pick up a hammer and, for no reason, fire it the whole length of the plant – and tough luck if somebody happened to be standing in the way." (Excerpt from a research interview transcript.) "George," interviewed by the same researcher, recalled that, "I worked in the cell plant from about 1963 on. ... They sent me to Winnipeg for a kidney biopsy in about 1969 – I was laid off for a year-and-a-half because of the mercury and I got some compensation. ... I sure was irritable back then ... I'd really blow up in a hurry. ... One summer they [Dryden Chemicals] had to put four of us outside to work because of our high mercury counts."

Then, in Kenora, there are the stories, many of them true, about the fits of rage, acts of violence, at White Dog and Grassy Narrows. The people of the reserves blame unemployment and liquor, but still say, "People get madder than they used to. ... People are always getting mad, shouting, fighting; I don't know why."

Dr. Harada (see p. 152) describes these mental and emotional symptoms of Minamata victims: " ... sleeplessness, tiring easily, not wanting to do anything, lack of ability to concentrate." And Haruhiko Tokuomi writes of: "Mental status: Slight intellectual deterioration [among postnatal cases], depression or marked emotional lability [instability] was noted in some patients."

Bruce Crofts, a Toronto insurance executive who worked with the people of White Dog and Grassy Narrows as an unpaid consultant, described a young electrician who helped to build a day-care centre: "The day he finished he just walked into the bush and shot himself. There was nothing else for him to do. ... He had worked, before, as a fishing guide and eaten a lot of the fish. ... Now he had no job and he was depressed most of the time."

In Iraq, of forty-three patients with methyl mercury poisoning studied 74.4% showed some degree of depression. The suicide rate at Grassy Narrows and White Dog is 200 times the national average. However, a neurologist employed by the Canadian government to study residents of White Dog and Grassy Narrows said during a tape-recorded research interview: "Depression is not a characteristic of mercury poisoning. ... Have you been to those reserves, seen them?. ... Golly, if I lived in White Dog, I'd get depressed too."

Mercury tends to concentrate in the thyroid gland; no one knows what potential damage may be done there. Dr. Harada also writes of the effect of methyl mercury on organs other than the brain: "For example, disturbance of the liver function, diabetes and hypertension are greater in the contaminated area than in the control area. ... Hypertension was found in 40% of those over 40."

Hypertension – high blood pressure – is directly related to heart disease. Soviet studies, not yet duplicated or verified in the West, claim to demonstrate a direct link between methyl mercury poisoning and coronary disease, going a step beyond the studies in Japan. Chapter 11 of a Russian book titled *Chronic Effects of Mercury on Organisms* (United States Dept. of Health, Education and Welfare Publication No. NIH 74-473, 1974) is titled "Cardiotoxic Effects of Mercury." It documents both human studies and animal experiments, describing chemical and tissue changes in the heart muscle resulting from exposure to methyl mercury, illustrating the report with cardiograms, noting the universally accepted fact that the heart is one of the organs in which the toxic heavy metal is concentrated by the human system; and it quotes these conclusions, from the study edited by I. M. Trakhtenberg, conducted by a series of Soviet scientists between 1949 and 1973: " ... among those subjected to prolonged exposure to mercury vapor under industrial conditions there was an increased number of cardiac ailments and a high percentage of arterial hypertension. ... We can conclude that the mercury effects produce specific shifts in both the biochemical dynamics of the cardiac muscle and in its response. ... Functional changes occur in centres regulating cardiac activity."

The only inquest ever held, in Northwest Ontario, into the death of an Indian who had been a heavy fish-eater took place on 26 January 1973. A coroner's jury found, on the advice of "expert" witnesses, that Thomas Strong, a forty-two-year-old fisherman and fishing guide, was killed by "an acute coronary thrombosis."

According to various newspaper reports of the inquest, Dr. Stopps suggested the coroner's jury ignore testimony that a post-mortem blood sample taken from Mr. Strong showed a mercury level of 224 parts per billion of mercury – eleven times the WHO "safe" threshold. Stopps said the blood sample had probably been contaminated or placed in a mercury-contaminated test tube. A former chief coroner of Toronto and several physicians and pathologists told researchers for this book that there is never any mercury present in a pathology laboratory which could contaminate such a sample; Dr. Stopps, in an interview in late 1976, said that it was impossible to draw a reliable blood sample after death. On arrival in Toronto the Thomas Strong sample had been a "greenish fluid" and impossible to identify.

There's a macabre footnote to the Thomas Strong inquest. In 1975 Professor Frank D'Itri was asked by the National Indian Brotherhood to test tissue samples from two cats which residents of Grassy Narrows and White Dog believed had exhibited symptoms of cat-dancing disease. The tests confirmed a diagnosis of fatal mercury poisoning. One of the cats had belonged to the Strong family, and shared their fish diet, a fact not known by Dr. D'Itri or noted by any officials at the time, or since.

Finally, three "silent" effects which may be attributable to methyl mercury poisoning and which may be lethal even when there are no overt symptoms of poisoning:

Exposure. Studies by J.P. Thaxton of the Department of Poultry Science of North Carolina State University show that levels of mercury poisoning too low to cause other symptoms have the effect of suppressing the body's ability to regulate temperature when ambient levels rise or fall. He concludes that it is "an intriguing question as to whether insidious levels of various pollutants, including the heavy metals, interact ... with climatic conditions in all animals, including man, to cause several yet-unidentified functional abnormalities." Experimenting with chickens, Thaxton demonstrated that mercury treatment which did not cause poisoning nonetheless impaired neural (brain) regulation of heat production and/or dissipation. When temperatures were drastically changed, the "control" chickens made the internal adjustments to maintain a safe body temperature; those given low-level methyl mercury doses couldn't and died. (J.P. Thaxton, "Diminution of Resistance of Mercury-treated Chickens to Elevated Environmental Temperature.")

For the Indians of White Dog and Grassy Narrows, where winter deaths from exposure are too common, it is more than an academic and "intriguing question."

Immunity. The body's immune system is centred in the liver – one of the organs which concentrates methyl mercury. A research chemist who has studied heavy metals poisoning said in an interview: "The immune response system is inhibited both by mercury and by lead. ... [The] body's already taxed to the limit by the mercury, to overcome that particular toxic effect. So what happens is that your resistance is down to other things, any other challenge to your system of immunity – from another poison, or a bacterial or virus infection." (Many Minamata patients died eventually from pneumonia – one of the most commonly fatal diseases of Grassy Narrows and White Dog.)

There's more than theory or hunch behind this suggestion about infection. In 1973 Dr. Loren D. Koller reported on experiments with male New Zealand white rabbits. He and his team had set out to determine whether a physiological system carrying heavy metal poison would produce the antibodies needed to fight off disease as efficiently as a mercury/cadmium/lead-free system. The answer was a graphic and resounding "No." In addition he found that mercury was by far the most inhibiting of the poisons.

On 27 March 1973, the American Journal of Veterinary Research received Dr. Koller's report titled "Immunosuppression Produced by Lead, Cadmium, and Mercury." Dr. Koller, a doctor of veterinary medicine, was then with the National Institute of Environmental Health Service – later with Oregon State University.

Four groups of rabbits were segregated: one was given lead acetate, another cadmium chloride, a third mercuric chloride, all in sterile water. In each case the dose was regulated to "an amount of each metal that would not produce overt symptoms" over the ten-week period of the initial phase of the experiment. The fourth ("control") group of test animals were given the same sterile water, with no poison added. The test rabbits were fed the heavy metal poisons daily. Even after ten weeks, "Overt clinical signs of toxicosis were not observed."

The rabbits were injected with a "viral antigen" – a substance (in this case one simulating a rabies infection) which acts like a virus and stimulates the production of antibodies in the system thus "attacked." The animals subjected to heavy metal exposure had "significantly lower antibody" levels than the "control" subjects. Rabbits given mercury, for example, produced average antibody levels only 30.869 per cent as numerous as those in the control animals, on day 78.

As for the comparative impact on immunity suppression, much less mercury by volume was administered than either of the other metals, as it is by far the most toxic. Allowing for those differences, mercury was, hands down, the most inhibiting of the poisons, on the basis of comparative dosage of the poisons. The actual ratios-of-effect on immunity suppression are: Lead

– 2.8; Cadmium – 16.7; Mercury – 405. As Dr. Koller noted, the "significant aspect of the present study is that *chronic exposure* to lead, cadmium or mercury produces immunosuppression to a viral agent." And this, possibly fatal, inhibition of the body's ability to fight disease was created at a level of poisoning at which medical examination revealed no symptoms of effect from the heavy metals.

Dr. Koller's findings were no great shock to chemists. Earlier studies had already shown that lead, arsenic, cobalt and PCBs (polychlorinated biphe-nyls) worked with viruses and bacteria to "increase the mortality of infected animals."

An article published in *Science* on 4 June 1971 disclosed the results of injecting lead-poisoned mice with salmonella bacteria. The authors were F.E. Hemphill, M.L. Kaeberle and W.B. Buck of Iowa State University. Again, the test animals were given "sub-clinical doses of lead," this time over a period of thirty days.

The animals were divided into three groups – one given no lead; one given a low level dosage; the third group given 2½ times more lead – but still not enough to cause symptoms of poisoning. Three days after introduction of the bacteria, all the mice in the high-lead group had died from the infection, as confirmed by autopsy; seven days after the bacterial infection, 54 per cent of the other lead-poisoned mice were dead – but only 13 per cent of the "control"mice. The rats carrying a burden of lead were killed by one-tenth the dose of bacteria needed to kill lead-free control animals; this despite the fact the lead-injected mice did not have high enough lead levels to exhibit any clinical symptoms of lead poisoning. And mercury, said Dr. Koller, has 144 times the effect of lead on antibody suppression.

The article concludes that *"the increased susceptibility to bacterial infection in the absence of lead toxicity is of paramount public health significance."* But although these experiments were partly funded by the US National Air Pollution Control Office, the message had still escaped both US and Canadian government health authorities six years later. That may explain why there have still been no epidemiological or post-mortem studies of victims of bacterial or viral disease from White Dog or Grassy Narrows to determine their antibody levels or measure a possible failure of their body's immunity response system.

In late 1976 health services officials of both the Ontario and Canadian governments told the author, who had asked if mercury and other heavy metals reduced immune responses: "There's absolutely no data to support that," and "That's just a crack-pot theory." In addition to the formal, published studies cited above, those gentlemen might refer to a further study by Dr. Koller ("Decreased antibody formation in mice exposed to lead,"

Nature, vol. 250, 12 July 1974).

There is also a study done with virus infections in mallard ducklings (H. Selye/B. Tuchweber/L. Bertok – Vol. 91, page 884 of the *Journal of Bacteriology*, 1966); and a similar experiment with chicks (reported by R.B. Truscott in the *Canadian Journal of Comprehensive Medical Veterinary Science*, vol. 34, p. 134 – in 1970).

For preliminary data on bacterial and viral infections at Grassy Narrows and White Dog one need only refer to infant mortality data, check deaths from pneumonia, or walk through either of the reserves and observe the number of children with skin infections, colds and influenza. There seems no reason to assume, on evidence easily available to anyone researching the literature, that heavy metal poisoning which is "sub-clinical" is also "sub-lethal."

The Breakdown of Alcohol. Again, a quotation from the research chemist:

> Mercury may also affect the body's ability to break down certain metabolites; the liver, of course, is your detoxification centre ... for the body. There is something called the drug-metabolizing enzyme complex in the liver – it's the general enzyme complex that chews up unwanted stuff; this is inhibited by lead, for example, and if you inject a particular drug or something like that, the drug will have a longer-lasting effect because of that heavy metal-induced inhibition.
>
> For instance, the liver enzyme system that takes alcohol and removes it from the system, breaks it down; if that's inhibited by mercury then ... the alcohol concentrations in the blood will just have to remain at a higher level – and longer, because of that.

In research interviews with the author, Dr. Brian Wheatley (the man charged with overseeing the Canadian government health program in respect of mercury poisoning), Dr. Stopps and Dr. Pritchard all agreed that alcohol was a major problem on the two reserves. All also agreed that the theory outlined above was fanciful.

We might refer them to "Enzyme and Metabolic Inhibitors," vol. 2, by J. Leydon Webb of the School of Medicine at the University of Southern California (Academic Press of New York and London, 1966). On pp. 792 and 793, Dr. Webb illustrates the effects on inhibition of enzymes by mercurials. Test results on a dozen enzymes are illustrated in the tables he gives there – among the enzymes "alcohol dehydrogenase," the specific one which breaks down alcohol in the human system. Citing the 1957 work of Wallenfels and Sund, Dr. Webb shows that a concentration of 20 ppb of mercury in a pure solution inhibits the action of the enzyme which breaks down alcohol in the human system *by 100 per cent.* In weaker solution the inhibiting influence is 50 per cent.

The mercuric used, p-MB, is one of our friends from the family of "organo-mercurials," – this one with two carbon atoms added to the atom of metallic mercury.

It should not be assumed that the Wallenfels/Sund data prove that organic mercury will totally inhibit the liver's capacity to "de-toxify" liquor whenever there is a concentration of 20 ppb of organic mercury present. First of all, the alcohol dehydrogenase used in the tests was produced by yeast, not in a human liver – it is a very similar enzyme to that in the human liver, but different in amino acid composition. Furthermore, the mercury concentration of 20 ppb was in a "pure solution," where its effect could be more concentrated and direct than in human tissue.

But even if we divided the results by five, we could still have an inhibiting influence of 50 per cent from a liver mercury concentration of only 50 ppb in humans and a 100 per cent inhibiting effect from mercury levels of 100 ppb – not unusual readings, at White Dog and Grassy Narrows, among those with elevated mercury burdens. And those cautious extrapolations apply if the mercury blocks enzyme action in a simple, linear, arithmetical progression dependent on the amount of mercury present. Tables edited by Webb indicate a much more geometric progress on the effect, an exponential impact in which 10 per cent more mercury, say, has much greater than 10 per cent more inhibitory impact.

Said a research chemist familiar with the Wallenfels/Sund data: "It is *conceivable* that at levels of mercury in the liver not too much higher than 50 – 100 ppb that *many* enzymes, among them alcohol dehydrogenase, could be significantly inhibited [his emphasis]." Not proved? Maybe not. But as another scientist said, "Not safe, either, until we know."

This comment from a worker at the Dryden Chemicals plant, in a tape-recorded research interview: "When we were working in the mercury cell plant, there, when our mercury levels was high, it was funny: we couldn't seem to drink. We'd go to the pub for a couple of beers after work and, first thing you'd know, just on one beer, or two, we'd be drunk. Just on a couple of beers."

APPENDIX EIGHT
LIVING BETTER ELECTRICALLY

General Electric's Canadian subsidiary makes and distributes mainly household appliances, covering a market in which federal import tariffs would make the prices of US-manufactured appliances prohibitive in competition with Canadian products. At its Montreal plant CGE makes automatic clothes washers; machines like those manufactured in GE's American plant in Louisville, but exempt from Canada import taxes and sold only in Canada. All of which leads us to examination of a classic example of the way industrial hazards may find a home in our basements and laundry rooms as well as our water systems or foods.

The following memo was received by the author in the third week of November 1976. It had been written, in 1974, by a senior executive of CGE:

cc: Ivan Feltham
September 10, 1974

A.M. Hurley
Vice President
Government & Public Affairs

Al–
Brian O'Malley, Product Planner, Major Appliance called me yesterday to discuss a possible recall program.

It has been known since November 1973 that 78,000 General Electric automatic washers (including 23,000 Viking models) already in the hands of consumers are potentially hazardous.

The machines have an easily corrected defect that could cause a fire or electrocution.

The only action taken so far has been to alert servicemen from

232

Consumer Products Division and Eaton's. Since November they have located and corrected, during service calls, just 4,000 washers.

The machines can be identified by serial number. The faulty washers were built between August 1972 and November 1973.

Bill Rooney and Francis Moskal [had] has been following the situation very closely. Moskal apparently is the officer who must make the decision to recall the washers, or alert those customers who have one of the 78,000 washers that are hazardous.

After delivering the memo, said its author, there were the following developments:

1) Ivan Fletham, legal counsel for the company then (now vice-president and general counsel), called the memo-writer and suggested it would be very bad for such incidents to become public knowledge. "We discussed the memo; he told me things like this could aid and comfort those people pushing for class action consumer legislation in Canada."

2) A. M. Hurley called the memo's author and invited him to Hurley's office, accompanied by all his own copies of the document. The executive kept back one copy of his memo, and went to Hurley's office with the others.

"Hurley told me to tear the copies up. I refused and pointed out that the situation seemed dangerous and that I could not be a party to tearing up such a document and possibly exposing myself to some liability later for being part of a cover-up. He then asked me to hand the copies to him. I did so. He tore them up and put them in his wastebasket."

3) Some weeks later, no public action having taken place, the executive who had written the memo resigned his job with CGE, "largely over the attitude that was so obvious in this situation."

When the memo reached this writer, in November 1976, it seemed that the hazards, if real, might still exist and that publication of the document ought not, therefore, to await publication of this book, some months later. Accordingly, I made copies of the memo *sans* the name of its author available to the CBC radio magazine program *As It Happens* and to Toronto newspapers. The *As It Happens* production staff called CGE, where startled executives demanded twenty-four hours to consider the allegations before making another of their legal counsel available for an on-air interview. He was a Mr. Fred Webber, and he confirmed all the essential data in the memo, and added some more. Here are some extracts from a transcript of his tape-recorded (and broadcast) responses to questions from program host Barbara Frum:

... That memo doesn't say anything at all that a number of other people high up in this company weren't already aware of for ten months. ...

> Something was done about it. ... We got our service people on top of it immediately and Eaton's service people on top of it immediately. ...

The hazard was created by a combination of two circumstances: a rubber drain hose which conducted electricity and a missing plastic shield over an electric terminal inside CGE's machines.

> We also examined the hazard; there's a possibility – it's not a fire in the sense of a holocaust or anything like that, it's more in the nature of a smouldering. ... We were able to determine, I don't know what the percentages would be, that a significant percentage of these potential fire hazards would go out by themselves and I guess, I'm a bit on weak ground here, Barbara, frankly, but I know we tested because I've got some information here. We can determine right now that you're not going to have a fire in most of those cases, you're simply going to have some smouldering and in most of these cases it's – the thing will go out by itself. There is an extremely small statistical possibility of having a real fire. I think we've heard of, I think, two cases where the fire department had to be called ...

Mr. Webber said the company had checked washers from the production run still in their warehouses and determined that only about 3 per cent of the machines had the plastic shield missing, making a potential total of 2,340 defective machines. This causes some confusion as the company had turned up 4,000 defective washers by the date the memo was written, 10 September 1974. And by Mr. Webber's testimony CGE engineers and experts only anticipated "finding" half of the defective machines through their passive correction program of having service personnel check for missing shields while making service calls for other purposes. Continuing with Mr. Webber's comments:

> We instructed them [Eaton's] and at the same time instructed our own product service people [in November 1973] that when their service people were doing any house calls ... they were to take a plastic shield which we supplied and correct this defect. ... When this problem first arose our engineers did an analysis of the problem and they were able to determine that a very high percentage, which I can't give you, but a very high percentage of the incidents would occur within the first year, and thereafter the problem would disappear. ...
>
> This company's been around since the turn of the century and one thing we have going for us is consumer confidence and we're not going to jeopardize consumer confidence in our products over two dollars times a couple of thousand machines ... We'd be crazy. We're a

three-quarters of a billion dollar outfit. We're not going to jeopardize our consumer confidence over a couple of thousand dollars. I mean, that's stupid.

I can assure you that CGE stands by its reputation.

Mr. Webber didn't know whether CGE would be prepared to release the serial numbers of the hazardous machines. Two days later, prodded by the press, they did so, along with disclosure that they knew of seventeen fires in the machines, reiterating that fire department help had been needed in only two. Assuming, of course, that all the cases of "smouldering" in people's laundry rooms had been traced to the faulty washing machines, and reported to CGE.

Have any homes burned down because of the machines? No one can ever know. Eaton's Department Stores, like CGE, stood silently by their reputation, too.

If you live in Canada and have a potentially hazardous "Viking" or CGE washer, (serial number prefixes: HH, JH, KH, LH, MH, AJ, BJ, CJ, DJ, EJ, FJ, GJ, HJ, JJ, KJ, LJ; suffix numbers following those letters range in sequence from 11,000 through 92,000 – example: KH25798) Eaton's and CGE say they'd like to hear from you. The repair, they announced, after reflection, would be free.

Notes

Chapter 1
[1]"Organic Mercury in the Environment," p. 18.

Chapter 2
[1]As reported by F.T. Matthes, R. Kirschner, M.D. Yow and J.C. Brennan in *Pediatrics*, vol. 22, p. 675, 1958.

Chapter 3
[1]Smith, Eugene and Aileen, *Minamata*, New York, 1975, p. 122.
[2]Kumamoto University Study of Minamata Disease, "Minamata Disease," Kumamoto University, Japan, 1968.
[3]Tests run by Professor Tejning of the University of Kund in Sweden demonstrated that, in five cases, foetal red blood cells, at birth, contained concentrations of methyl mercury averaging levels twenty-eight per cent higher than those in the mother's blood. Another series of tests in Japan showed infant levels at birth to be thirty per cent higher than those of the mother.
[4]*Ibid.*, p. 4. The author is Shigeru Nomura, Professor of Public Health at Kumamotu University.
[5]Such massive atrophy occurs occasionally in non-fetal victims of the disease, but usually the loss of cells is less dramatic. In one fetal case, a child which died at two years of age, the brain weighed 650 grams as compared to a "normal" 960 grams. In a three-year-old victim of congenital Minamata Disease, the brain weighed 630 grams at death. The "normal" weight of a child's brain at the same age is 1,125 grams.

Chapter 4
[1]Most toxicologists now regard 70 days as the "average" half-life. However, there is no data yet on individual differences in victims; it's known both that some individuals have a longer retention period and that some are more sensitive to the poison than others – Japanese data suggests a half-life of 120 days in the brain. Moreover the whole half-life sequence is only "operative" when people at risk stop

236

eating mercury-contaminated fish; a continuing fish diet obviates the benefit of half-life excretion of methyl mercury already in the system.

[2]It was known that small amounts of organic mercury could be "created" from inorganic mercury, via biomethylation, within the body of a fish or animal; but the process was thought to be slow and to involve only a tiny fraction of the body's burden of inorganic mercury, which, anyway, has a very short half-life in the system relative to organic mercury – and so may be excreted before much damage has taken place. However, several scientists suspected that something similar might be possible in water systems; if so, they reasoned, it would occur most efficiently where there was the least oxygen present.

[3]"Minamata Disease: The Outbreak of a Neurological Disorder in Minamata, Japan, and Its Relationship to the Ingestion of Seafood Contaminated by Mercuric Compounds." The three US scientists who wrote the paper were Leonard T. Kurland of the Epidemiology Branch of the National Institute of Neurological Diseases and Blindness, Public Health Service, Bethesda, Maryland; Stanley N. Faro, an epidemiologist with the Communicable Disease Centre; and Howard Siedler, with the Neurological Unit at Boston City Hospital.

[4]Both inorganic mercuric chloride and its cousin, an organic salt called methyl mercury iodide, were long used as fungus-inhibiting agents in treating seeds.

[5]October 1968. The authors were Dr. Carl Rosen, Dr. J.M. Wood, a vitamin researcher at the University of Illinois, and F.S. Kennedy.

[6]The team included: Dr. John T. Allin, Habitat Protection Biologist, Fisheries Branch, Ontario Ministry of Natural Resources; Dr. Fennell F. Archdekin, Special Advisor to the Minister of Health; Dr. John S. Crawford, Ophthalmologist-in-Chief, The Hospital for Sick Children, Toronto; Dr. Henry Landis, QC, General Counsel, Ontario Ministry of the Environment; Dr. Jan Muller, Chief, Environmental Health Studies Service, Community Health Division, Occupational Health Protection Branch, Ministry of Health; Dr. John Stobo Pritchard, Neurologist-in-Chief, Hospital For Sick Children; Mr. Gerard C. Ronan, Director of Laboratory Services Branch, Ontario Ministry of the Environment; Dr. Brian Russell, Chief, Newborn Service, Lake of the Woods Hospital, Kenora; Dr. G. James Stopps, Associate Professor, Department of Preventative Medicine and Biostatics, University of Toronto.

[7]The formal order said:

"considering that Dryden Chemicals Limited owns and operates an industrial enterprise (herein after referred to as the plant) for the production of caustic soda and chlorine at Dryden, Ontario;

"And considering that the electrolytic process of the plant utilizes mercury as an electrode and in a variety of ways the plant releases mercury that is a source of contamination of the environment;

"And considering that the Commission is of the opinion that the arrangements of any industrial establishment for the collection, transmission, treatment or disposal of its sewage are unsatisfactory if mercury is released in any quantity at all to the environment;

"And considering that the Commission, by letter of February 27, 1970, advised

Dryden Chemicals Limited that it must take immediate steps to eliminate any discharge of mercury from the plant to the water environment,

"The Ontario Water Resources Commission ... Hereby requires you, Dryden Chemicals Limited, pursuant to the provisions of Section 50 of the Ontario Water Resources Commission Act, R.S.O. 1960, Chapter 281, as amended,

"(1) ... to assure that all mercury contaminated condensate from hydrogen coolers, not returned to the process, is treated for the removal of mercury;

"(2) ... to provide facilities to ensure that mercury-contaminated brine is not discharged to the environment under any circumstances. ...

"(3) to isolate all floor trenches, drains and sumps, that may receive mercury, with resultant contamination of water, so that the mercury collected therein, or the water contaminated thereby, is treated and/or returned to process;

"(4) to handle all sludges resulting from treatment of brine that may contain mercury so as to eliminate the possibility of the release of mercury to the environment.

"(5) to dispose of any drying agent used to dry chlorine containing mercury, whether such disposal be to waste or to re-use, in such a way that no mercury will be released to the environment."

And there was more: orders for the company to sample and test effluents, to install or construct sewage and effluent treatment facilities as needed (this latter by 1 May 1970) – or later if a requested postponement was agreed to by the Commission on or before April 24 – to maintain, repair and operate clean-up facilities as directed by the Commission.

[8]Mercury is sometimes used in the amalgam process of refining gold and silver; the company suggested mercury in the river may have come from old silver mines – never identified or located geographically. As late as August 1975, President Robert Billingsley of Reed Paper said, "We have data on fish biology throughout the area and recognize a high background level of mercury in this area. There is a high mercury burden in plankton in the Wabigoon upstream from the Dryden mills. We must recognize there is a high background level in this area and that other influences such as mining play a role in high mercury levels. There may always have been high mercury levels in some lakes in the area."

And sixteen days earlier his prepared statement in the Kenora *Miner and News*, 5 August, had said: "Subsequently, it was established that the area has a high background mercury level, the result of natural mineral deposits that release mercury into the environment." A change, at least, from claims about old silver mines. However, insofar as the water systems around the Dryden mill are concerned, the claim is patently untrue.

Fact: In a letter of 9 March 1976, S.M. Irwin, Chief of Survey Programs for the Water Resources Branch of the Ontario Ministry of the Environment, quoted "mercury data in sediments collected upstream and downstream from the Reid [sic] Paper Mill at Dryden for the period 1972 to 1974," and noted following the figures: "As can be seen from this data very little mercury exists naturally in the sediment of Lake Wabigoon and the Wabigoon River upstream from the Reid Paper Mill at Dryden and quite high levels of mercury are found in the sediments downstream from the mill." Mr. Irwin's figures showed "downstream" maximum levels were *780 times higher* than those upstream in 1972; 333.75 times higher in 1973; 273.33 times higher in 1974.

Fact: Government studies in 1970 showed only insignificant mercury levels in crayfish caught immediately above the dam located 800 metres upstream from the mill's effluent pipe. Forty miles downstream crayfish carried very high mercury burdens.

Fact: In samples taken and tested in the years from 1970, there were these differences in sediment separated by only the 800 metres between upstream dam and mill effluent pipe:

In 1975, a sample from below the mill showed 332.4 times as much mercury as a sample from above the dam. (13.3 ppm as contrasted with .04 ppm.)

In 1974 the downstream sediment was 173.4 times as high as the above-dam test. (8.67 v. .05.)

In 1973 the ratio was 305.4 times.

In 1972 there was 227 times more mercury downstream than up.

In 1970 the ratio would have been 832.5 times if the upstream sample had read as high as those of later years; but in 1970 the upstream sediment sample contained so little mercury (that "background mercury burden") that it could not be measured or identified at all. There was, at most, less than one-tenth as much as in samples taken from 1972 onwards – which made the downstream ratio something in the order of 8,000 plus times more mercury in the final year in which Dryden Chemicals operated prior to the order to stop dumping mercury.

[9]Introduction to "Mercury in Water and Sediment of the Wabigoon-English River System," Ontario Ministry of the Environment, 1976, p.i.

Chapter 5

[1]Final Report of the Task Force on Organic Mercury In The Environment, Appendix B, "A report on Mercury in the Environment in the Communities of White Dog and Grassy Narrows: The Dietary Aspects and Problems of Communicating with the Local Populations" by Ignatius E. La Rusic.

[2]Ibid.

[3]Ibid.

Chapter 6

[1]"Alternative Pollution Abatement Policies for the Ontario Pulp and Paper Industry." Report prepared by Ontario's Ministry of the Environment.

[2]In 1968 the Water Resources Commission said: "Dissolved oxygen depletion below the pulp mill was critical to a distance of 39 miles. ... Emission of offensive odours was detected from the surface waters of the Wabigoon River between the point of discharge of the mill effluent and the 27-mile range. ... Surface waters of the entire river below the mill and the eastern portion of Clay Lake [*52 miles downstream*] exhibited a high potential to foam. ... *Pulp wastes were observed to blanket the entire river bottom to a distance of 27 miles below the mill.* Isolated beds of these same wastes were common downstream to the 39-mile range. Visible conditions of the river and its shoreline were aesthetically objectionable down-

stream to the 27-mile range. Surface water discolouration, foaming, bubbling of escaping gases, shoreline litter, sludge-bank formations and floating fibre mats were characteristic of this upper river reach."

[3]According to a 1972 study by the Resource Products Division of the Ontario Department of Lands and Forests.

[4]Over the province of Ontario as a whole, the average annual commercial catches in all the rivers and lakes closed because of mercury pollution totalled 2,789,000 pounds; revenue lost to fishermen closed down by mercury contamination averaged $881,000 per year.

Chapter 8

[1]Internal federal government memo extract from D.B. Dewar, Assistant Deputy Minister of the Medical Services Branch, National Health and Welfare, to Dr. N.J.B. Wiggin, Director General, Research Programs, National Health and Welfare. Federal government file number 850-5-8 (M67), 15 August 1975.

[2]"Mercury Levels in Fish from Northwestern Ontario, 1970-1975," Ontario Water Resources Branch of the Environment Ministry.

[3]*Ibid.*, pp. 60-63

Chapter 9

[1]Jones resigned his directorship of Dryden Chemicals effective 28 June 1974 according to a formal "Notice of Change of Directors" filed under requirements of the Corporations Information Act, 1971, by the company – on 22 July 1974.

[2]Report by Norman Webster in the Toronto *Globe and Mail*, 12 May 1973.

[3]*Ibid.*

Chapter 10

[1]From a press release of speech notes "for release at 12 noon" to the First Northwestern Ontario International Trade Mission at the Royal Edward Hotel, Thunder Bay, Ontario.

[2]5% of Chisso's inorganic mercury *was* methylating inside the factory, but the crucial methylation was always that in Minamata Bay.

[3]The company's 1970 Annual Report states: "Batch treatment commenced April 29, 1970, i.e. all effluent was discharged as batches after that date. Following April 29, 1970, the absence of data for a given day indicates that no batch was discharged that day and hence there was no discharge of contaminated effluent." Here are figures for some of those days – when the company said there was no discharge, but when Ontario's Ministry of the Environment took samples anyway. Those samples, by the company's testimony, should have tested near zero parts per billion of mercury in the water:

30 July 1970:	4,600 ppb
31 July 1970:	6,500 ppb
29 August 1971:	190 ppb
15 August 1973:	116 ppb
28 April 1975:	78 ppb
28 November 1973:	61 ppb

All on days when, according to Dryden Chemicals, samples tested should have shown *no* mercury, because none was "lost" on those dates.

[4]A 1976 Ministry of the Environment study says: "Our data did not show a significant decrease with time in mercury concentrations in sediment in the Wabigoon River from Dryden to Clay Lake [54 miles downstream from the chemical plant and mill] during the period 1970-1975. ... Significant amounts of methyl mercury were found in Wabigoon River sediment. If sediment conditions remain unchanged, continued high levels of methyl mercury can be expected. ... Because of the nature of certain Wabigoon River sediments, it is expected that mercury-enriched sediment is still being transported down the Wabigoon River system."

[5]"Mercury In The Effluents From Chlor-Alkali Plants: Second Survey At Dryden, October, 1975." Appendix III, p. 56.

[6]"Size" is a substance used to give finish or "body" to paper or cloth (such as dress material); in the form of a "semi-glutinous substance" (OED) it gives paper or cloth more substance and makes it easier to imprint colours and patterns.

Chapter 11
[1]"Alternative Pollution Abatement Policies ... The Ontario Pulp and Paper Industry." Report prepared by the Ontario Ministry of the Environment, 1973.

Chapter 12
[1]Letter to Marion Lamm from Claude Desjardins, Correspondence Secretary to the Prime Minister, 7 August 1974.
[2]Letter to Marion Lamm from Claude Desjardins, 12 September 1974.
[3]Letter to Marion Lamm from Irvin Goodleaf, Special Assistant to the Minister of Indian and Northern Affairs, 6 November 1974.
[4]The committee's "Minutes of Proceedings and Evidence," pp. 63:12 and 63:25.
[5]*Ibid.*, pp. 63:28-63:31.

Chapter 13
[1]To: Regional Director,
ONTARIO REGION
From: Zone Director,
THUNDER BAY ZONE
Date: March 15, 1973
Subj.: Mercury Pollution
Grassy Narrows and Whitedog Reserves
Progress Report

I still believe that when this whole issue was opened their motivation was limited to the "juvenile" prospect of compensatory "treats". It is dubious if any of them had seriously considered all the consequences of their actions including the most obvious present political solution of removal of the reserve yet again to a new location. It is less than ten years since they were moved to their present location with its total social and cultural upheaval which is partly responsible for the present problems in this community.

It is understood that the people of these reserves did receive some financial compensation approximately three years ago which may have set a precedent but on the other hand in view of the current information it may be regarded that that was a once forever payment. If the Provincial Government does provide any financial compensation to these communities it would be setting an extremely expensive precedent which will undoubtedly be brought out at regular intervals for every bit of smoke, bad weather or any other adverse factors which may affect the communities in the future.

I will keep you informed of progress.

Dr. Peter J. Connop

[2]Ontario Legislature question by Leo Bernier, legislative member for Kenora constituency, to the Minister of Lands and Forests, 2 November 1970.

[3]Letter from R.M. Connelly, Director, Community Affairs Branch of the federal ministry of Indian and Northern Affairs, to D.A. Davidson, a colleague, and accompanying a report on mercury blood levels in northern Canadian natives, 31 May 1973.

[4]Letter from John Munro, Federal Minister of Health and Welfare, to a fellow MP, 27 September 1971.

Chapter 14

[1]There's little doubt about the lowered fish diet on the reserves during the winter; a few families fish through the ice for an occasional meal, but they are the exceptions. Here are a handful of the replies typed on to the "MERCURY SURVEY" sheets provided by the author. Each box marked "Date Sample Taken" has the answer 30 April 1970. Each reply comes from a reserve resident with a blood level later found to be well over the 20 ppm maximum "normal" level:

"When was the last meal of fish? –LAST FALL
LAST FALL
LAST FALL"

Asked about frequency of fish-eating, here are some of the responses: "EATS FISH MAY TO OCTOBER ABOUT TWICE A WEEK: NO FISH EATEN DURING WINTER"; "EATS FISH NEARLY EVERY DAY IN SUMMER: EATEN FISH FROM OFF-RESERVE ABOUT FIVE TIMES THIS WINTER"; "EATS FISH TWICE A WEEK IN WINTER: FIVE TO SEVEN TIMES A WEEK IN SUMMER."

[2]Letter from John Munro to a fellow MP, 27 September 1971.

[3]The Ontario Law regarding inquests is relatively simple and clear (and available to anyone willing to spend $1.50 for a rather modest, forty-page, blue-covered booklet titled "The Coroners Act, 1972"). As amended in 1974 and by regulatory changes in 1973 and 1975, the Act, Chapter 98 of the Ontario statutes, permits any coroner to call an inquest as well as the Chief Coroner of Ontario or the cabinet minister in charge, the Solicitor General. The mandate is very broad; under Section Nine, subsection "g" of the Act, all deaths must be reported to a coroner "under such circumstances as may require investigation." With regard to the suggestion that pathology samples now being collected by the Ontario Health

Ministry may not be collected in a totally by-the-book manner, Section Ten reads: "No person who has reason to believe that a person died in any of the circumstances mentioned in Section 9 shall interfere with or alter the body or its condition in any way until the coroner so directs by his warrant."

The act goes on to give any "spouse, parent, child, brother, sister, or personal representative of the deceased person" the right to request an inquest, the right of a reply in writing and the right of appeal if the inquest is denied. The Act also, in Section 23, notes that, "A coroner may at any time during an investigation or inquest issue his warrant for a post mortem examination."

As for the Chief Coroner, (Section 21(1)), "The chief Coroner may direct the coroner having jurisdiction in respect of any death to issue a warrant to take possession of the body, conduct an investigation or hold an inquest, or may direct any other coroner to do so or may intervene to act as coroner personally for any one or more of such purposes."

And the Solicitor General is covered too, in Section 19: "Where the Minister has reason to believe that a death has occurred in Ontario in circumstances that warrant the holding of an inquest, he may direct any coroner to hold an inquest ... "

As for the recommendation of the Thomas Strong jury that all reserve deaths involving people who might have high mercury levels become coroner's cases, the Coroners Act, Section 4, subsection "d": " ... Chief Coroner for Ontario ... shall, (d) bring the findings and recommendations of coroners' juries to the attention of appropriate persons, agencies and ministries of government."

4"Organic Mercury in the Environment," National Health and Welfare, p. 10.
5See "Review of the Physiological Impact of Mercurials," Office of Research and Development of the US EPA, 1974.

Chapter 15

1"Exposure to Methyl Mercury in Grassy Narrows and White Dog Reserves — An Interim Report."
2*Bulletin of the Institute of Constitutional Medicine*, pp. 169-193. Their paper was also presented at the International Congress of Scientists on the Human Environment at Kyoto, Japan, 20 November 1975.

Chapter 16

1"Study of the Medical Toxicological Effects of Organic Mercury in Northwest Quebec." Quotations from pp. 121, 139 and 170 respectively.
2Barbeau, *op. cit.*, p. 178.

Chapter 17

1Report EPS 5-AP-73, "Ambient Air Levels of Mercury in the Vicinity of Chlor-Alkali Plants," prepared by M.J. Bumbaco, J.H. Shelton and D.A. Williams for the Surveillance Division, Air Pollution Programs Branch.

Chapter 18

1In the Louisiana survey, cancer mortality figures ranged from 10% to 20% higher among populations drinking municipally treated Mississippi River water than among those in communities relying on well water in the northern parts of the state.

In a report published in *Science* on 2 July 1976 (Volume 103, No. 4247) Dr. Harris and his colleagues from Case Western Reserve University and Resources for the Future, Inc. state: " ... analysis indicates a statistically significant relation between cancer mortality rates in Louisiana and drinking water obtained from the Mississippi River. This is true for total cancer, cancer of the urinary organs, and cancer of the gastrointestinal tract ... this ... study supports the hypothesis that there is a link between carcinogens in drinking water and cancer mortality."

[2]Five years after DDT was banned in the Great Lakes area some fish were still testing at DDT levels too high for safe human consumption. In the spring of 1976, trout were sampled from the western portion of Lake Superior. In a study coordinated by the US Federal Department of Agriculture, the Federal Bureau of Fisheries and Wildlife and the Michigan State Departments of Natural Resources, Public Health and Agriculture, 38 per cent of all sampled fish were found to contain over-the-limits DDT levels.

[3]The US National Cancer Institute of Bethesda, Maryland, reported on experimental studies with rats and mice on 1 March 1976. In the rat subjects " ... a decrease in survival rate ... was evident for all tested groups" (groups given chloroform). Among the "control" rats given none of the carcinogen, there were no kidney tumors – 8 per cent of those on a low dosage of chloroform developed the tumors however, as did 24 per cent of those getting a higher dose. Among the mice, 98 per cent of males and 95 per cent of females on the "high dose" developed cancer of the liver, as did 36 and 80 per cent of those on a low dosage of chloroform; the "control" animals had no cancer.

[4]G.R. Harvey of the Woods Hole Oceanographic Institute says there's a dramatic drop in PCB levels in the mid-Atlantic, evidently because the highly volatile compounds are evaporated as they move away from shore and blown to colder climates where they fall with natural precipitation.

[5]Each participating company holds two shares and has two representatives on the board of directors; the four remaining shares are held by the remaining board members. In 1976 these men were the Deputy Minister of Natural Resources, his Assistant Deputy Minister, a retired Deputy Minister, and the corporation's president, Byron Flieger.

[6]*The Lancet*, 6 July 1974. Briefly stated, the study involved applying liquid topically (it was "painted on") to mice; the "control" group were "painted" with corn oil; others were treated with Fenitrothion in one case, with DDT alone in another group, and with a combination of Fenitrothion and DDT in a third. All the mice were then injected with a sub-lethal dose of virus infection.

The virus did not kill any of the mice in the control group.

In groups of mice treated with DDT alone, up to 17 per cent died within 10 days.

In mice treated with Fenitrothion alone, up to 9 per cent died.

In mice treated with both pesticides, up to 60 per cent died.

And the mice died, not with the common symptoms of the virus with which they'd been infected, a normally "harmless" virus dose which should have induced only mild illness, but with paralysis, convulsions and, in post mortem examination, degeneration and fatty changes in the liver.

[7] "Measurement of concentrations of Fenitrothion in forest products has not reinforced the disintegration-time found in the laboratory but has shown a much longer persistence of the chemical. Yule has reported that Fenitrothion is retained in its pure state in trees much longer than in its free state. Francis and Barnes, in their studies of mammalian toxicity, note the "very prolonged effect from a single dose" of Fenitrothion ... suggesting that a large part of the compound must be stored soon after administering and then slowly released ... "

[8] Originally published in the *Bulletin of Environmental Contaminants Toxicology*.

[9] In 1974 a lab technician working with Dr. Crocker became acutely ill with symptoms of Fenitrothion poisoning. She had been exposed by a vial of the poison in her car, containing less than two ounces, which had leaked. She was hospitalized, treated with a specific antidote and evidently recovered. In 1975, while on a self-imposed diet, the woman experienced a resurgence of the symptoms (as her body, during the diet, began drawing on reserves of fat). Then in November 1976 she was hospitalized for surgery. Following the operation the symptoms of Fenitrothion poisoning recurred and, again, had to be treated with the specific antidote. (This while, in the post-operative recovery period, the woman was on intravenous feedings which, again, required her body to draw on stored reserves of fatty tissue.) Said Dr. Earl Reid, her physician, when interviewed for the CBC network TV program, *Ombudsman*:

> ... We've been told that Fenitrothion was not cumulative in the tissues – but the technician's behaviour would suggest that it is stored in the tissues. One has to look at the tissues that have a relatively slow turnover – and this primarily is fat tissue ... Now the implication ... would be that if, in the human population, they're exposed ... repeatedly to smaller doses that this may have a cumulative effect and [be] stored in fat tissues and released over a period of time where, in an acute illness or something of this sort they could get ... the symptoms. And we really don't know for instance what would happen to dairy herds if they happened to be sprayed and stored Fenitrothion in their fat tissues; then during the winter of course when they're not eating green grass and, rather, are on hay, and grain supplements ... with any weight loss they could also have Fenitrothion released in their milk.

Bibliography

TECHNICAL PAPERS

Allan, R.J., E.M. Cameron & I.R. Jonnasson.
"Mercury and Arsenic Levels in Lake Sediments from the Canadian Shield,"
Geological Survey of Canada, Ottawa, Canada.

All Japan Committee of Members of the Legal Profession Against Pollution.
*"Environmental Pollution and Role of Jurists in Japan."*1975.

Amin-Zaki, L., S. Elhassani & M.A. Majeed, University of Baghdad, Baghdad, Iraq,
& T.W. Clarkson, R.A. Doherty & M.R. Greenwood, University of Rochester,
Rochester, NY, USA.
"Prenatal Methylmercury Poisoning in Iraq."

Annett, C.S., M.P. Fadow, F.M. D'Itri & M.E. Stephenson, Michigan State
University of Agriculture and Applied Science, East Lansing, Mich., USA.
"Mercury Pollution and Lake Erie Fishes."

Armstrong, F.A.J., & A.L. Hamilton, Fisheries Research Board of Canada, Freshwater Institute, Winnipeg, Man., Canada.
"Pathways of Mercury in a Polluted Northwestern Ontario Lake."

Azzaria, L.M., Assoc. Prof., Dept. of Geology & Minerology, & Fathi Habashi, Prof.,
Dept. of Mines & Metals, Laval University, Laval, Quebec, Canada.
"Mercury Pollution – An Examination of Some Basic Issues."

Baker, Robert A., Director, Environmental Sciences, Teledyne Brown Engineering,
Research Park, Huntsville, Ala., & Ming-Dean Luh, Fellow, Carnegie-Mellon
University, Mellon Institute, Pittsburgh, Pa., USA.
"Mercury Analyses and Toxicity: A Review."

Berlin, Maths, MD, Crawford A. Grant, DVM, Jan Hellberg, Jonas Hellstrom,
Andrejs Schutz, from respectively: Dept. of Environmental Health, University of
Lund, Sweden; Dept. of Pathology, Karolinska Hospital, Stockholm; Dept. of
Psychology, University of Lund, Sweden; Dept. of Occupational Medicine, University
Hospital, Lund, Sweden.
"Neurotoxicity of Methylmercury in Squirrel Monkeys."

246

Brinck, J.W. & L. Van Wambeke, Commission Communautés Européennes Bruxelles, Belgium.
"World Resources of Mercury."

Burrows, W.D., K.I. Taimi, P.A. Krenkel, Associated Water and Air Resources Eng. Inc., Nashville, Tenn. & Tennessee Valley Authority, Chattanooga, Tenn., USA.
"The Uptake & Loss of Methylmercury by Freshwater Fish."

Charbonneau, S.M., I.E. Munro, E.A. Nera, R.F. Willes, T. Kuiper-Goodman, F. Iverson, C.A. Moodie, D.R. Stoltz, F.A.J. Armstrong, J.F. Uthe & H.C. Grice, Food Research Laboratories, Dept. of National Health & Welfare, Ottawa, Canada.
"Subacute Toxicity of Methylmercury in the Adult Cat."

Clarkson, T.W., J. Crispin Smith, D.O. Marsh & M.D. Turner, University of Rochester School of Medicine and Dentistry, Rochester, NY, USA.
"A Review of Dose-Response Relationships Resulting from Human Exposure to Methylmercury Compounds."

Clarkson, T.W. & David O. Marsh, University of Rochester School of Medicine and Dentistry, Rochester, NY, USA.
"The Toxicity of Methylmercury in Man: Dose-Response Relationships in Adult Populations."

Clarkson, T.W., University of Rochester School of Medicine and Dentistry, Rochester, NY, USA.
"Recent Advances in the Toxicology of Mercury with Emphasis on the Alkylmercurials."

Cooke, N.E. & A. Beitel, Engineering, Canadian Industries, Ltd.
"Some Aspects of Other Sources of Mercury to the Environment."

Cranston, Raymond E., & Dale E. Buckley, Marine Geology, Atlantic Geoscience Centre, Bedford Institute, Dartmouth, NS, Canada.
"Mercury Pathways in a River and Estuary."

Crocker, J.F.S., K.R. Rozee, R.L. Ozere, S.C. Digout & D. Hutzinger, Dalhousie University, Halifax, NS, Canada.
"Insecticide and Viral Interaction as a Cause of Fatty Visceral Changes and Encephalopathy in the Mouse."

Dennis, C.A.R., & F. Fehr, Prairie Institute of Environmental Health, Regina, Sask., Canada.
"Mercury Levels in Whole Blood of Saskatchewan Residents."
"The Relationship between Mercury Levels in Maternal and Cord Blood."

D'Itri, Frank M., Assoc. Prof., Dept. of Fisheries & Wildlife, Michigan State University, East Lansing, Mich., USA.
"The Politics of Methylmercury Poisoning (A Formal Discussion of the Distribution of Mercury in Fish and its Form of Occurrence, by Jun Ui and Rikuo Doi)." Dec. 1973.

D'Itri, Frank M., Charles S. Annett & Ario W. Fast, Michigan State University, East Lansing, Mich., USA.
"Comparison of Mercury Levels in an Oligotrophic and a Eutrophic Lake."

D'Itri, Frank M., Charles S. Annett, J.R. Ford & H.H. Prince, Michigan State University, East Lansing, Mich., USA.
  "Mercury in Fish and Waterfowl from Ball Lake, Ontario."

Emerson, D.G., CBE.
  "The Industrial Uses of Mercury."

Eyl, Thomas B., MD, St. Clair, Michigan.
  "Methyl Mercury Poisoning in Fish and Human Beings," Clinical Toxicology, June 1971.

Federation of Ontario Naturalists.
  "Summary re Strategic Land Use Programme," Jan. 1975.

Fehr, Florence, & C.A.R. Dennis, Prairie Institute of Environmental Health, Regina, Sask., Canada.
  "The Use and Health Hazard of Mercury in Saskatchewan." June 1975.

Ferens, Catherine M., University of Georgia, Athens, Georgia, USA.
  "A Review of the Physiological Impact of Mercurials prepared for Office of Research and Development, US Environmental Protection Agency, Washington, DC."

Fimreite, Norvald, Dept. of Zoology, University of Western Ontario, London, Ontario, Canada.
  "Mercury Uses in Canada and their Possible Hazards as Sources of Mercury Contamination." 1970.

Fimreite, Norvald, W.N. Holsworth, J.A. Keith, P.A. Pearce & I.M. Gruchy.
  "Mercury in Fish and Fish-eating Birds near Sites of Industrial Contamination in Canada." (Reprinted in Canada from the *Canadian Field-Naturalist*, July-Sept. 1971, Vol. 85. No. 3.)

Fimreite, Norvald, & Lincoln M. Reynolds, from respectively: University of Tromso, Tromso, Norway & Ontario Research Foundation, Sheridan Park, Ont., Canada.
  "Mercury Contamination of Fish in Northwestern Ontario," Journal of Wildlife Management 37 (1) 1973.

Fimreite, Norvald, University of Tromso, Tromso, Norway.
  "Mercury Contamination of Aquatic Birds in Northwestern Ontario." 1973.

Friberg, Lars, Karolinska Institute, Stockholm, Sweden.
  "Mercury in the Environment. A Toxicological and Epidemiological Appraisal," Nov. 1971.

Fyfe, R.W., J. Campbell, B. Hayson & K. Hodson, Canadian Wildlife Service, Edmonton, Alberta, Canada.
  "Regional Population Declines and Organochlorine Insecticides in Canadian Prairie Falcons." 1969.

Fyfe, R.W., Canadian Wildlife Service, Edmonton, Alberta, Canada.
  "Pesticide – Wildlife Problems in Canada."

George, J.G., Dept. of Energy, Mines & Resources, Ottawa, Canada.
  "Mercury." 1973.

Ghosh, Mriganka M., & Paul D. Zugger, Dept. of Civil Engineering, University of Maine, Orono, Maine, USA.
  "Toxic Effects of Mercury on the Activated Sludge Process."

Giovanoli-Jakubczak, Teresa, Michael R. Greenwood, J. Crispin Smith & T.W. Clarkson, from respectively: Medical Academy, Warsaw, Poland and University of Rochester, Rochester, NY, USA.
  "Determination of Total and Inorganic Mercury in Hair by Flameless Atomic Absorption, and of Methylmercury by Gas Chrometography." 1974.

Goldwater, Leonard J., Duke University, Durham, N. Carolina, USA.
  "Biological Effects of Mercury in the Environment."
  "Standards and Regulations for the Control of Mercury in the Environment."

Harada, Masazumi, Tadashi Fujino, Taketoshi Akagi & Susumu Nishigaki, from respectively: Dept. of Neuropsychiatry, Inst. of Constitutional Medicine, Kumamoto University; Dept. of Physiology, School of Medicine, Kumamoto University; Dept. of Environmental Medicine, Tokyo Metropolitan Research Laboratory of Public Health.
  "Epidemiological and Clinical Study and Historical Background of Mercury Pollution on Indian Reservations in Northwestern Ontario, Canada."

Hunter, Donald & Dorothy S. Russell, Dept. for Research in Industrial Medicine (MRC) and The Bernhard Baron Institute of Pathology, The London Hospital, London, England.
  "Focal Cerebral and Cerebellar Atrophy in a Human Subject due to Organic Mercury Compounds," Journal of Neurology, Neurosurgery & Psychiatry, 1954.

Iijima, Nobuko, Dept. of Health Sociology, School of Health Sciences, Faculty of Medicine, University of Tokyo, Japan.
  "Life of Canadian Indians and the Influence of Mercury Poisoning on It." Nov. 1975.

International Joint Commission, Great Lakes Water Quality Board.
  "Toxic and Hazardous Polluting Substances, 1975 Annual Report."
  "Asbestos in the Great Lakes Basin, with emphasis on Lake Superior." Feb. 1975.

Irukayama, Katsuro, Dept. of Hygiene, Kumamoto University Medical School, Kumamoto, Japan.
  "Source of the Organomercury Compound in the Fish and Shellfish from Minimata Bay."

Jackson, N.H., BSc, A.I.M. Anglo-American Research Laboratories, Johannesburg, South Africa.
  "Mercury in the Gold Mining Industry."

Jensen, S. & A. Jernelov, Institute of Analytical Chemistry, University of Stockholm, & Swedish Water and Air Pollution Research Laboratory, Stockholm, Sweden.
  "Biological Methylation of Mercury in Aquatic Organisms," 1969.

Katz, Arthur, Massachusetts Institute of Technology Laboratory for Nuclear Science, Cambridge, Mass., USA.

"Mercury Pollution: The Making of an Environmental Crisis." (Critical Reviews in Environmental Control, 1972, vol. 2, Issue 4).

Krenkel, P.A., Dept. of Environmental and Water Resources Engineering, Vanderbilt University, Nashville, Tenn., USA.
"Mercury: Environmental Considerations" (Critical Reviews in Environmental Control, 1973, vol. 3, Issue 3).

Kurland, Leonard T., Stanley N. Faro & Howard Siedler, Epidemiology Branch, National Institute of Neurological Diseases and Blindness, Public Health Service, Bethesda, Md, USA.
"Minamata Disease. The Outbreak of a Neurologic Disorder in Minamata, Japan, and Its Relationship to the Ingestion of Seafood Contaminated by Mercuric Compounds." 1960.

Lambou, Victor W.
"Hazards of Mercury in the Environment with Special Reference to the Aquatic Habitat."

Lander, Lars, Swedish Water and Air Pollution Research Laboratory, Institutet for Vatten– Och Luftvardsforskning, Stockholm, Sweden.
"Restoration of Mercury Contaminated Lakes and Rivers, 1970."

Langley, D.G., Laboratory Division, T.W. BEAK CONSULTANTS LTD., Toronto, Ont., Canada.
"Mercury Methylation in an Aquatic Environment. Journal WPCF (Jan. 1973).

Lin, F.M. & C. Romero-Sierra, Queen's University, Kingston, Ont., Canada.
"Non-addiction Alcohol (sake) Drinking Effects on Acute Methylmercury Chloride Toxicity."

Lovejoy, H.B., P.P.G. Industries, Lake Charles, Los Angeles, USA.
"The Correlation of Mercury Exposure Evaluations with Human Urine Mercury Excretion."

Maghazaji, H.I., Dept. of Medicine Medical College, Baghdad University, Baghdad, Iraq.
"Psychiatric Aspects of Methylmercury Poisoning," Journal of Neurology, Neurosurgery & Psychiatry, 1974.

Marsh, D.O., M.D. Turner, J. Crispin Smith, J. Wun Choi & T.W. Clarkson, University of Rochester, Rochester, NY, USA.
"Methyl Mercury (MeHg) in Human Populations Eating Large Quantities of Marine Fish. 2. American Samoa; Cannery workers & fishermen."

McGill University, Montreal, Quebec, Canada.
"Environmental Aspects of the Pulp and Paper Industry in Quebec" (ed. Fikret Berkes, Bruce Ott, Michael J.A. Butler & William A. Ross).

Mee, J.M.L. & C.C. Brooks, University of Hawaii, Honolulu, Hawaii.
"Mercury Contamination in Hawaii Molasses, Feedstuffs and Selected Fish."

Mercury Pollution Action Group of British Columbia.
"Mercury & Our Environment: A General Survey of the Environmental Impact

of Mercury." Presented on the occasion of the United Nations Conference on Human Settlements, June 1976.

Merten, D. & G. Wortley, International Atomic Energy Association.
"Report on an 'Expert Meeting on Mercury Contamination in Man and His Environment,' " Amsterdam, 13 May 1967. (Distributed by the World Health Organization to all Departments of Health).

Minnesota, State of Minnesota, Department of Natural Resources Division of Game & Fish.
"Mercury Levels in Minnesota Fish, 1970-71."

Mukai, S. & Y. Nakahiro, Dept. of Mineral Science and Technology, University of Kyoto, Japan.
"Study on the Removal of Inorganic and Organic Mercury in Waste Water by the Flotation Method."

Munro, I.C., S.M. Charbonneau & W.P. McKinley, Dept. of Health & Welfare, Ottawa, Canada.
"Studies on the Toxicity of Methyl Mercury." 1973.

Novak, Milton, Troy Chemical Corporation.
"The Nature of Toxicity and Hazards of Mercury Compounds." Paper presented before the New Jersey Academy of Science, April 1971.

Olotka, Fred T., Environmental Control, Hooker Chemical Corporation, Niagara Falls, NY, USA.
"Can Mercury Cell Plants Continue to Comply With New Mercury Pollution Regulations?"

Olszewski, Walter A., K.K. Sivasankara Pillay, Chester A. Glomski & Harold Brody, Buffalo General Hospital and State University of New York at Buffalo, NY, USA.
"Mercury in the Human Brain."

Organization for Economic Co-operation and Development, Environment Directorate.
"Polychlorinated Biphenyls, Their Use and Control." Paris, 1973.

Ramel, Claes., University of Stockholm Wallenberg Laboratory, Lilla-Frescati S-10405 Stockholm 50, Sweden.
"The Mercury Problem – A Trigger for Environmental Pollution Control."

Reimers, Robert S., W. Dickinson Burrows, & Peter Krenkel, Dept. of Environmental and Water Resources Engineering, Vanderbilt University, Nashville, Tenn., USA.
"Total Mercury Analysis: Review and Critique," Journal of Water Pollution Control Federation 45 (5) 814-828, May 1973.

Rekers, C.J.N. & G.J. Jong, Akzo Chemie, Hengelo, Holland.
"The Akzo Process for Removal of Mercury from Waste Water."

Romero-Sierra C. & F.M. Lin, Queen's University, Kingston, Ont., Canada.
"The Influence of Ethanol on the Acute Toxicity of Methylmercury."

Rustam, Hussain, MD, Rudolph Von Burg, PhD, Laman Amin-Zaki, MD, Sami El

Hassani, MD, College of Medicine, University of Baghdad, Iraq. (Dr. Rudolph Vonburg, University of Rochester, Rochester, NY, USA.)
  "*Evidence for a Neuromuscular Disorder in Methylmercury Poisoning,*" *Environmental Health*, American Medical Assoc., 1975, Vol. 30.

Shephard, David A.E., FRCP.
  Mercury Article, *Canadian Medical Association Journal*, 6 March 1976, Vol. 114, 463-472.

Stopps, Gordon J., Mary E. Maxfield, Martha McLaughlin, Haskell Laboratory for Toxicology and Industrial Medicine, and Sidney Pell, Medical Division, E.I. du Pont de Nemours & Co. (Inc.) Wilmington, Delaware, USA.
  "*Lead Research: Current Medical Developments,*" Paper presented at 31st Annual Meeting of the Industrial Hygiene Foundation, Pittsburgh, Pa., USA, 18-19 Oct., 1966.

Suzuki, Tsuguyoshi, Tomoyo Miyama & Haruo Katsunuma, Dept. of Human Ecology, School of Health Sciences, Faculty of Medicine and Dept. of Public Health, Faculty of Medicine, University of Tokyo, Hongo, Bunkyo-Ku, Tokyo, Japan.
  "*Mercury Contents in the Red Cells, Plasma, Urine and Hair from Workers Exposed to Mercury Vapour.*" *Industrial Health,* 1970.

Takeuchi, T., F.M. d'Itri, P.V. Fischer, C.S. Annett, & M. Okabe from respectively, Kumamoto University, Kumamoto, Japan; Michigan State University, East Lansing, Mich., USA; 2 Indian Valley Crescent, Toronto, Ont.; Michigan State University, Mich., USA; Kumamoto University, Kumamoto, Japan.
  "*The Outbreak of Minimata Disease (Methyl Mercury Poisoning) in Cats on Northwestern Ontario Reserves.*" (Correspondence to be sent to D'Itri.)

Thaxton, J.P., Dept. of Poultry Science, N. Carolina State University, USA.
  "*Diminution of Resistance of Mercury-treated Chickens to Elevated Environmental Temperature.*"

Thaxton, J.P., Dept. of Poultry Science, N. Carolina State University, USA.
  "*Reproductive Dysfunction and Abnormal Mating Behavior of Japanese Quail as caused by Mercury.*"

Tomlinson, G.H., Domtar.
  "*The Problem of Mercury in Fish and Man in Northwestern Quebec,*" Oct. 1975.

Torrie, Jill, Mercury Project Staff, National Indian Brotherhood, Kenora, Ont., Canada.
  "*The Human Mercury-Level Monitoring Programme: A Critical Review of Five Years of Testing on the Grassy Narrows and Whitedog Indian Reserves.*" Presented to the Standing Committee on Mercury in the Environment, Ottawa, 23 July 1975.

Trakhtenberg, I.M. (translated from Russian by the Geographic Health Studies Program of the John E. Fogarty International Centre for Advanced Study in the Health Sciences, 1974.
  "*Chronic Effects of Mercury on Organisms.*" U.S. Dept. of Health, Education &

Welfare Public Health Service, National Institutes of Health, DHEW Publication No. (NIH) 74-473.

Turner, M.D., D.O. Marsh, C.E. Rubio, J. Chiriboga, C. Collazos Chiriboga, J. Crispin Smith & T.W. Clarkson.
"Methyl Mercury in Population Eating Large Quantities of Marine Fish."

Ui, Jun, University of Tokyo, Dept. of Urban Engineering, Shoji Kitamura, University of Kobe, Dept. of Public Health.
"Mercury Pollution of Sea and Fresh Water. Its Accumulation into Water Biomass." Presented to 4th Colloquium for Medical Oceanography, Naples, 2-5 Oct. 1969.

Uthe, J.F., Freshwater Inst., Winnipeg, Man., Canada, F.M. Atton & L.M. Royer, Saskatchewan Fisheries Laboratory, Dept. of Tourism and Renewable Resources, Sask., Canada.
"Uptake of Mercury by Caged Rainbow Trout (Salmo Gairdneri) in the South Saskatchewan River, 1973."

Vermeer, K., Canadian Wildlife Service, Edmonton, Alberta; Canada; F.A.J. Armstrong, Fisheries Research Board of Canada, Winnipeg, Man.; D.R.M. Hatch, Oak Lake, Manitoba, Canada.
"Mercury in Aquatic Birds at Clay Lake, Western Ontario." Journal of Wildlife Management, 37 (1), 1973.

Von Burg, R., F. Farris & J.C. Smith, Dept. of Pharmacology and Toxicology, University of Rochester School of Medicine and Dentistry, Rochester, NY, USA.
"Determination of Methylmercury in Blood by Gas Chromatography." Journal of Chromatography, 97 (1974) 65-70.

Vostal, J.J., MD, PhD & T.W. Clarkson, PhD, University of Rochester, Rochester, NY, USA.
"Mercury as an Environmental Hazard." Journal of Occupational Medicine, August 1973, vol. 15, no. 8, 649-656.

Webb, J. Leyden, School of Medicine, University of S. California, Los Angeles, Cal., USA.
"Enzyme and Metabolic Inhibitors." Academic Press, New York, vol. 2, 1966.

Yusho, Kanemi, Japan.
"PCB Disease."

BOOKS AND MAGAZINES

Bauer, Erwin A., "Witness To Outrage," *Sports Afield*, Nov. 1970, vol. 164, no. 5.

Carter, Luther J., "Michigan's PBB Incident: Chemical Mixup Leads To Disaster," *Science*, 16 April 1976, vol. 192, pp. 240-43.

Commission Of The European Communities, "Problems of the Contamination of Man and his Environment by Mercury and Cadmium," Luxembourg, 3-5 July 1973.

CRC Press (A Division of the Chemical Rubber Co., Cleveland, Ohio) "Mercury in the Environment," 1972, vol. 2.

Dunlap, Lloyd, "Mercury: Anatomy of a Pollution Problem," *Chemical & Engineering News*, 5 July 1971.

Goldwater, Leonard J., *Mercury, A History of Quicksilver,* York Press, 1972.

Holmes, Jay, "Mercury Is Heavier Than You Think," *Esquire*, May 1971.

Kahn, Ephraim, MD, "A No-Nonsense Report On Mercury In Fish," *Redbook*, May 1971, vol. 137, no. 1.

Knap, Jerome J., "Mercury Poisoning (or) The Fish You Catch Can Kill You," *Field and Stream*, July 1970.

Krehl, Willard A., MD, PhD, "Mercury, The Slippery Metal," *Nutrition Today*, Nov./Dec. 1972, vol. 7, no. 6.

Kumamoto University Study Group of Minamata Disease, "Minamata Disease," Kumamoto University, Japan, 1968.

Metals Week, "The Realities Of Mercury Pollution," *Metals Week*, 18 Jan. 1971.

Montague, Katherine and Peter, *Mercury,* Sierra Club Battlebook, 1971.

National Institute of Public Health, Stockholm, Sweden, "Methyl Mercury In Fish," Suppl. 4, Stockholm, 1971.

Ontario Economic Council, Northern Ontario Development, "Issues And Alternatives," 1976.

Organization for Economic Co-operation and Development, "Mercury and the Environment," Paris, 1974.

Putnam, John J., "Quicksilver And Slow Death," *National Geographic*, Oct. 1972, vol. 142, no. 4.

Royal Society Of Canada, "Mercury in Man's Environment," Proceedings of the Symposium, 15-16 February 1971.

Smith, Eugene and Aileen, *Minamata*, Holt, Rinehart and Winston, New York, 1975.

Van Coevering, Jack, "The Truth About Mercury," *Field and Stream*, May 1971, vol. 76, no. 1.

GOVERNMENT REPORTS
PROVINCIAL
Ministry of the Environment – Ontario

Air Quality Dryden – Annual Report 1975, Pub. 1976, (H.D. Griffin, Chief, Air Quality Assessment).

Alternative Policies for Pollution Abatement ... The Ontario Pulp and Paper Industry – 1974 Draft For Discussion, (Dr. J. Donnan & Dr. P. Victor).

Ibid. Appendices.

Ibid. Summary Report.

Ibid. Summary and Update.

Environmental Protection Act, 1971.

The Environmental Assessment Act, 1975.

Inventory of Research Projects, 1975-6, AR-3.

Mercury in Sediment and Water in the Wabigoon-English River System, 1970-1975, June 1976 (J.W. Parks).

Mercury in the Effluents from Chlor-Alkali Plants: First Survey at Dryden, July 1975, Pub. August 1975.

Mercury in the Effluents from Chlor-Alkali Plants: Second Survey at Dryden, October 1975, Pub. Feb. 1976.

Mercury Levels in Fish from Northwestern Ontario, 1970-1975, Pub. April 1976, (J.N. Bishop & B.P. Neary).

Ontario Water Resources Commission – Status of Mercury Pollution in Northwestern Ontario, 11 Aug. 1970.

Ontario Water Resources Commission – Water Pollution Survey of the Wabigoon River 1969, (M.J. German).

Ontario Water Resources Commission – Water Use Study, Wabigoon River Below Dryden, 1970.

Ministry of Natural Resources

Guidelines for Land Use Planning (revised edition), 1 Jan. 1974.

Impact of Mercury Contamination on the Ontario Commercial Fishery, Jan. 1972, (G.F. Adams).

Interim Report Analysis of Northwestern Ontario Inland Commercial Fishery, Report prepared by Ontario Research Foundation for Ministry of Natural Resources, Dec. 1971, (A.T. Wren).

Strategic Land Use Plan – Background Information and Approach to Policy, Northwestern Ontario, Sept. 1974.

Ministry of Health

Government of Ontario Task Force Report on Mercury, 1973.

Mercury Poisoning in Iraq and Japan – A Report Of A Team Sent By Ontario Ministry Of Health, Nov./Dec. 1975.

The Public Health Significance Of Methyl Mercury, Feb. 1972. Released 8 Nov. 1974.

GOVERNMENT OF CANADA

Environment Canada

Ambient Air Levels Of Mercury In The Vicinity Of Selected Chlor-alkali Plants (Surveillance Report EPS 5-AP-73-12), July 1973.

An Investigation into the Source and Distribution of Mercury in the Environment In Northwestern Quebec, May 1972.

Le Mercure dans le Nord-Ouest Quebécois (Situation Actuelle et Recommandations) 1976.

Mercury in Canadian Fish and Wildlife Used in the Diets of Native Peoples, No. 35, Canadian Wildlife Service (P. Desai-Greenaway & I.M. Price).

Mercury Levels in the Rivers of Western Canada 1970-1976 (Social Science Series No. 16), Water Quality Branch.

National Inventory of Sources and Emissions of Asbestos, Beryllium, Lead and Mercury, EPS 3-AP-74-1, Jan. 1974.

National Inventory of Sources and Emissions of Mercury 1970 (by James F. MacLaren Ltd., Environmental Consultants, Ontario).

Review of Environmental Control of Mercury in Japan – Water Pollution Control Directorate, Aug. 1976.

National Health & Welfare

Background to the Regulation of Polychlorinated Biphenyls (PCB) in Canada – A Report of the Task Force on PCB, April 1 1976 to the Environmental Contaminants Committee of Environment Canada and Health and Welfare Canada.

Epidemiological Study on Effects of Mercury Pollution on Health on Grassy Narrows and White Dog Reserves, Non-Technical Description (Brian Wheatley, Senior Staff Medical Officer, Medical Services Branch).

Occupational Health Review, vol. 15, no. 2

Occupational Health Review, vol. 15, no. 3

Exposure to Methyl Mercury in Grassy Narrows and White Dog Reserves – An Interim Report (T.W. Clarkson).

"The Potential Hazards of Mercury in Fish," (D.G. Chapman), Health Protection Branch.

A Report on Mercury in the Environment in the Communities of White Dog and Grassy Narrows: The Dietary Aspects and Problems of Communicating with the Local Population, 31 July 1973, (Ignatius E. La Rusic).

The Significance of Reports of Mercury in Various Body Tissues in the Perspective of Studies in Various Canadian Populations (Aaron D. Bernstein, MD, FRCP).

Task Force Report on Organic Mercury in the Environment – Grassy Narrows & White Dog, Ontario, Final Report.

Fisheries & Forestry

"Environmental Factors Affecting the Utilization of Great Lakes Fish as Human Food," (E.G. Bligh), Fisheries Research Board of Canada.

"Marine Mercury Pollution In Canada," (E.G. Bligh and F.A.J. Armstrong), Fisheries Research Board Of Canada.

"Mercury in the Aquatic Environment: A Summary of Research carried out by the

Freshwater Institute 1970-1971," (ed. J.F. Uthe) – Fisheries Research Board of Canada Manuscript Report Series No. 1167.

"Mercury Pollution," (E.R. Hearnden), *Fisheries Of Canada*, May-June 1970, vol. 22, no. 1.

Miscellaneous

"A Clear and Present Danger," transcripts of the CBC radio broadcasts of 6 and 7 Nov. 1974, in the series *As It Happens.*

"Environmental Danger of Mercury Contamination," prepared for communication to Mr. Richard Phaneuf, National Indian Brotherhood by Donald R. Miller, National Research Council Laboratories, 30, Jan. 1976.

"Fenitrothion: The Effects of its Use on Environmental Quality and its Chemistry," National Research Council Of Canada, NRCC no. 14104.

"the fifth estate," transcripts of interviews filmed for the CBC telecast of 23 Sept. 1975.

"Forest Spray Program and Reye's Syndrome," Report of the panel convened by the Government of New Brunswick, 27 April 1976.

Mercury Brief of The United States Environmental Protection Agency as filed with The Administrative Law Judge, Judge Levinson.

"Mercury Contamination of Fish and Aquatic Birds in Northwestern Ontario," Acres Consulting Services Ltd. for National Research Council of Canada.

"Mercury in the Natural Environment: A Review of Recent Work," Department of Energy, Mines and Resources Paper 70-57 (I.R. Jonasson).

"Mercury Pollution in Canada: Health and Jurisdictional Aspects," prepared by Research Branch, Library of Parliament (Project Officers: Tom Curren, Louanne Labelle), completed 6 Oct. 1975.

Minutes of the Meetings of the Federal-Provincial Standing Committee on Mercury & the Environment.

Minutes of the Meetings of the Standing Committee on Mercury in the Environment.

Ombudsman, transcripts of interviews filmed for the CBC telecast of 9 Jan. 1977.

"Pollution of The Wabigoon River," Acres Consulting Services Ltd., Toronto, 14 July 1972.

"Three Perspectives on Mercury In Canada: Medical, Technical & Economic," Prepared by Clarence T. Charlebois, Science Advisor, Science Council Of Canada. Contributions by Drs. A. Barbeau & J.F. Jaworski.

W-5, transcript of interviews filmed for the CTV telecast of 17 Oct. 1976.

Index

For reference to government departments, see under Government of Canada, Government of Ontario, etc.

259